GW00374910

ELIAS LANDOLT / KRYSTYNA M. URBANSKA

OUR ALPINE FLORA

ELIAS LANDOLT

Professor of Geobotany
at the
Swiss Federal Institute of Technology
Zurich

OUR ALPINE FLORA

with 120 colour plates
after photographs by Hans Sigg and other collaborators
as well as drawings by Rosmarie Hirzel

1st English edition
translated from the 5th German edition, entirely revised

by

Professor Krystyna M. Urbanska
Geobotanical Department
Swiss Federal Institute of Technology
Zurich

SAC Publications

Phototypeset and printed by Gasser AG Chur
Colour prints by Effingerhof AG Brugg
Photolithographs by Rapid SA Yverdon
Bound by Burkhardt AG Mönchaltorf-Zürich
Printed in Switzerland

ISBN 3-85902-098-6
3000   7.89

Foreword

«Alpine Flora» constitutes, since its first appearance, a very precious item in the long list of the publications sponsored by the Swiss Alpine Club. It has constantly enjoyed an enthusiastic response from the public, and its translation into French in 1986 brought still more interested readers. Switzerland is rather well-known for botanical research; we hope that the translation of «Alpine Flora» into English will help to recognize this good fame within a further, large and important area of the world.

The translation of «Alpine Flora» into English is a full realization of the idea budding already in the first edition of the book, where the list of Latin plant names was accompanied by the corresponding common names in French, Italian, Rhaeto-Romanic and English.

The publication of the English version of «Alpine Flora» coincides with the 125th anniversary of the Swiss Alpine Club. May it be a sign of a genuine comradeship and a solidarity bond with the Association of British SAC Members in England, celebrating now, too, its own 125-year-jubilee.

The English translation has been done by Professor Dr. Krystyna M. Urbanska from Geobotanical Institute, SFIT Zurich. A specialist in alpine plant ecology herself and a close associate of Professor Elias Landolt, the author of the original book, she rendered precisely the scientific character of the German text, and took an expert care of the linguistic details important to English-speaking readers. Her meticulous work is greatly appreciated.

With these remarks, we wish to congratulate the author once more for his successful book, and to offer our most sincere thanks to the translator. Together with the Publications Committee, we are glad to be able to offer a reference-book which hopefully will find many new friends in Great Britain and other English-speaking countries. May it also be of interest to English-speaking visitors in the innumerable resorts of Switzerland.

July 1989, Altdorf (UR) and Münster (VS)

Central Committee of the Swiss Alpine Club

President	Head of the Publications Committee
Franz Steinegger	Hansjörg Abt

CONTENTS

Preface

This guide is the first English translation of «Unsere Alpenflora» originally published in German over 25 years ago. The translation is based on the fifth German edition of 1984, but the text has been revised and corrected throughout.

Since our guide is written primarily for interested amateur, we have tried to avoid using specialized terms. Nevertheless, there were numerous occasions where this proved to be impossible. For example, we distinguished «Alpine» plants in some chapters from «alpine» in others. These are not typing mistakes, but refer instead to the geographical term «Alpine» as opposed to the ecological term «alpine» referring to plants or areas above the timberline. Similarly we describe water and temperature «budgets» which may not immediately be apparent. Our reasons for doing this is to show that plants, like man, also live on a budget to keep their household in order.

For a better understanding of the Alpine flora and vegetation, the reader needs information on its past and the life conditions in the Alps. We hope that the brief outline of the evolutionary development and characteristics of the Alpine environment given in the first part of our booklet will achieve this aim.

It has only been possible to describe the more important plants and vegetation types occurring in the Alps above 1500 m. In making our choice we have selected plants and communities that are particularly characteristic, to give the reader an idea about the richness of life forms and environmental niches in the Alps.

The Alpine ecosystems are fragile; they are disapearing fast under human influence. It is in our common interests to protect and preserve the green world of the Alps and the main purpose of this guide is to help understand this importance. Please keep the beauty of our Alpine flora intact – don't contribute to its destruction, so that you can come back and enjoy it again.

E. L.

K. M. U.

1. Origin and formation of the Alpine flora[1,2]

1.1. Flora of the Tertiary[3] period

About 50 million years ago, when the formation of the Alps began, large parts of Europe were still under water. Scandinavia, mostly not covered by the shallow sea, was at that time connected to Greenland and North America. A large land bridge extended in the north from North America to Central and East Asia. South of the partly sea-covered Sahara lay the continent of Africa which still earlier was connected to South America. Land bridges, at least temporary ones, existed thus between nearly all continents and plants were able to expand from a given area over large parts of the Earth. Central Europe, not covered by sea at that time, was inhabited by subtropical/tropical vegetation. Camphor and cinnamon trees, magnolias, laurels, tulip-tree, soapberry, persimmon, sweet-gum tree, sumac, and numerous other plants which nowadays are partly extinct or occur in southern areas only, formed a belt of mostly evergreen forests over large surfaces. In dry habitats acacias prevailed whereas humid and cool sites were inhabited by mammoth trees and bald cypresses. The mean annual temperature was over 20°C, thus much higher than now (Zurich has 9°C), the lowlands being free of frost even in winter. On the other hand, the climate of the Alps slowly forming over millions of years was rather harsh. It was more extreme than in the lowlands, sub-zero temperatures occurring frequently during the night and in winter. The air was less humid, desiccating winds and solar radiation much stronger

---

[1] The term: *flora* denotes all plant species occurring in a given area. *Vegetation* is the plant cover of a given place or area; the term refers to all individual plants as well as plant communities.

[2] Reconstruction of the formation of floras is largely based upon *fossil* findings and phytogeographical data. Fossils of Alpine plants are, unfortunately, rather rare because plant part could only have been preserved without access of air (e.g. as deposits in bogs, lakes, or seas). Such conditions occurred only seldom in the Alpine area. Patterns of the present distribution of particular species and their close relatives often indicate when, and from where the plants immigrated to Central Europe. As far as the postglacial development is concerned, *pollen analysis* is very helpful. In bogs that grow a little higher every year, pollen has been preserved in humid layers of the bog-moss over thousands of years; the oldest pollen deposits form the bottom layer, whereas the most recent pollen is contained in the uppermost part. Since pollen grains of various plants have distinct form and sculpture of their cuticle, migration paths of various species can be rather well documented in palynological data. The C_{14} (radio-carbon) method is very valuable when a precise dating of a given pollen sample is required.

[3] *Tertiary* is the name of a geological epoch that began about 60 million years ago, and ended about one million years ago i.e. at the beginning of the Quaternary.

than at low altitudes. Only very few plants from the adjacent plants could endure these life conditions and colonize high altitude sites in the Alps. The sea barrier precluded the immigration of Scandinavian plants adapted to rough climates and they would not have been able to compete with the plants of the lowlands anyway. Thus the first colonization of the Alps involved nearly exclusively plants from the neighbouring Balkan mountains, the Carpathians, the Appenines, and the Pyrenees. These mountains are as old as the Alps or older; in the past, they had floristic exchanges with old massifs and the highlands of Asia and Africa. At present these connections are broken, particular areas being separated from each other by lowlands or sea. Most of the plants inhabiting the Alps during the Tertiary period originated from Central Asia or the eastern part of this continent: these old lands with their mountains and highlands were obviously a better developmental center for plants than Central Europe which was repeatedly subjected to flooding. The Tertiary vegetation occurring in the highlands of Asia was similar to the contemporary one and consisted partly of steppes. Similarly to high mountains, steppes have a climate characterized by extreme temperatures, limited air humidity, and strong solar radiation. The steppe plants were thus able to live at high altitudes. Closely related species of our edelweiss grow nowadays in steppes of Asiatic highlands.

While the rocky strata of the Alps were lifted up, thrust over each other, and eroded again and again, innumerable plants immigrated into the Alpine area. Some were still identical to their ancestors growing in the homeland, but many of them evolved in the course of their journey and were in fact new species. For instance, the original alpenrose (small-flowered relative of numerous Asiatic rhododendrons and azaleas) has given rise to two species viz. 1/ hairy alpenrose *(Rhododendron hirsutum)* which is competitive on calciferous substrata only and 2/ rust-leaved alpenrose *(R. ferrugineum)* which grows mostly in acid soils.

The ancestors of the following Alpine plants came, among others, from Central or East Asia: aconite *(Aconitum)*, columbine *(Aquilegia)*, alpenrose *(Rhododendron)*, primrose *(Primula)*, rock-jasmine *(Androsace)*, milk-vetch *(Astragalus)*, oxytropis *(Oxytropis)*, gentian *(Gentiana)*, lousewort *(Pedicularis)*, wormwood *(Artemisia)*, hawk's-beard *(Crepis)*. Primarily from Mediterranean and North African mountains originate gypsophila *(Gypsophila)*, campion *(Silene)*, pheasant's eye *(Narcissus)*, crocus *(Crocus)*, kidney-vetch *(Anthyllis)*, toadflax *(Linaria)*, globularia *(Globularia)*, and bellflower *(Campanula)*. The following genera came from America, presumably not before glaciations: bearberry *(Arctostaphylos)*, goldenrod *(Solidago)*, aster *(Aster)*, fleabane *(Erigeron)*, and arnica *(Arnica)*. Only a few genera viz. St. Bruno's lily *(Paradisia)*, moehringia *(Moehringia)*, snowbell *(Soldanella)*, rampion *(Phyteuma)*, adenostyle *(Adenostyles)* and coltsfoot *(Homogyne)* have their origin in the mountains of Central Europe e.g. the Alps.

In this way, by the end of the Tertiary, a very rich Alpine flora appeared which constituted the foundation of the present-day world of

1.2. Flora

Alpine plants have exceedingly beautiful, brightly-
-haracteristic of steppes and deserts but also of

ions

Towards the ...iary the climate slowly turned cooler. Tropical and subtr... the evergreen forests had to retreat southward and were re... ...ciduous and coniferous species.

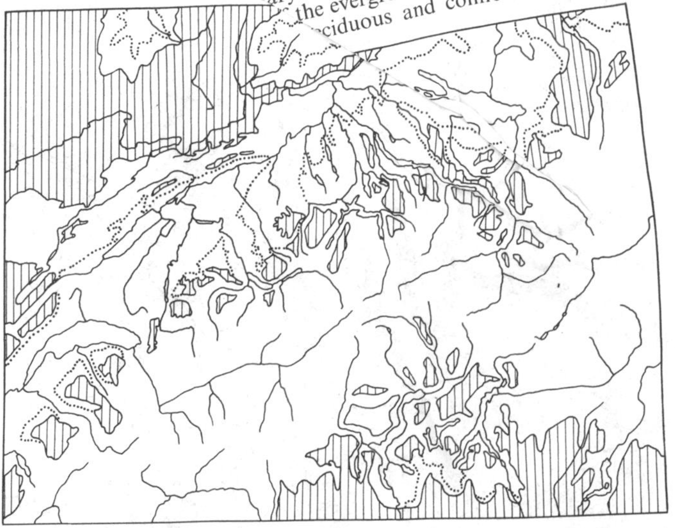

Fig. 1. The Swiss Alps during the period of glaciations (after *3.e.*, modified). The areas hatched were ice-free, also during the largest glaciation (the Riss). The dotted line corresponds to the ice sheet boundary of the last glaciation (the Würm).

Now and then, the temperature grew warmer over longer periods and some of the flora could return but the warmth-loving plants were again forced south by recurrent cooling. Snow-rich winters resulted in the growth of glaciers in the Alps, the temperatures of the cool summers not being sufficient to melt the snow mass. Glaciers grew slowly, filling out the mountain valleys and then advancing to the foreland. So began, about one million years ago, the period of glaciations. Valleys of the Central Alps filled out with ice up to more than 2000 m; the lowland flora was driven away into milder Atlantic and Mediterranean areas. Some high-altitude plants were able, however, to stay above the glacier currents in sheltered sites of the Central Alps e.g. in southern Wallis and the Engadine; both these areas are rather …ed by strong solar radiation. The survival sites we… on south-facing slopes or cliffs and wind-protected … temporarily snow-free in winter. Numerous plants … the calcareous Northern Alps on mountain tops ju… ice (e.g. the Dent de Morcles, the Vanil Noir, the … Alps of Brienz, the Pilatus, the Churfirsten). In th…ps, life conditions were more advantageous: many pla…ugia in the massifs of South Tyrol, the Bergamo Alps, th… Mt. Generoso, the Grajic Alps etc. Numerous warmth… and highly specialized species perished whereas the oth…ved in vast non-glaciated areas of the SW or SE Alps and i…alkan mountains (Figs 1–2).

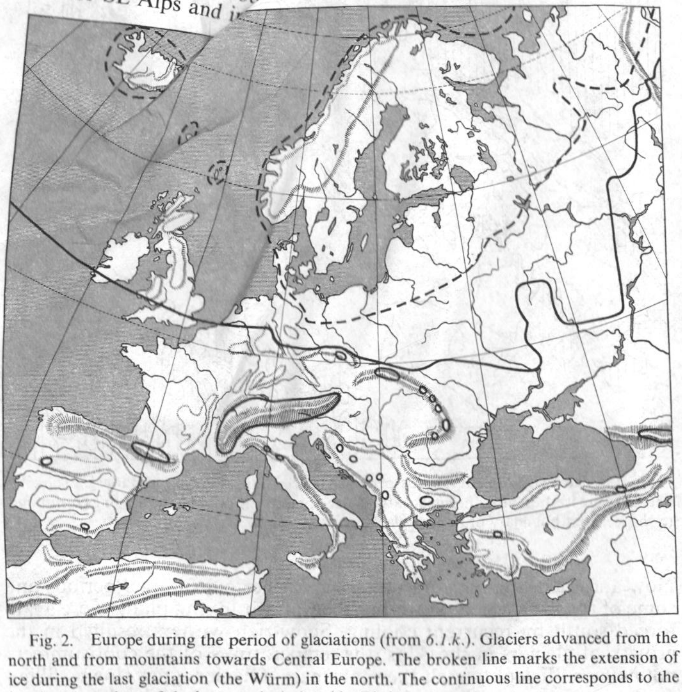

Fig. 2. Europe during the period of glaciations (from *6.1.k.*). Glaciers advanced from the north and from mountains towards Central Europe. The broken line marks the extension of ice during the last glaciation (the Würm) in the north. The continuous line corresponds to the ice sheet boundary of the largest glaciation (the Riss).

Not only in the Alps but also in all other mountains of the northern temperate zone as well as in the Arctic the existing glaciers grew and new ones appeared. An ice sheet expanded from Scandinavia south to the East and the North Sea. Many northern (Arctic) plants migrated over the Carelic Strait to the eastern part of Europe and from there to Central Europe; they competed north of the Alps with Alpine plants. Other northern plants e.g. dwarf buttercup *(Ranunculus pygmaeus)* reached the Central Alps from Central Europe over the Sudety Mts., the Carpathians and the Eastern Alps. Some Alpine plants e.g. bearded bellflower *(Campanula barbata)*, purple gentian *(Gentiana purpurea)*, black vanilla orchid *(Nigritella nigra)* migrated the other way round into the neighbouring mountains or up to the border of the Scandinavian ice sheet and subsequently followed its retreat north.

The climate changed frequently in the course of many thousands of years. When temperatures rose higher for a longer period, the glaciers retreated a little; ice-free areas were then colonized by plants which had survived in nearby places, some newly-formed taxa having more success than their ancestral species. In particular, hybrids originating from crosses between closely-related species and genetically isolated through doubling of their chromosome number frequently demonstrated a great potential for expansion; numerous plants which nowadays grow in meadows belong to this group. With increasing rise in temperature more demanding plants returned from the south, the southeast or the southwest. The Alpine plants were thus forced back to their high altitude sites and the vegetation regained its preglacial aspect. However, numerous original species disappeared completely, some northern plants became established, and some slightly different new taxa were born.

One warmer period was soon followed by a colder one and the plants had to yield ground to the advancing glaciers. In this way cold and warm phases alternated; at present, four major glaciation viz. Günz, Mindel, Riss, and Würm as well as numerous lesser glaciations are recognized. On the whole, glaciers came down to the Alpine foreland about ten times. During the last glaciation viz. the Riss, the ice sheet extended north of the Alps to the areas beyond the Jura and Lake Constance (Figs 1–2). The Swiss Midlands, too, were mostly covered by ice during the last glaciation.

1.3. Postglacial flora

At the beginning of the ice retreat after the last glaciation viz. about 16 000 years ago, Europe was covered (except for the glaciers) by a treeless vegetation consisting of grasses, herbs, mosses, and lichens. In favourable sites alpenrose and willow shrubs as well as dwarf birch rose above the low vegetation carpet. However, an increasingly warm and dry climate caused a rapid expansion of mountain pine and Scots pine. Alpine plants and numerous northern species followed the retreating ice back into the Alps and were replaced in the lowlands by the immigrating forest species; they have been able to survive only in a few favourable sites (e.g. bogs, gullies, and north-facing slopes with scanty woodland. On the Uetliberg near Zurich e.g. dwarf mountain pine *(Pinus mugo)*, yellow mountain saxifrage *(Saxifraga aizoides)*, small bellflower *(Campanula cochleariifolia)* and paradoxial butterbur *(Petasites paradoxus)* survived. Some Alpine plants e.g. narcissus-flowered anemone *(Anemone narcissiflora)* or yellow gentian *(Gentiana lutea)* have been able to withstand competition from lowland taxa also in the Canton of Schaffhausen and in the Hegau, outside the glaciated areas.

Not all the plants returned into the Alps. The Alpine foreland and outer Alpine ranges are mostly built of calciferous substrata; a plant that is able to grow solely upon acidic soil which is poor in calcium therefore finds only few places in these areas where it can grow and remain competitive. Calcium may sometimes be washed out from the uppermost soil layer so that the calcium-avoiding plants may after all grow in some sites however, such soil changes frequently take hundreds of years. Many calcium-avoiding species were therefore unable to immigrate rapidly into the Alps and were either outcompeted by better-adapted plants thriving in a warm climate, or forced back into cold acidic bogs in the Alpine foreland or in the Jura. For instance, dwarf birch *(Betula nana)* occurs today only in a few bogs within the Alpine foreland (e.g. Einsiedeln) and in the Jura; the northern species low birch *(Betula humilis)* can be seen nowadays in Switzerland only in the surroundings of Abtwil (Canton of St. Gall). Both these dwarf shrubs with small round leaves are, on the other hand, still widely distributed in the Arctic. Chickweed wintergreen *(Trientalis europaea)* which also belongs to this relictic[4] group can be found at present only in very few places in Switzerland (Oberhasli, valley of Urseren, Einsiedeln, St. Bernardino, the Morteratsch, the Cavaglias).

Numerous steppe plants which arrived from eastern Europe together with pines, and some before and afterwards them (about 10 000 years ago), found suitable life conditions and as yet not competition in the increasingly warm and dry climate. They expanded over the valley of the Danube into the areas of Lake Constance and the surroundings of the Rhine, along the southern foot of the Alps, and over the valley of the Inn into the central and southern Alpine valleys (the Vintschgau, Lower Engadine, the Wallis, the Aosta valley). Characteristic representatives of these plants are e.g. feathergrass *(Stipa pennata)* and savin *(Juniperus sabina)*. A little later, Mediterranean plants arrived from the south to the Ticino and the valley of the Rhône; they proceeded north to the Wallis, and along the southern foot of the Jura or through the valley of the Saône, entering the lowlands of the Upper Rhine over the Belfort Gap and the Saverne. However, only a few of these species e.g. viper's bugloss *(Echium vulgare)* or erucastrum *(Erucastrum nasturtiifolium)* were able to reach high altitudes. Hazel, oak, and other foliage trees also arrived at this time. In the Midlands large mixed forests of oak appeared; in particularly warm sites developed the southern forests of white oak which included many Mediterranean plants. At higher altitudes and in central Alpine valleys appeared pine

---

[4] *Relics* are species which immigrated long time ago (under different climatic conditions) into a given area, and have been able to remain in places where competition was not too strong. They give evidence of the past.

16

forests (Scots pine, mountain pine, Arolla pine) which partly climbed over the present-day timberline.

About 5000–7000 years ago, the increasing humidity promoted the immigration of plants from areas with oceanic climate. Various Atlantic species arrived from the west to Switzerland; they found suitable life conditions above all in the Ticino and in the western part of the country. This group, however, did not play an important rôle in the formation of the Alpine flora, the climate of the Alps being insufficiently balanced. Beech and white fir which colonized the southern side of the Alpine chain much earlier, expanded north of the Alps together with the Atlantic plants; spruce arrived a little later. These trees drove away oak and pine from middle and high altitudes in the outer Alpine ranges.

During the last 3000 years the constantly fluctuating climate turned cooler again. Numerous warmth-loving plants disappeared and occur nowadays only in a few favourable sites (foehn valleys, central Alpine valleys, the southern foot of the Alps and the Jura); they are clearly a relictic element there.

Pollen analysis permitted one to establish fairly precisely the origin and the time of immigration of particular tree species; it is thus possible to recognize putative areas of their survival *(l.e.)*. Arolla pine *(Pinus cembra)* came from the east and probably survived on the eastern and the southern flank of the Alps; spruce *(Picea excelsa)* presumably survived in the northern Balkans. In contrast, white fir *(Abies alba)* came to the Alps from the southwest and it is conceivable that it found a refugium in the Apennine Peninsula. Oak *(Quercus)* and beech *(Fagus)* immigrated from various areas, the former tree coming from the southeast, the south and the southwest, whereas the latter arrived from the southeast and the west.

1.4. Human influence upon vegetation and flora of the Alps

After the retreat of the glaciers Man also expanded within the Alpine area. Mountain farming and animal husbandry have been influencing the region for some 5000 years; as a result, the natural vegetation has become more and more repressed. Human activity in the Alps has increased appreciably since the Middle Ages. Forests have been cleared, giving way to new land for farming and grazing. In all places below the timberline where villages, crop fields, hay meadows, and pastures occur nowadays, large forests would have grown naturally; only cliffs, watercourses and isolated mires were not covered by woods in the past. Natural forests are confined today to less fertile hilltops, steep slopes, and/or river banks, this tendency being particularly distinct in the mountains. Forests are present in steeper slopes which are difficult to mow, offer bad conditions for grazing, or are avalanche-endangered; however, as soon as a slope becomes less steep forest is replaced by pastures, mountain hay meadows, or small crop fields. The timberline was frequently lowered by some hundred metres to obtain more Alpine land for grazing; trees have been used as firewood in houses and smelters, or as timber for construction. Numerous Alpine passes (e.g. the Bernina, the Gotthard, the Furka, the Grimsel, the Simplon) which are treeless at present would have been covered by woods, were it not for human intervention. The areas where alpine huts were built were also formerly woodland.

Most of the present forests in Switzerland are not natural, however. In the lowlands, foreign trees have frequently been planted, economically important species being given preference; for instance, all forests of spruce and larch occurring in the Midlands were planted by Man; genuine spruce forest grows nearly exclusively above 1000 m in our country.

Very numerous Alpine forests are grazed, and the straw is still occasionally used. Establishment of young trees is therefore nearly impossible; forests become increasingly sparse, avalanches and landslides being unavoidable. Forest is often kept light artificially, and some tree species are selected to assure good grazing; for instance, most of the pure larch forests in the Engadine and in the Wallis are man-made. Such artificially created pure stands suffer frequently from diseases which would seldom have been dangerous in healthy natural forests (e.g. dieback of sweet chestnut in the Ticino, bark-beetle in spruce forests, larch bud moth in the Engadine). Incidentally, the damage to trees resulting from exhaust fumes is largely independent of the natural or artificial origin of the forest affected.

In our country truly natural meadows and pastures are confined to the areas above the timberline. Swiss meadow plants growing nowadays within the areas formerly inhabited by forests relate only marginally and only at higher altitudes to the original alpine grassland as plants of forests, mires, stream banks, cliffs, and scree competed with each other in sites newly open to colonization by the clearing of forests. It goes without saying that only the plants able to grow successfully in habitats influenced by Man and to withstand e.g. intensive fertilization, mowing, or grazing could have survived. Many such species evolved under strong competition and gave rise to specialized taxa. Plants nowadays inhabiting our strongly managed meadows and pastures were often formed rather recently (during the last glaciation). Numerous plants arrived in Switzerland as a result of grass seed exchange; they too became established in meadows.

Together with agricultural plants Man brought many weeds to Switzerland; they originate primarily from the Mediterranean area or West Asia, partly also from America (only the species introduced more recently). Weeds are only seldom competitive enough against native plants; on the other hand, they successfully colonize some artificially cleared sites e.g. arable land, gravel pits, roadsides, railway banks, etc. They usually remain until the native vegetation takes over and a closed plant cover is formed.

The human impact is less striking above the timberline (1800–2000 m in the outer Alpine ranges, ca. 2000–2400 m in the Central Alps), but changes in vegetation are rather easily recognizable, especially in much grazed pastures. Plants which are not sensitive to grazing or trampling, as well as species avoided by grazers (because they are poisonous, bitter-tasting, or prickly) are able to expand at the expense of more sensitive species. Even in places not longer affected by human intervention (the National Park, nature reserves) nature is barely able to regain its primary balance. Wolf, bear, lynx, and eagle being eliminated by Man, red deer, chamois, marmots, and other herbivores form large populations when not hunted; they graze forests and meadows often as intensively as do cattle, goats, or sheep.

Flower-picking and collecting of plants are very specific human interferences in life of Alpine species. Gathering of spectacular or rare plants in large amounts for bouquets, decorations, and pharmaceutical purposes resulted in the total extinction of many plants while others (e.g. edelweiss, alpine columbine, orchids) retreated into almost inaccessible sites. This impoverishment of Alpine flora is unnecessary and should be avoided. It should be realized that beautiful and rare things must not be taken away only to prove that one has seen it all or to show how successful and clever one can be. Incidentally, the Alpine flowers mostly wither already while carried into the valleys or live for a few days only; dried plants lose much of their original beauty too, so that the work involved is really not worthwhile. A flower left undisturbed in its natural habitat may, on the other hand, stay open for several weeks giving delight to many a tourist; apart from the esthetic value, it can bear seed and the population will remain competitive because of its rejuvenation. Fortunately enough, the times are gone when shoe-boxes filled with gentians and alpenroses were mailed home as the customary souvenir from holiday places. The nature protection rules are nowadays very strict in many cantons (see Chapter 7). However, the regulations are so complex that it is nearly impossible to remember them all; any plant should therefore be considered potentially worthy of protection and picked only when its stand is sufficiently large. It should be kept in mind, however, that many tourists will possibly gather plants at the same site; one should thus never pick more than ten flowers, the common species included. Detailed regulations and limitations are given in further on in this book, together with descriptions of particular species. Obviously plants must not be pulled up with their roots; Alpine plants are generally not suited to lowland sites and most of the transplanted species do not come up to expectations, on the contrary: they are rather poorly or die off.

Flower-picking is, incidentally, not the biggest hazard to Alpine vegetation nowadays; power-supply industry, tourism, and agriculture affect the original beauty of nature and the diversity of plant species in a much more drastic way. Intact and species-rich areas are still being flooded as a result of dam construction, further power stations are planned e.g. in the Greina, the basin of Gletsch, the Lakes Macun. The areas mentioned are famous for their irreplacable vegetation; for instance, the surroundings of the Lakes Macun are the only Swiss site of dwarf buttercup *(Ranunculus pygmaeus)*.

Construction of machine-graded ski runs is also exceedingly damaging. The ruinous exploitation of nature is in this case carried out without a second thought, though everybody knows that a successful revegetation of graded ski runs above the timberline is virtually impossible without large investments; the humus accumulated over centuries is destroyed and the newly-formed bare scree surfaces are exposed to erosion. Seed mixtures used in revegetation attempts are not suited to the Alpine climate (native seeds are as yet not available on the market). Should the construction of graded ski runs be further permitted by irresponsible authorities in large Alpine areas, our beautiful mountain landscape, so appealing to tourists, will be largely reduced to scree fields and summer tourism will be deprived of its basis.

Agricultural practices in the Alps have changed greatly since the last world war. Remote alps are practically no longer used, wild hay meadows not being mown either. These changes lead to alteration of the mountain landscape because forests begin to reappear in many places. The familiar scenery, rich in varied culture-influenced elements, slowly turns into a more monotonous landscape; lookouts with fine views over valleys and mountains become overgrown by trees. Steep slopes with wild meadows not mown anymore become more than ever endangered by erosion; incidentally, wild hay plots represent the most brightly-coloured and spectacular meadows of the Alps. As a substitute for the original management, very large herds of sheep spend the summer in the Alps; they do not leave a single flower behind and expose numerous sites to erosion. Both the preservation of a landscape that offers interest to tourists and a good opportunity of recreation, as well as the conservation of a species-rich and healthy world of plants and animals in any Alpine area nowadays require particular care and understanding.

2. Distribution of Alpine plants

2.1. Phytogeographic regions

Distribution of each plant family, genus, or species is influenced by the time and place of its formation, its potential for expansion, and its ecological requirements. Various continents e.g. Africa, South America, and Australia were separated from one another some millions years ago, and floristic exchanges have been precluded ever since. Plants in various continents therefore evolved different morphological features even if the ecological conditions were comparable. The situation in mountains separated from each other by plains was analogous, if on a more limited scale; for instance, the Pyrenees house numerous plants unknown in the Alps and vice versa.

The distribution areas of many plants often overlap; it is thus possible to divide the Earth into phytogeographical regions. Delimitation of such regions is therefore based, on the one hand, on ecological factors and, on the other hand, on the geographical and historical situation.

Temperate and cool climatic zones of the northern hemisphere are assigned to the holarctic floristic kingdom. The plant families having their principal distribution here include the pine family *(Pinaceae)*, rush family *(Juncaceae)*, willow family *(Salicaceae)*, birch family *(Betulaceae)*, buttercup family *(Ranunculaceae)*, saxifrage family *(Saxifragaceae)* and maple family *(Aceraceae)*. Numerous genera are confined to this floristic kingdom. The phytogeographic regions of Europe are shown in Fig. 3.

2.1.1. Arctic region

The Arctic region comprises the plant world of the Arctic, the Scandinavian part being to some extent autonomous. Many Arctic plants were able to migrate south during the glaciations, or soon afterwards, and occur today in the Alps; they are called Arctic-Alpine species and represent the Arctic element in the Alpine flora. Numerous species of this group are rather inconspicuous and wind-pollinated. They make up about 8% of the plant cover above 1500 m in the Swiss Alps, only 1% being limited to the European part of the Arctic. Typical *Arctic-Alpine plants* include Scheuchzer's cottongrass *(Eriophorum scheuchzeri)*, dwarf willow *(Salix herbacea)*, dwarf buttercup *(Ranunculus pygmaeus)* and mountain avens *(Dryas octopetala)*. Glacier crowfoot *(Ranunculus glacialis)* and rock speedwell *(Veronica fruticans)* are confined to Europe.

21

Fig. 3. Floristic regions of Europe (from *6.1.k.*).
1. Arctic region
2. Boreal region
3. Central European region
4. Atlantic region
5. Mediterranean region
6. Pontic region
7. Mountains of Central and Southern Europe

2.1.2. Boreal region

The Boreal region includes coniferous woods of the northern hemisphere; these are above all plants of forests, mires, as well as tall-herb communities. The Eurasian part of the Boreal region is inhabited by very numerous, characteristic species which are called Eurosibirian. The European part, too, includes various representative species (North European-Alpine species). Twenty-three percent of the plants which occur in the Swiss Alps above 1500 m correspond to the Boreal element, 8% being Eurosibirian-North American, 12% Eurosibirian, and 3% European-Alpine. *Eurosibirian-North American plants* include e.g. dwarf juniper *(Juniperus nana)*, marsh-marigold *(Caltha palustris)* and cowberry *(Vaccinium vitis-idaea)*; Eurosibirian *species* are represented e.g. by juniper *(Juniperus communis)*, Martagon lily *(Lilium Martagon)*, common bistort *(Polygonum bistorta)* and blueberry *(Vaccinium myrtillus)*. The *North European-Alpine* spruce *(Picea excelsa)* and spring pasqueflower *(Pulsatilla vernalis)* are confined to the European part of the region.

2.1.3. Central European region

The Central European region comprises the largest part of the area inhabited in Europe by summer-green foliage woods. Many typical species grow in forests or at intermittently dry sites on steep slopes covered by light woods. Eight percent of the plants which occur in the Swiss Alps above 1500 m correspond to the *Central European element;* typical species include beech *(Fagus silvatica)*, blue sesleria *(Sesleria coerulea)*, and spring snowflake *(Leucojum vernum)*.

2.1.4. Atlantic region

The Atlantic region comprises European lowlands which have an oceanic climate (relatively high air humidity, mild winters). The climate in the Alps above 1500 m is characterized by cold winters and periods of pronounced dry air and no species of this floristic region are able to grow there.

2.1.5. Mediterranean region

The Mediterranean region is confined to the southern part of Europe and characterized by mild, humid winters and warm, dry summers. Numerous species form part of a sclerophyllous woodland; geophytes with bulbs or thick rhizomes, and also annual plants are frequent. The Alpine climate at high altitudes is unsuitable for these plants; therefore they occur only seldom, mostly as species introduced by Man (e.g. viper's bugloss, *Echium vulgare)*.

2.1.6. Pontic region

The Pontic region is limited in Europe to the southeast. It comprises for the most part *East European-Central Asiatic steppe plants* which are able to endure dry conditions and great fluctuations of temperature. The few representatives of this group occur mostly in central Alpine valleys (in Switzerland: the Wallis, the Engadine, the valley of the Rhine; in the adjacent southern areas: the Tarentaise, the Mauritienne, the Aosta valley, the upper Veltlin and the Vintschgau). Pontic plants represent only low percentages of the plant cover in the Swiss Alps above 1500 m. Typical examples are savin *(Juniperus sabina)*, feather-grass *(Stipa pennata)*, large-flowered hemp-nettle *(Galeopsis speciosa)* and downy-beaked oxytropis *(Oxytropis pilosa)*.

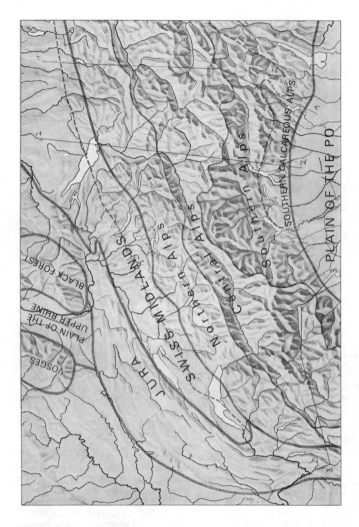

Fig. 4. Phytogeographical classification of the middle part of the Alps (from *6.1.k.*). 1–3.
Migration limits:
1. Valley of Lech – Val Camonica
2. Hinterrhein – Lake of Como
3. Tarentaise – Aosta valley

24

2.1.7. Mountains of Central and Southern Europe

The floristic region of Central and South European mountains comprises, apart from the Alps, the Pyrenees, the Apennines, the Carpathians, and northern mountains of the Balkans. Plants inhabiting cliffs, scree, and grassland prevail. About 56% of the species occurring at high altitudes in the Swiss Alps belong to this group. Nearly half of them are *distributed over a large part of the mountains listed;* to this group belong both very common species e.g. alpine sedge *(Carex curvula),* adenostyle *(Adenostyles alliariae),* or cilliated moehringia *(Moehringia ciliata)* as well as very rare taxa e.g. coriander-leaved callianthemum *(Callianthemum coriandrifolium)* or Mt. Baldo anemone *(Anemone baldensis).* About 8% of these species occur preferably in the eastern or in the western part of the mountains. Eastern species occur in the Alps, too, above all in the eastern part; on the other hand, Western plants are mostly distributed in the western part of the Alpine chain. *In the east* occur e.g. green alder *(Alnus viridis),* tufted bellflower *(Campanula thyrsoides)* and Carniol groundsel *(Senecio carniolicus),* whereas St. Bruno's lily *(Paradisia liliastrum),* alpine clover *(Trifolium alpinum)* and flesh-coloured rock-jasmine *(Androsace carnea)* belong to *Western species.* Some plants e.g. wild peony *(Paeonia officinalis),* white asphodel *(Asphodelus albus),* alpine scull-cap *(Scutellaria alpina)* and fire lily *Lilium bulbiferum)* are mostly *distributed in the southern part of the mountains* and thus relate genetically to the Mediterranean region.

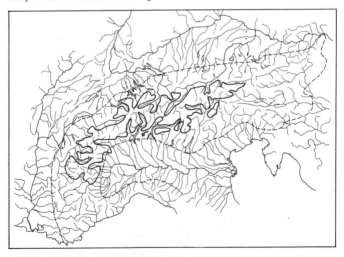

Fig. 5. Distribution of stinking primrose *(Primula hirsuta)* in the Alps. The species occurs almost everywhere upon siliceous substrata. After MERXMÜLLER *2.d.).*

Some species were able to expand north during the glaciations and have remained there in isolated habitats ever since; they are called *Scandinavian-Alpine* plants. To this group belong e.g. black vanilla orchid *(Nigritella nigra)* and purple gentian *(Gentiana purpurea)*. About 13% of the species occurring at higher altitudes in the Swiss Alps are specifically Alpine; about one-third (5%) of these are distributed over the whole Alpine chain or nearly so (Alpine or pan-Alpine plants) whereas 3–4% each occur only in the eastern Alps or in the western part of the Alpine chain. Barely 1% of the Alpine plants are confined to the southern part of the Alps. *Typical Alpine plants* include alpine rockcress *(Arabis alpina)*, Fleischer's willowherb *(Epilobium fleischeri)*, Swiss rock-jasmine *(Androsace helvetica)*, king of the Alps *(Erytrichium nanum)* and whitish hawkweed *(Hieracium intybaceum)*. Stinking primrose *(Primula hirsuta)* is typically distributed over the whole Alpine chain (Fig. 5) but it expands farther west into the Pyrenees. As far as the plants inhabiting only a part of the Alps are concerned, the species-group of hoary groundsel *(Senecio incanus* s.l.) is a good example (Fig. 6): of the three vicariant taxa (vicariance, see p. 56) one is typical of the eastern Alps, another occurs in the western Alps, and the third grows within the western part of the Rhaetic-Bergamo area. *Eastern Alpine plants* (Figs 7–8) include e.g. snow dock *(Rumex*

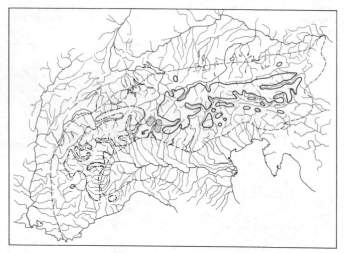

Fig. 6.   Distribution of the species-group of shaggy groundsel *(Senecio incanus* s. 1.). *Senecio incanus* s. str. occurs in the western Alps (broken/dotted line) and is also known from an isolated locality in the Apennines. *Senecio carniolicus* occurs in the eastern Alps and in the Carpathians (continuous line). *Senecio insubricus* is confined to the westernmost part of the Rhaetic Alps/Bergamo Alps (hatched); its area of distribution corresponds exactly to the migration limit: Hinterrhein – Lake of Como. After MERXMÜLLER *(2.d.)*.

nivalis), glacial pink *(Dianthus glacialis)*, saxifrage with naked stems *(Saxifrage aphylla)*, hairy alpenrose *(Rhododendron hirsutum)*, black yarrow *(Achillea atrata)* and musk yarrow *(Achillea moschata)*. *Typical plants of the western Alps* (Fig. 9) are e.g. alpine columbine *(Aquilegia alpina)*, five-fingered lady's mantle *(Alchemilla pentaphyllea)*, hoary groundsel *(Senecio incanus)*, dwarf yarrow *(Achillea nana)*, alpine scullcap *(Scutellaria alpina)*. *Plants of the southern Alps* (Fig. 10) which have survived the glaciations at the southern foot of the Alps e.g. in the Bergamo Alps mostly do not longer occur in Switzerland; they are exemplified by tassel rampion *(Synotoma comosum)* or glossy cinquefoil *(Potentilla nitida)* which still grows in the area of the Lake of Como. An exception is Mt. Baldo sedge *(Carex baldensis)* which still occurs in the area of the Ofen pass and also in two habitats in the Bavarian Alps.

Numerous plants of the eastern Alps survived the glaciations on the non-glaciated eastern flank of the Alpine chain (NE or SE Alps); they again expanded into the Swiss Alps only during the postglacial period. Plants of the western Alps had their refugia mostly in the SW Alps and returned from this area. The lines: Lech valley-Val Camonica, the Hinterrhein-Lake of Como and the Tarentaise-Aosta valley (Fig. 4) are frequently considered as the western migration limits of plants typical of the eastern Alps. Fern-leaved lousewort *(Pedicularis aspleniifolia)* does not pass the first border mentioned; the second one is the western limit of occurrence of beaked lousewort *(Pedicularis rostrato-capitata)* and dwarf valerian *(Valeriana supina);* hairy alpenrose *(Rhododendron hirsutum)*, black yarrow *(Achillea atrata)* and musk yarrow *(Achillea moschata)* stop at the third line. On the other hand, the plants of the SW Alps stay behind this line and do not reach the Swiss Alps at all or only barely so (e.g. alpine scullcap, *Scutellaria alpina,* Fig. 9). The borderline Lech valley-Val Camonica is not crossed by Mt. Cenis bellflower *(Campanula cenisia)* and alpine columbine *(Aquilegia alpina)*. Various plants originating from calcareous regions have been able to expand farther in the Southern Alps than in the Northern Alps; for instance, ascending lousewort *(Pedicularis ascendens)* is distributed in the northern part of the Alps from the west up to the Furka pass, but in the Southern Alps it reaches only to the eastern part of the Bergamo Alps.

In contrast to the eastern and western Alps, the middle part of the Alps has practically no species of its own because this area was strongly glaciated; branched gentian *(Gentiana ramosa)* occurring between the Aosta valley and the Brenner pass may be included in this category. Some species have very limited distribution areas and have presumably not expanded beyond their glacial refugia; such refugia centers do not occur in Switzerland but in the adjacent area at the southern foot of the Bergamo Alps. None of these southern plants came back to Switzerland; on the other hand, some species which survived the glacial era in the northern part of the Bergamo Alps and north of the Lake of Como occur nowadays in Switzerland, mostly in the southern part of the Grisons. These *Rhaetic-Bergamo species* are represented e.g. by

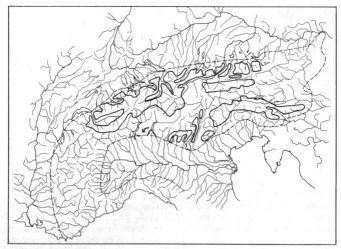

Fig. 7. Distribution of black yarrow *(Achillea atrata)*. The species occurs in the western Alps and in the middle part of the Alpine chain; it does not expand south beyond the borderline: Tarentaise – Aosta valley. After MERXMÜLLER *(2.d.)*.

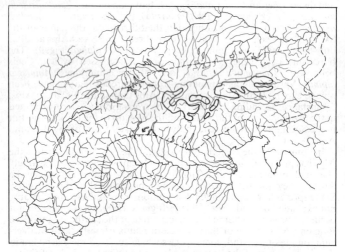

Fig. 8. Distribution of glacier pink *(Dianthus glacialis)*. The species occurs almost exclusively in the inner Alpine ranges and represents a typical plant of the eastern Alps reaching west to the borderline: Hinterrhein – Lake of Como. After MERXMÜLLER *(2.d.)*.

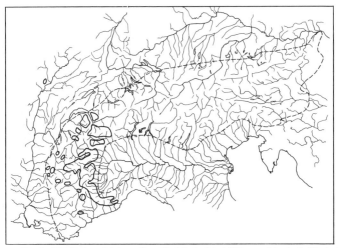

Fig. 9.   Distribution of alpine scullcap *(Scutellaria alpina)*. This mountain plant of Central and Southern Europe occurs mostly in the south; in the Alps it is distributed similarly to the Western Alpine taxa. It presumably immigrated from the Apennines, and crosses the borderline: Tarentaise – Aosta valley a little northwards, but not eastwards. After MERXMÜLLER *(2.d.)*.

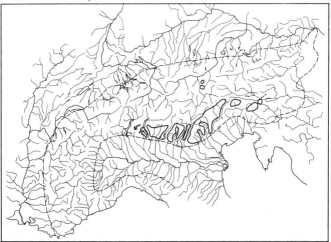

Fig. 10.   Distribution of tassel rampion *(Synotoma comosum)* showing its typical southern area. Calcareous substrata reaching from the east only to the Ticino, plants of the Southern Alps do not occur farther than the Lake of Como. After MERXMÜLLER *(2.d.)*.

insubrian groundsel *(Senecio insubricus)*, short rock-jasmine *(Androsace brevis)*, Rhaetic knapweed *(Centaurea rhaetica)*, antique yellow-rattle *(Rhinanthus antiquus)* and Rhaetic rampion *(Phyteuma hedraianthifolium)*. Some plants occurring at present in the southern part of the Wallis probably survived the glaciations in the Graian Alps south of the Aosta valley and subsequently came back from this region. These *Graian-Pennine plants* (Fig. 11) include e.g. yellow soapwort *(Saponaria lutea)*, incised bellflower *(Campanula excisa)*, spickenard *(Valeriana celtica)* and one-headed groundsel *(Senecio uniflorus)*. Hardly any plants are exclusive to the Swiss Alps. Dwarf rampion *(Phyteuma humile)* is known only from the area of the Monte Rosa whereas Ladin draba *(Draba ladina)* occurs only in the Dolomites of the Lower Engadine. Primrose of the Daone valley *(Primula daonensis)* has, too, a very restricted distribution from the Oetz valley to Val Camonica, in Switzerland it occurs solely in the valley of Münster.

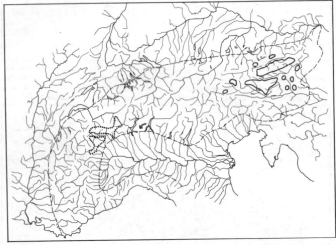

Fig. 11. Distribution of spikenard *(Valeriana celtica)*. The species occurs in the area of the Graian/Pennine Alps. The Northern Alps are inhabited by the vicariant taxon ssp. *norica* Vierhapper. After MERXMÜLLER *(2.d.)*.

2.2. Flora of particular areas

Diverse geographic situations, diverse possibilities for survival of the glaciation period in the Alps, different distances from glacial refugia and, last but not least, diverse climate and soil conditions contributed to the formation of diffferent floras in particular Alpine areas. The following pages bring more details on the subject.

The middle part of the Alpine chain can be divided into three floristically different sectors viz. Northern Alps, Central Alps, and Southern Alps (Fig. 4, p. 24). The adjacent Jura will be treated briefly first.

2.2.1. Jura

Situation. The Jura is adjacent to the western Alps. Its altitude decreases from the southwest to the northwest (the Reculet: 1717 m, the Dôle: 1677 m, the Hasenmatt: 1445 m, the Randen: 924 m). Together with the decreasing altitude the diversity of species also decreases, mountain plants being mostly eliminated from the middle part of the Jura as a result of planting of forests. The mountain flora becomes again a little more diversified in the area of the Schwäbische Alb which has various humid and dry rocky sites. As far as the Swiss Jura is concerned, the Dôle, the Creux du Van, and the Chasseral belong to the floristically most interesting areas. Here arrived from the western Alps e.g. mountain kidney-vetch* *(Anthyllis montana)* which can be found up to the Creux du Van; milk-white rock-jasmine *(Androsace lactea)* which reaches to the Hauenstein and the Schwäbische Alb; Carinthian buttercup* *(Ranunculus carinthiacus)* which occurs up to the Röthifluh and the Schwäbische Alb, and Thora buttercup which reaches to the Dôle; poisonous aconite *(Aconitum anthora)* with its distribution limit at the Creux du Van, alpine cephalaria *(Cephalaria alpina)* at the Aiguilles de Baulmes and large-flowered sandwort *(Arenaria grandiflora* on the Chasseral. None of these species occurs in the eastern Swiss Alps. Even the Lägern still house some special mountain plants e.g. white mountain saxifrage *(Saxifraga aizoon)* and alpine rockcress *(Arabis alpina)*. As far as alpenroses are concerned, only the rust-leaved species *(Rhododendron ferrugineum)* immigrated into the Jura up to Mont Tendre because of the few suitable sites; hairy alpenrose which would have found favourable sites in the Jura migrated west only up to the Lake of Geneva and had therefore no possibility to enter the Jura. Only few mountain plants arrived to the Jura from the Northern Alps (esp. the Canton of Schaffhausen and the Hegau); these plants include e.g. narcissus-flowered anemone *(Anemone narcissiflora)* and superb pink *(Dianthus superbus)*.

Substrata. The Jura consists mostly of limestone and marl. Plants of siliceous mountains are thus mostly absent.

Glaciations. Large parts of the Jura stayed free of ice during the glaciations. Some plants which nowadays do not occur in the Swiss Alps (e.g. mountain pennycress, *Thlaspi montanum,* alpine hogweed* *Heracleum alpinum* and rocky toadflax* *Linaria petraea)* have been able to survive in the Jura.

Climate. The climate of the Jura is humid and rather oceanic. At the southern foot it may be temporarily very warm and arid owing to the strong solar radiation. Numerous subatlantic species which have their main distribution in the Atlantic region but may reach to the Central European region and do not climb very high occur in the Jura. Here

* species neither included in colour Plates not described in Chapter 6.

31

belong e.g. stinking hellebore* *(Helleborus foetidus)*, watery figwort* *(Scrophularia aquatica*, heath pea* *(Vicia orobus)*. Diverse fens and bogs in the Jura include rare Nordic plants e.g. goat's saxifrage* *(Saxifraga hirculus)*, dwarf birch* *(Betula nana)*, upright sandwort* *(Minuartia stricta)*. Many submediterran plants (species which are mostly distributed within the Mediterranean region and north of it) grow at the southern foot of the Jura. Good examples of this group are white oak* *(Quercus pubescens)*, St. Lucie's cherry* *(Prunus mahaleb)*, Italian maple* *(Acer opalus)*, lizard orchid* *(Himantoglossum hircinum)*. Numerous steppe plants of East Europe e.g. common pasqueflower* *(Pulsatilla vulgaris)* and blackish broom* *(Cytisus nigricans)* occur in the northern part of the Jura. Various southern and southwestern species of Central European and South European mountains e.g. narrow-leaved red valerian* *(Kentranthus angustifolius)*, hyssop-leaved ironwort* *(Sideritis hyssopifolia)*, mountain kidney-vetch *(Anthyllis montana)* and Jurassic figwort* *(Scrophularia juratensis)* are also characteristic of the Jura.

2.2.2. Northern Alps

Situation. On account of the floristic composition the northern boundary of the Northern Alps was accepted as the line formed by the Napf, the Rigi, the Rossberg, and the Speer; these molasse mountains rise up to more than 1200 m. The southern boundary of the Northern Alps corresponds to the principal ancient Alpine chain and follows the line: Dents du Midi – Dents de Morcles – Finsteraarhorn – Dammastock – Oberalpstock – Panix pass – Calanda – Rätikon. Valleys in the Northern Alps run mostly along the South-North axis.

Substrata. The Northern Alps consist mostly of calciferous substrata viz. limestones, dolomites, marl, nagelfluh (see Fig. 19, p. 46). Substrata poor in calcium occur only in a few areas (e.g. granites of the massifs of Aare and Gotthard in the northern Bernese Oberland and in the Canton of Uri; verrucano in the Glarus Alps east of the Linth and also in the St. Gall Oberland; rare sandstones and schists poor in calcium in the areas of flysch). The flora of the Northern Alps thus consists mostly of plants typical of calciferous substrata; species requiring siliceous substrata are confined to the areas mentioned above and may also be seen occasionally on a few leached-out hilltops, ridges, or plateaus.

Glaciations. The Northern Alps were rather strongly glaciated, only the mountains situated at the northern border and the highest summits being the ice-free nunataks (non-glaciated knolls). Nunataks were e.g. the Grammont, the Dent de Morcles, the Vanil Noir, the Stockhorn range, the Brienzer Rothorn, the Pilatus, the Napf, the Pizol, the Speer, the Churfirsten, the Rätikon. The nunatak areas are nowadays richer in species than the glaciated areas; particularly characteristic is the isolated occurrence of some species e.g. Seguier's buttercup *(Ranunculus seguieri)* in the area of the Brienzer Rothorn (the nearest localities are the Reculet in the Jura and the area of Judicaria NE of the Lake of Garda) or Austrian hogweed* *(Heracleum austriacum)* at the Napf (the nearest locality is near Berchtesgaden and on Mt. Baldo, 530 km east). Diverse species e.g. Oeder's lousewort *(Pedicularis oederi)*, alpine eryngo *(Eryngium alpinum)*, hoary draba *(Draba incana)*, Sendtner's poppy *(Papaver sendtneri)* occur in Switzerland nearly exclusively in the Northern Alps. Orange-red saxifrage *(Saxifraga mutata)* is distributed mainly in the Alpine foreland. Milky rock-jasmine *(Androsace lactea)* which reached the Hohgant immigrated from the west; mountain pansy *(Viola lutea)* expanded to the Reuss, western poppy *(Papaver occidentale)* to the Brienzer Rothorn; Carinthian buttercup* *(Ranunculus carinthiacus)* with, today, its main limit of distribution at the Hohgant and an isolated location on the Rigi as well as Thora buttercup *(Ranunculus thora)* which can be seen up to the Vanil Noir also arrived from the west. On the other hand, pannonic gentian *(Gentiana pannonica)* which reached the Churfirsten, and Sendtner's poppy *(Papaver sendtneri)* which can be found up to the Pilatus immigrated from the east.

Climate. The climate of the Northern Alps is humid and rather oceanic. Warmer temperatures and stronger solar radiation are confined to valleys influenced by the foehn. Similarly to the Jura, the foreland of the Northern Alps includes bogs with rare Nordic plants e.g. dwarf birch* *(Betula nana)* or holy-grass* *(Hierochloe odorata)*. Warmth-loving plants are characteristic of the foehn valleys; there one can find e.g. woodruff of Turin* *(Asperula taurina)*, European cyclamen *(Cyclamen europaeum)*, stemless primrose* *(Primula acaulis)*, pinnate bladdernut* *(Staphylea pinnata)* or coris St. John's wort* *(Hypericum coris)*.

2.2.3. Southern Alps

Situation. The Southern Alps comprise the southern Alpine ranges. Their northern boundary corresponds to the line: Graian Alps – Monte Rosa – Simplon – Gotthard – St. Bernardino – Maloja – Bernina pass – Tonale pass. The southern limit is defined by the border of the plain of the Po. The valleys run mostly from north to south.

Substrata. The substrata in the northern and western part of the Southern Alps are almost exclusively cristalline and poor in calcium. On the other hand, the south-eastern part (south of the line: Luino – Lugano – Val Colla – Valsassina) consists as a rule of calciferous substrata, dolomite being frequent (see Fig. 19, p. 46). The flora of the northern part of the Southern Alps corresponds at high altitudes to the plant cover of the Central Alps. Typical plants of the Central Alps requiring siliceous substrata e.g. larch-leaved sandwort *(Minuartia laricifolia)*, Scheuchzer's rampion *(Phyteuma scheuchzeri)*, pyramidal saxifrage *(Saxifraga cotyledon)* or paniculate fescue* *(Festuca paniculata)* occur almost exclusively below the timberline. The flora of the southern calcareous part of the Southern Alps is very rich, the

Bergamo Alps being particularly interesting; species representing this flora in Switzerland occur only near the Lake of Lugano and their number is rather limited.

Glaciations. The northern part of the Southern Alps was rather strongly glaciated except for some high summits; the southern part was, on the other hand, only slightly glaciated and included some survival centers. The flora of the southern areas is thus particularly rich in various plant species, endemics (taxa which occur only in a given area) being numerous especially in the southern Bergamo Alps. Typical species include Elisabeth's campion* *(Silene elisabethae)*, saxifrage of Presolana* *(Saxifraga presolanensis)*, Tonzig's toadflax* *(Linaria tonzigii)*, Rainer's bellflower* *(Campanula raineri)*, waterwort-like bellflower *(Campanula elatinoides)*, splendid ox-eye *(Buphtalmum speciosissimum)*. Some rare endemics occur, too, in the northern part of the Southern Alps which consists of substrata poor in calcium; here one can see e.g. Rhaetic knapweed* *(Centaurea rhaetica)*, antique yellow-rattle* *(Rhinanthus antiquus)*, short rock-jasmine *(Androsace brevis)*, Rhaetic rampion *(Phyteuma hedraianthifolia)*, burnet of Bergamo* *(Sanguisorba dodecandra)* and Comolli's violet* *(Viola comollii)*.

Climate. The climate of the Southern Alps is characterized by high precipitation and strong solar radiation; lower areas enjoy mild winters. At lower altitudes numerous characteristic species which are distributed at the southern foot of the Alpine chain occur. They include e.g. dubious knapweed* *(Centaurea dubia)*, bract-shaped knapweed* *(Centaurea bracteata)*, red bedstraw *(Galium rubrum)* and also various Mediterranean plants e.g. sage-leaved cistus* *(Cistus salviifolius)*, tree heath *(Erica arborea)*, and some subatlantic species e.g. broom* *(Cytisus scoparius)* and gorse* *(Ulex europaeus)*. Some warmth-loving plants e.g. German broom *(Genista germanica)*, elder orchid *(Orchis sambucina)* etc. are well-distributed in the Southern Alps but rare in the Central and Northern Alps.

Some local taxa characteristic only of a particular insubrian climate e.g. insubrian gentian* *(Gentiana insubrica)* or cisalpine eye-bright* *(Euphrasia cisalpina)* are apparently of postglacial origin.

2.2.4. Central Alps

Situation. The Central Alps form the inner part of the Alpine chain between the Northern and the Southern Alps. Characteristic of this area are valleys running from west to east or vice versa. The Central Alps comprise the highest Alpine massifs; plants of high altitudes that are rare or absent in outer Alpine ranges (e.g. alpine rock-jasmine *Androsace alpina*, king of the Alps *Eritrichium nanum* or globularia-leaved rampion *Phyteuma globulariifolium)* thus occur abundantly in this area.

Substrata. The Central Alps consist mostly of substrata poor in calcium; calcium-rich (in particular marl-like) substrata occur scattered throughout this part of the Alpine chain. Pure calcareous areas may be exemplified by the Lower Engadine and the region of Arosa (see Fig. 19, p. 46). Plants typical of siliceous substrata prevail in the Central Alps but calcium-indicating species are in general also well-represented; the areas in which both substratum types occur are thus very rich in species. The Central Alpine areas with calcareous schists have some characteristic species of their own e.g. corymbose pennycress *(Thlaspi corymbosum)*, Hoppe's draba *(Draba hoppeana)*, short-stemmed hutchinsia *(Hutchinsia brevicaulis)* and fringed sandwort *(Arenaria ciliata)*.

Glaciations. The Central Alps were strongly glaciated, only few mountain tops jutting above the ice sheet within the highest massifs e.g. near Zermatt and in the region of the Bernina. Endemic plants are thus rare in this part of the Alps; they are confined to a few high massifs. For instance, incised bellflower *(Campanula excisa)*, one-headed groundsel *(Senecio uniflorus)*, large-flowered houseleek* *(Sempervivum grandiflorum)* and Christ's eye bright* *(Euphrasia christii)* occur in the eastern part of the Pennine and Graian Alps; dwarf rampion *(Phyteuma humile)* grows solely in the area of the Monte Rosa; primrose of the Daone valley* *(Primula daonensis)* is found exclusively in the Ortler area; Ladine draba *(Draba ladina)* occurs only in the Dolomites of the Lower Engadine. Flesh-coloured rock-jasmine *(Androsace carnea)*, yellow rock-jasmine *(A. vitaliana)*, glacial wormwood *(Artemisia glacialis)*, hoary groundsel *(Senecio incanus)* occur exclusively in the western part of the Central Alps. On the other hand, glacial pink *(Dianthus glacialis)* and Carniol groundsel *(Senecio carniolicus)* can be found only in the eastern part of the Central Alps.

Climate. The climate of the Central Alps is rather continental (low annual precipitation, great fluctuations in temperature, strong solar radiation). For instance, Grächen in the Wallis has a summer precipitation of only 15 cm whereas Engelberg in the Northern Alps has 70 cm. Nearly all plants inhabiting the Central Alps climb higher than those growing in the Northern and the Southern Alps. Characteristic of the Central Alps are numerous steppe plants occurring especially in the Wallis and the Aosta valley; they include e.g. feathergrass species *(Stipa pinnata* s. l., *S. capillata)*, various species of milk-vetch* *(Astragalus exscapus, A. onobrychis)*, downy-beaked oxytropis *(Oxytropis pilosa)* or Austrian dragonhead* *(Dracocephalum austriacum)*. Swiss ephedra* *(Ephedra helvetica)*, alpine stock *(Matthiola vallesiaca)*, knapweed of Wallis* *(Centaurea vallesiaca)* and Haller's pasqueflower *(Pulsatilla halleri)* are representative of the Central Alpine steppes.

3. Climate and soil of the Alps

Climatic and edaphic differences lead to the formation of different types of vegetation. The diversity of Alpine vegetation and differences between the plant world at high altitudes and in the lowlands are thus only comprehensible when something is known about the climatic factors and the soils. This chapter deals in particular with differences between the lowlands and the Alpine areas. Unless otherwise mentioned, most of the data originate from Schroeter *(3.k.)*.

3.1. Atmospheric pressure

Atmospheric pressure decreases with altitude. The average pressure at sea level is about 760 mm; in Zurich (411 m) it corresponds to 727 mm, in Grächen (1600 m) to 628 mm, and at the Mt. Blanc (data from a station at about 4300 m) it reaches about 450 mm.

Atmospheric pressure has only an indirect effect upon plants since the humidity of the air and the carbon dioxide content per volume unit decrease with diminishing pressure (thus with increasing altitude). For this reason plants lose more water when their stomata (regulated openings, mostly on the leaf underside, which serve for gas exchange) are open. Also, the stomata must stay open for a longer time if a mountain plant is to get the same amount of CO_2 and to synthesize the same amount of sugar as a corresponding plant in the lowlands. The water budget of mountain plants is therefore rather precarious if the water supply is limited.

3.2. Temperature

3.2.1. Air temperature.
The temperature of the air decreases in annual mean value of $0.55°C$ per 100 m with increasing altitude. This decrease corresponds to only $0.4°C$ in fall and winter but runs up to $0.7°C$ in spring and summer. The mean annual temperature in Zurich (480 m) is $8.5°C$, in Seewis (954 m) it is $6.6°C$, in Davos (1561 m) $2.7°C$, and at the Julier pass (2237 m) it stays below zero ($-0.7°C$). A small part of the solar radiation is absorbed by the air (on an average, about 20% above the ground); it is fairly permeable in the visible part of the spectrum. Another part is reflected and dispersed, partly through water particles of the clouds as well as dust particles. The amount of solar radiation taken up from the surface of the ground is appreciably larger; thus it is by far

the most important source of heat to the atmosphere, emitting energy as a/ long-wave or infra-red radiation, b/ heat stored in the ascending water vapour and c/ through turbulent movement of the air. The long-wave radiation is greatly absorbed in the air, especially by the water vapour and CO_2. The lowest air layers are heated most because they are nearer to the surface of the ground than the heat source, and particularly since they contain much water vapour, CO_2, and dust particles. An inversion may occur during the stable anticyclone in autumn and/or winter: the air layers closest to the ground cool off increasingly as the low sun supplies less heat in the short daytime than is lost during the night. This cold air remains enclosed over the Midlands between the Alps and the Jura. During an anticyclone the air in higher layers flows down slowly and at the same time is warmed up because of the compression. With the same water vapour content per 1 kg air, the relative humidity decreases with increasing altitude (good visibility at high altitudes, above the cold air layer). A persistent high cloud cover reinforces the thermic contrast. The mean temperature decrease with increasing altitude is therefore less sharp in autumn and winter than in spring and summer.

Numerous life functions being temperature-dependent, temperature plays an important rôle in plants. On the whole, speed of life processes (thus also of growth) increases with increasing temperature up to some plant-specific threshold. The growth of plants in high altitudes which have low temperatures is thus less intensive than that of lowland plants.

3.2.2. Solar radiation. *Solar radiation is appreciably stronger at high altitudes than in the lowlands.* It is more than twice as strong at 1800 m as at sea level, only some rays being reflected or dispersed in the high-mountain air poor in dust or water droplets. Notwithstanding much lower temperatures, objects are thus heated more at higher altitudes than in the lowlands. The difference between an object exposed to the sun and one remaining in the shade may easily exceed $50°C$ at an altitude higher than 3000 m whereas it often does not amount to more than $10°C$ at sea level within the same geographical latitude. Rock temperatures of $50°C$ and more are not infrequent above 2000 m.

Owing to the strong radiation plants growing on south-facing slopes of the Alps are able to compensate, at least partially, for the low mean temperature; plants in those sites nearly always climb much higher than those inhabiting north-exposed places. However, sharp thermal contrasts and great temperature fluctuations make some demands on plants, water budget being particularly affected (See chapter 4.1).

The Central Alps have low precipitation and limited cloudiness, solar radiation being particularly strong; many plants are thus able to climb higher than in outer Alpine ranges, even if mean temperatures at a comparable height are not very different in the latter areas. In the Southern Alps, too, radiation is stronger than in the Northern Alps but weaker than in the Central Alps. The high precipitation being very intensive, average cloudiness in the Southern Alps is lower than in the Northern Alps.

3.2.3. Nocturnal heat emission. *Nocturnal heat emission becomes stronger with increasing altitude.* It increases by 40° between 300 m and 3000 m. The temperature drop during clear (dry) and calm nights may be more than 20°C; in addition, temperature directly on the surface of the ground is lower by 2–8 degrees than that 2 m above. In the lowlands, dust hanging in the air absorbs a large part of the emitted heat which is then sent again towards the ground. A small part retained by water vapour and CO_2 remains in the air.

As far as plants are concerned, strong nocturnal heat emission in the mountains signifies frost danger nearly throughout the year; the plants must therefore be frost-resistant, also during their period of growth.

3.2.4. Temperature and large massifs. *Large massifs have high mean altitude above sea level (in Switzerland mostly the Central Alps esp. the Wallis and the Engadine). During the daytime and in summer they warm up more than isolated mountain groups e.g. the Jura or the outer Alpine ranges* (Fig. 12, p. 39).

Owing to the direct solar radiation the soil is heated much more than the surrounding air. Compared to its surrounding air mass, the soil which can be heated is much larger in large massifs than in isolated mountains; the balancing influence of the air is therefore rather weak and the temperature drop during the night or in winter may be very pronounced. The occurrence of large massifs reinforces the influence of solar radiation which is strong because of little cloud; temperature fluctuations are thus very great in these areas. For instance, mean air temperature in July at 1:00 p.m. and at 1500 m is 14°C on the Rigi (an isolated mountain in the Northern Alps) but reaches 19°C in the Engadine, although the mean annual temperatures of these two areas differ from one another only by 0.5°C (Fig. 13).

Plants living in the Central Alps must endure more extreme temperatures than species inhabiting the outer Alpine ranges. On the other hand, the plants can grow higher in the Central Alps because the diurnal temperature rise is stronger there. Warmth-loving (but frost-resistant) species which otherwise occur only in southern areas or steppes are able to inhabit places at rather high altitudes in the central part of the Alpine chain.

3.2.5. Cold air pools. *Valleys and gullies are colder during the night and in winter than the surrounding slopes and hilltops.* Bever (1712 m) in the Upper Engadine has a mean January temperature of –9.8°C, the Julier pass (2237 m) – that of –8.3°C whereas the isolated Rigi (1775 m) has only –4.3°C. The frigid air, heavier than the warm air, flows into vallyes and gullies and becomes trapped there.

Plants growing in valleys, gullies, and hollows must withstand extreme temperature fluctuations and prolonged periods of frost.

3.2.6. Soil temperature. *Soil stores up the solar radiation.* Owing to the strong solar radiation at higher altitudes the soil in the mountain becomes more heated than in the lowlands. At an altitude of 600 m a. s. l. the mean annual soil temperature 1.2 m below the ground is

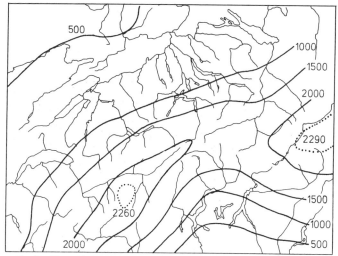

Fig. 12. Mean altitudes above sea level (calculated in m for squares with lateral length of 64 km). After LEHNER (from *3.b.*).

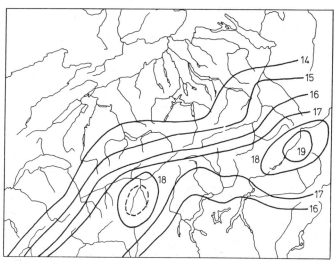

Fig. 13. Mean July temperatures (°C) measured at 1:00 p. m. at 1500 m. a.s.l. After DE QUERVAIN (from *3.k.*).

39

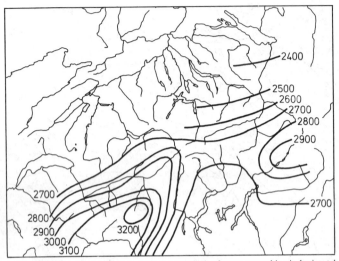

Fig. 14. Climatic snow limit in m a.s.l. (mean limit of snow not melting in horizontal surfaces). After JEGERLEHNER (from *3.k.*).

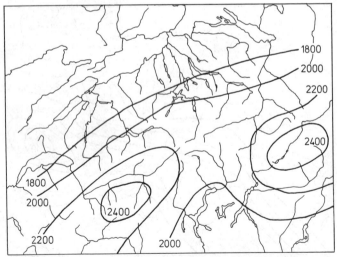

Fig. 15. Mean altitude of the timberline in m a.s. l. (after data and observations on the highest growing trees and tree groups).

40

0.5°C higher than the mean air temperature; the corresponding difference at 1500 m is 1.7°C and that at 3000 m – 2.9°C. South-facing slopes obviously store more heat in the soil.

The heat of the soil influences the air layers close to the ground; low-growing plants, able to take full advantage of the warm air, therefore occur very often in the Alps. Evaporation in warm soils being strong, they may dry out rapidly on the surface. Plants occurring above the timberline are mostly dependent on soil heat.

3.3. Light

Light intensity increases with altitude. At 1600 m it is twice as strong in summer, in winter even six times as strong, as at sea level (sun protection at high altitudes!) and the ultraviolet part is conspicuously greater. *Light intensity difference between sunny and shady places also increases with altitude.* At 3000 m light intensity is 6.5 times higher in sun than in shadow whereas at 2000 m it is only twice as high. Similarly to heat waves, light rays (esp. ultraviolet rays) are partly absorbed in the atmosphere so that fewer rays reach the lowlands. Part of the light is dispersed by the haze particles in the air; in this way light reaches shady places, too. The air in the lowlands being dusty and hazy, more light becomes dispersed and shadowy places are lighter.

High light intensity is favourable to sugar synthesis (assimilation) in plants; in spite of low temperatures, plants are able to build up a sufficient amount of sugar. On the other hand, plants have to protect themselves from too intense light (esp. the ultraviolet rays) with pigmentation, hairiness, thick cuticle (cuticle is a layer coating external cell-walls in plants; it contains wax which protects tissues). Bright colours of flowers often result from an intensive synthesis of dye compounds in a strong light.

3.4. Precipitation and humidity

3.4.1. Amount of precipitation.
Annual precipitation increases with altitude and with the proximity of the Alps. In the area of Zurich it amounts to about 1 m and increases to more than 3 m on the north side of the Alps at 3000 m. When humid air cools off, part of its moisture is eliminated in the form of precipitation (rain, snow, hail). Air in the proximity of mountains flows upwards and therefore cools off; this process explains the high precipitation in the Alps (Fig. 16). It can be accepted as a rule of thumb that precipitation increases by 100 mm/ 100 m between 500 and 2500 m a. s. l.

The precipitation is particularly high in the outer ranges of the Southern Alps because they rise very steeply from the plain of the Po. In contrast to the Northern Alps, precipitation intensity is, however, much higher there; the Southern Alps have thus rather long periods of aridity and, above all, strong solar radiation.

The Central Alps are more arid than the outer Alpine ranges. Humid air masses that reach the Alps from the south, west, or north, flow

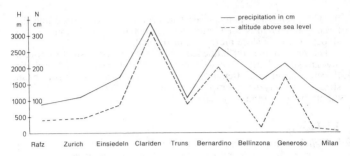

Fig. 16. Mean annual precipitation in the Alps along a gradient Zurich–Milan.

upwards over the outer ranges and there release the largest part of their moisture; the valleys of the Central Alps situated on the lees, thus receive little precipitation. The lowest precipitation in Switzerland is reported from the Wallis and the Lower Engadine; outside Switzerland, the Aosta valley and the Vintschgau are still more arid (Figs 16–17).

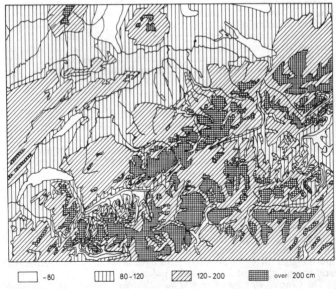

| | -80 | | 80-120 | | 120-200 | | over 200 cm |

Fig. 17. Mean annual precipitation in the Swiss Alps (after 3.e., simplified).

42

It can be seen in Fig. 18 that precipitation in the Central, Northern and Southern Alps is comparable as far as higher altitudes are concerned; differences in precipitation are thus hardly of importance to plants inhabiting the alpine and subnival belt (above the timberline).

Since the amount of precipitation is low, lower altitude sites in the Central Alps are often inhabited by steppe plants which are widely distributed on shallow soils on south-facing slopes, in places where forest has been cleared by Man. The driest areas are typically inhabited by pine forest. Fertilized meadows must be irrigated. At higher altitudes and in outer Alpine ranges the soil is sufficiently humid for most of the Alpine plants; it may temporarily dry out only on steep slopes and wind-exposed ridges.

	Altitude	Northern Alps	Central Alps	Southern Alps
precipitation in cm	500 m	100–170	50–70	140–200
	1000 m	160–180	50–80	200–240
	1500 m	180–220	50–120	200–260
	2000 m	200–280	80–180	200–280
	2500 m	200–300	160–250	200–300
mean temperature in °C — year	500 m	8–9	8,5–10	9,5–10,5
	2000 m	0,5–2,5	0,5–2	1–2,5
summer	500 m	16–17	17,5–19	17–18
	2000 m	7–8,5	9–10	8–9,5
winter	500 m	−1,5–0,5	−0,5–1	1–2,5
	2000 m	−4,5– −6,5	−5,5– −10	−4– −6,5

Fig. 18. Temperature and precipitation at different altitudes in the Swiss Alps (after the data from *3.1.* and *3.m.*).

3.4.2. Air moisture content. *The absolute air moisture (g water vapour per m³) diminishes with increasing altitude.* During a period of fair weather the air may become exceedingly dry (the pure mountain air, great thirst during mountain trips!). At 2000 m the air is on an average only half as moist as in the plains; it retains less moisture since it is less dense and cooler.

Because of the dry air plants growing high in the Alps lose more water by transpiration than lowland species living in otherwise comparable conditions. The danger of wilting is thus very real, cool water not being readily supplied in the soil.

3.5. Snow

3.5.1. Snow cover and snow limit. *Duration of the snow cover increases with altitude.* On the north-facing side of the Central Alps the average snow-free period amounts to nine months at 600 m, the corresponding data for 1000 m, 1300 m, 1800 m, and 2500 m being eight, seven, five, and two months, respectively; the snow-free period thus decreases in length by about ten days per 100 m upwards. On the south-facing side of the Central Alps the snow-free period is about one month longer at lower altitudes and up to two months longer at higher altitudes. *The climatic snow limit* (i.e. the limit at which the snow on horizontal surfaces still melts in summer) corresponds to 2400–2700 m in the Northern Alps, to 2700–3200 m in the Central Alps, and to 2700–2800 m in the Southern Alps (Fig. 14, p. 40). Snow may lie late at lower altitudes in shady places and the avalanche paths; on the other hand, south-facing slopes and cliffs may be snow-free in summer up to the summit. Snow limit is influenced by summer temperatures and precipitation level. In the Central Alps (esp. the Wallis and the Engadine) summer temperatures are higher and precipitation lower than in the outer Alpine ranges; the snow limit thus lies higher.

Flowering plants can grow only in places that are snow-free at least for a brief period (two months on average) every year since temperature and light intensity under the snow cover are not sufficient to ensure successful growth.

3.5.2. Insulating snow cover. *Snow cover is insulating.* At an air temperature of 17°C below zero, the temperature measured in the snow at 20 cm depth was –8°C, at 40 cm depth – –3°C, and at 50 cm depth i.e. directly on the ground it was only –1.6°C. Snow is a bad heat conductor; given a sufficiently thick snow cover, the temperature of the soil remains at about freezing point notwithstanding the temperature of the air; the ground under snow is thus hardly frozen.

A thick snow cover protects plants from frost and desiccation; should the snow fail to come in winter, plants are often destroyed. The winter snow cover is also an important water reserve that keeps the soil moist later in season.

On the other hand, the snow cover keeps light away from the plants. They receive only 30% of the light through a snow layer that is 5 cm thick; if the snow cover is 20 cm thick, only 5% of the light can reach the plants *(4.g.)*. However, the plants are able to synthesize a small amount of sugar below a shallow snow cover if the temperature does not fall much below freezing point.

3.6. Wind

Mean wind velocity increases with altitude. On the Säntis (2400 m) the wind is three times as rapid as in Zurich (7.2 m per second vs 2.5 m per second). Wind velocity diminishes close to the ground because of friction.

The wind may influence plants in various ways and sometimes does it quite drastically. It may inflict purely mechanical damage to plant parts or tear out whole plants; it may blow the snow away and thus expose plants to frost; it may appreciably shorten the growing period by accumulating snowdrifts. In general, wind increases evaporation in plants. Alpine plants growing in wind-exposed places must therefore be well anchored to the ground, resistant to mechanical damage, and effectively protected against evaporation.

3.7. Substrata

Substrata in the Alps are very varied and in some areas form a mosaic pattern. *The Northern Alps are mostly built of calciferous rocks* (nagelfluh, marl, limestone, calciferous sandstone, calcium-bearing schists etc.). Rocks poor in calcium are rather infrequent (e.g. some schists in the verrucano and the flysch of the Glarus Alps east of the Linth, and in the St. Gall Oberland; cristalline rocks in the massif of the Aare in the Bernese Oberland). *The Central and Southern Alps consist mostly of siliceous* (i.e. partly formed by salts of the silicic acid) *rocks;* they are mostly poor in calcium and weather to clayey soils. However, calciferous rocks are well-distributed in the Bernese Alps west of the Lötschenpass, in the central and northern Grisons, the Lower Engadine and southern Ticino. Calciferous substrata may also occur in other areas; for instance, the Bündnerschiefer schists comprise both calcium-rich and calcium-poor rocks and frequently also contain serpentine which is very poor in nutrients (Fig. 19).

Some plants prefer calcium-rich substrata, others grow better in soils poor in calcium; depending on the type of substratum, the plant cover may therefore be quite distinct and pronounced differences occur between vegetation inhabiting various substrata even if the climatic conditions are almost identical.

3.8. Soil

Soil is formed as a result of physical and chemical weathering of the mother rock (due to frost, temperature stress, root pressure, colume increase during hydration of salts esp. from anhydride to gypsum, chemical alteration through dissolving, oxidation, and hydrolysis). Further processes contributing to soil development are formation of humus compounds from decaying organic matter (microorganisms, roots, litter, animals living in the soil) and the shifting of components, derived from weathering and decaying, into the soil profile and out of it (leaching of soluble compounds by seepage; supplying by downslope water flow, ground-water or heavy rainfall; burrowing of animals in the soil; erosion and accumulation of debris). Soil development depends on the mother substratum, climate, organisms and the time available.

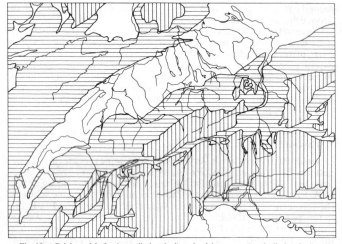

Fig. 19. Calcium-rich (horizontally hatched) and calcium-poor (vertically hatched) rocks in the Swiss Alps. The substrata of the Swiss Midlands were not distinguished between but they mostly contain calcium. After *3.e.,* simplified.

A vertical cut through the soil called *soil profile* is usually differentiated into various layers (horizons). Such profiles are often visible along roads that have been cut into the soil. Depending on the soil profile various types of soil can be distinguished. *Raw soil* in areas near the snow limit and on unstable slopes (talus, scree, landslips) consists nearly exclusively of a slightly weathered mother rock. All transitions between the raw soil and the fully-developed soil may occur in a given area. Special wet soils (e.g. mire soils, soils of wet woodlands, gley soils etc.) occur on impermeable layers, in particular on those which are rich in clay (e.g. flysch and also in places constantly or intermittently irrigated (banks of streams, lakesides, flushes etc.). Alpine soils can otherwise be classified as follows:

3.8.1. Podsols. The uppermost layer is up to 50 cm thick and often consists of pure organic humus with pH values[5] of 3.5–4.5 (acid). Underneath occurs a light-grey, bleached mineral layer from which soluble mineral compounds, iron and aluminium have been washed out. The deepest layer of accumulation ist rust-red; it contains iron and aluminium hydroxide together with humus compounds. Podsols

[5] *pH values* refer to acidity of a given solution. They form a scale from 0 to 14. pH 7 signifies a neutral solution; pH below 7 corresponds to an acidic solution, and pH above 7 – to alkalic one. A soil with pH below 4.6 is referred to as strongly acid, that with pH of 4.6–5.8 is considered as acid, whereas pH between 5.8 and 6.6 determines weakly-acid soils. Samples with pH between 6.6 and 7.3 are neutral, those with pH above 7.3 – alkalic or basic.

develop above on substrata poor in calcium, in moist areas characterized by cold winters and rather warm summers; upon calciferous substrata podsolization is hindered. Podsols are widely distributed in the Alps under coniferous forests (spruce, Arolla pine) and dwarf shrubs; they mostly occur between about 1200 m and the timberline (1800–2500 m). Podsols are humid, very acid, and poor in nutrients; the plants must therefore be quite specialized to grow there.

3.8.2. Brown earths. Mineral and organic components are intricately mixed within the upper soil layer. Alkalic salts and calcium are leached out from the upper layers but iron and aluminium remain. The upper soil layer is brown-grey, the lower layer containing less humus is rust-brown. Brown earths develop upon calciferous substrata in moderately moist areas (in arid areas, they appear also upon substrata poor in calcium). Brown earths occur in the whole of Switzerland under meadows and pastures; in forests they occur mostly up to about 700 m only and then change gradually into podsols. Brown earths are moderately humid and rather nutrient-rich, weakly acid to acid. They can be inhabited by most plants and the competition there is accordingly great.

3.8.3. Limestone rendzina. The uppermost layer is stony, rich in humus and calcium, neutral to weakly basic (pH 6–8). In the lower layers the soil turns gradually into the mother substratum. Limestone rendzinas develop upon substrata very rich in calcium and poor in clay, in dry to moist areas, particularly on slopes. In Switzerland, they are distributed upon limestone and dolomite up to and above the timberline. Limestone rendzinas are rather dry, rich in calcium, and frequently also in nutrient, neutral to weakly basic. They are mostly inhabited by specialized plants.

3.8.4. Marl rendzina. The uppermost layer contains only a little humus. The soil consists of grey layers rich in clay and calcium, impermeable and therefore intermittently humid. It is neutral to weakly basic. Marl rendzina develops from the marl (i.e. calcium-rich clay) on slopes; it occurs throughout the whole of Switzerland and can be found at any altitude. It is frequently very dry in summer, but otherwise remains moist to wet; it is rich in calcium and usually also in nutrients, neutral to weakly basic. Marl rendzina is inhabited by specialized plants.

3.8.5. Siliceous humus soils or **rankers.** The uppermost layer of the soil is rich in humus and also stony; it lies directly upon physically weathered mother rock that is poor in calcium. Siliceous humus soils develop above the timberline upon substrata poor in calcium; they are moist, weakly acidic, and contain only a limited amount of nutrients. Plants inhabiting this type of soil must be specialized similarly to those growing on podsols. Soils above the timberline which develop upon substrata poor in calcium mostly represent transitions between podsols, rankers, and raw soils. Particularly frequent are soils which have no typical bleached horizon but otherwise are rather similar to podsols.

4. Alpine plants and their environment

Form and life function in plants are determined by genetic and ecological factors. Various individuals of a given species differ a little from each other in their genetic make-up and their environmental responses are thus different. Plants in their original site usually respond suitably towards external factors. Should the conditions of the site (e.g. climate) change, the plants become less competitive and may eventually be ousted from their habitat. Species which remain competitive over large areas are in fact genetically/ecologically[6] differentiated into various races. Marguerite *(Chrysanthemum leucanthemum)*, dandelion *(Taraxacum officinale)* or yarrow *(Achillea millefolium)* grow in a number of sites from the lowlands to over 2000 m. The lowland races, however, are not sufficiently competitive in the Alps and are replaced there by specialized races which are morphologically only a little different; vice versa, the Alpine races are not competitive enough in the lowlands.

4.1. Water budget

Should a plant lose more water than it can take up from the soil, it wilts and will eventually perish if the water loss is not replaced in a short time. Pronounced dryness of the air and strong desiccating winds cause a high evaporation in Alpine plants. A rapid replacement of the water lost is hampered because the soil is cold esp. in the morning, irrigated by melting snow, or even frozen (water is taken up more rapidly at higher soil temperatures than at lower ones). Influence of frost is often due to desiccation: when the air becomes warm again, during sunny and/or windy weather, the plant loses water by evaporation but is unable to take it up from the frozen soil. Soil also dries out very rapidly on cliffs, steep south-facing slopes ridges, etc. Despite high precipitation, the danger of desiccation is generally more serious in the Alps than in the lowlands; Alpine plants have thus evolved numerous protective characters. Only the plants inhabiting shady, wind-protected, long snow-covered slopes and hollows over the timberline do not need any particular protection against evaporation. The following adaptations are characteristic of Alpine plants:

a. Nanism. Dwarf growth permits a maximum use of the heat of the soil and offers protection against desiccation by wind. Wind velocity is

[6] *Ecology* deals with relationships between various organisms, and also with those between organisms and their environment.

relatively low directly above ground, the evaporation in low-growing plants being therefore less intensive than in tall individuals: also, the water can be supplied much more rapidly. Dwarf plants are better protected by snow in winter, too. Plants living in an Alpine climate are mostly low-growing on account of the high light intensity and cold night temperatures. Plants kept in the shade elongate in the same way as Alpine plants brought to the lowlands; on the other hand, characteristic dwarf growth of Alpine plants is genetically controlled, this control being generally absent in plants from the plains. Nanism can take various forms:

Flat cushions. The principal shoot branches out just over the ground and numerous densely-leaved lateral shoots form a closed, domed structure. Similarly to mosses, cushion plants are able to suck up large amounts of water (water reserve); evaporation is reduced because a layer of calm air is formed beneath the dense leaf canopy. Cushion plants are exemplified by stemless moss campion *(Silene acaulis)*, mossy cyphal sandwort *(Minuartia sedoides)*, Swiss rock-jasmine *(Androsace helvetica)*, blue saxifrage *(Saxifraga caesia)*, cushion sedge *(Carex firma)*. Cushion plants are particularly common on stabilized scree slopes and upon cliffs at high altitudes.

Rosettes. The leaves are mostly grouped in a compact flat circle, only the flowering shoots being taller. Good examples are white mountain saxifrage *(Saxifraga aizoon)*, draba *(Draba)*, primrose *(Primula)* daisy-leaved speedwell *(Veronica bellidioides)*, hawkbit *(Leontodon)*. The buds are protected within the rosettes. Rosette-forming plants are the most frequent growth type in alpine grasslands.

Tussocks. Each plant forms numerous, densely-clustered tufts, as exemplified by mat-grass *(Nardus stricta)*, coloured fescue *(Festuca varia)*, alpine sedge *(Carex curvula)*, stellar hare's ear *(Bupleurum stellatum)*, wood pink *(Dianthus silvester)*. The buds and young leaves are protected by old leaves. Tussock plants occur frequently in meagre grasslands and on cliffs.

Carpets. Prostrate leaves and stems of a plant trail over the ground as e.g. in net-leaved willow *(Salix reticulata)*, mountain avens *(Dryas octopetala)*, trailing azalea *(Loiseleuria procumbens)*, purple saxifrage *(Saxifraga oppositifolia)*. Carpet plants use the heat of the soil optimally. They grow preferably in places not much influenced by competition, mainly in windy corners and stabilized scree.

b. Large root-system and ample underground organs. The larger the root-system, the more water and nutrients can be taken up from the soil. Roots and underground parts of the stem serve partly as water-storage organs and anchor plants in the soil. Plants with large underground organs are able to survive an occasional frostbite or desiccation of the aboveground parts. Some alpine plants that are barely 10 cm tall e.g. small willows *(Salix)* or French honeysuckle *(Hedysarum)* develop exceedingly long roots and underground stems.

c. Protection against evaporation in leaves. Water evaporates through the leaf stomata; water loss through the epidermis is less serious because the cell walls of the external cell layer are mostly sealed with waxy compounds. Stomata are for the most part situated on the underside of leaves; they regulate the gas exchange, above all the uptake of carbon dioxide (CO_2) and the release of oxygen (O_2) during the synthesis of sugar (assimilation[7]). Assimilation can only proceed in the light: thus stomata must remain open during the day-time. Water is supplied through the veins of the leaf. The farther the part of the leaf lie from the veins, the more pronounced is the danger of desiccation; leaves in Alpine plants are therefore generally small (except for plants living in shady places), but – unlike those in steppe plants – relatively broad. In order to take up a sufficient amount of CO_2 which is less concentrated at high altitudes, they have more stomata per surface unit than the leaves of lowland plants.

Special features as protection against evaporation are:

Dense hairiness (esp. on the leaf underside). Hairs hold off a part of the solar radiation, above all the damaging UV-rays; they surround the leaf with a layer of moist calm air so reducing evaporation. As stomata are generally on the leaf underside, hairs are often confined to this part of the leaf whereas the upper part is usually protected by a thick layer of wax. In some cases, plants are able to take up dew of fog droplets with their hairs. Densely pilose leaves occur e.g. in edelweiss *(Leontopodium alpinum)*, pussytoes *(Antennaria)*, wormwood *(Artemisia):* mountain avens *(Dryas octopetala)* has leaves that are hairy on the underside only.

Wax coating. Waxy external cell walls occur rather seldom in Alpine plants. They can be seen e.g. in rubble dock *(Rumex scutatus)*, bird's eye primrose *(Primula farinosa)*, glabrous cerinthe *(Cerinthe glabra)*.

Leathery leaves. Evergreen leaves with particularly thick-walled epidermis occur generally in dwarf shrubs and semi-shrubs. They are rather resistant against desiccation; their firmness guarantees water replacement, even after a prolonged period of drought. Leather leaves occur e.g. in cowberry *(Vaccinium vitis-idaea)*, common bearberry *(Arctostaphylos uva-ursi)*, trailing azalea *(Loiseleuria procumbens)*, shrubby milkwort *(Polygala chamaebuxus)*, alpine rockrose *(Helianthemum alpestre)*.

Rolled leaves. Margins of leathery leaves may be rolled under to reduce evaporation. Such leaves are often needle-like as e.g. in crowberry *(Empetrum hermaphroditum)*, ling heather *(Calluna vulgaris)*, common heath *(Erica carnea)*. In some species leaves may be folded lengthwise.

Bristle-like leaves. Many grasses and sedges have stiff, bristle-like leaves with margins curved in to reduce evaporation. Similar but cylin-

---

[7] *Assimilation* or *photosynthesis* in plants is the process in which sugar and starch are built from carbon dioxide (CO_2) and water. Assimilation is possible only in light; solely the chlorophyll can use the light energy for the sugar synthesis. During assimilation plants take up CO_2 from the air and release free oxygen. *Respiration* is a catabolic process in which starch, sugar, and other carbohydrates are burned to obtain energy; respiration requires uptake of oxygen from the air and results in release of CO_2.

drical leaves occur in rush *(Juncus)* and chives *(Allium schoenoprasum)*.

Succulence. Thick fleshy leaves or stems frequently occurring in halophytes or desert plants partly serve as water-storing organs. Succulence in Alpine plants is rather rare; it occurs in some species growing on exposed cliffs or scree e.g. in houseleek *(Sempervivum)*, stonecrop *(Sedum)* as well as some species of saxifrage *(Saxifraga)*.

4.2. Temperature budget

Many life processes are, partly or totally, chains of chemical reactions. Speed of a chemical reaction increases with increasing temperature (double to threefold per 10°C). Respiration, assimilation, growth, and many other life functions proceed much more rapidly at higher temperatures than at lower ones. At the same annual or diurnal temperature, plants therefore grow better in areas characterized by greater temperature extremes. The timberline thus lies at a much lower annual temperature level in the Central Alps than in the outer Alpine ranges (in Zermatt, at –0.6°C, on the Rigi – at +2.1°C).

No more growth occurs below a minimal temperature threshold and the plants become dormant. The minimal temperature varies from one species to another and often also from one individual to another. Tropical and subtropical plants mostly have rather high minimal temperatures (melons and date-palms, for instance, between 15°C and 18°C). Arctic and alpine species are still able to grow at sub-zero temperatures: many plants synthesize sugar (assimilate) at –6°C and less *(4.q.)*. Respiration, too, may still proceed at low temperatures even if it slows down very much.

On the whole, growing plants are more frost-sensitive than dormant ones. For instance, Arolla pine *(Pinus cembra)* remains undamaged at winter temperatures of –40°C but cannot endure summer temperatures below –8°C; newly-formed needles are still more sensitive and frostbite may occur already at –3°C in summer *(4.o.)*. Rust-leaved alpenrose *(Rhododendron ferrugineum)* becomes damaged by frost at ca. –28°C in winter, but already at –3°C in summer. During the dormant period, the stomata are closed; the plants therefore lose less water and are less exposed to desiccation. In addition, water content of cells is reduced during the dormancy period but the sugar content is high (lower freezing-point!) so that the danger of mechanical damage by ice is not very great. Dormant spruce, larch, and Arolla pine are able to withstand temperatures reaching –40°C (Sibirian coniferous trees – even –70°C); some seeds, bacteria, algae, and fungi (as spores) may also remain undamaged at very low temperatures indeed (ca. –190°C).

Lowland plants mostly stop growing as long as there is danger of frost. In the Alps, however, there is frost danger throughout the year; thus, the plants must be able to withstand sub-zero temperatures during the vegetation period. In this respect they behave similarly to the early-spring flora in the plains. A constantly high sugar content in the cells (as a result of the high light intensity, plants synthesize much sugar that is not all turned into starch at low temperatures) lowers the freezing-point; on the other hand, specialized protective structures, just discussed, prevent desiccation that might be caused by frost.

Alpine plants are able to withstand high temperatures, too. For instance, cushion sedge *(Carex firma)* still assimilates at temperatures approaching 47°C and becomes damaged only at 54°C; the corresponding values for glacier crowfoot *(Ranunculus glacialis)* which usually grows in less-exposed places are 39°C and 48°C, respectively *(4.q.)*.

Characteristic to the way of life of Alpine plants are *(4.p.)*: a/ broad temperature optimum for assimilation which allows plants to use the wide range of diurnal temperatures. b/ metabolic processes and growth proceeding at low temperatures (at 0°C, alpine plants are able to take up about 30–50% of the CO_2 used at optimal temperatures, and differ in this respect from the lowland plants), c/ a rapid beginning of assimilation after the nocturnal frost.

4.3. Vegetation period and reproduction

A plant always respires a little, also in a dormant state; its reserves are thus used during the dormancy period, organic compound being catabolized to obtain energy during respiration. Plants unable to store a sufficient amount of reserves during the growing period must die of hunger; every plant therefore needs a vegetation period, be it a minimal one. Flowering plants with most modest demands (snow-patch inhabitants e.g. dwarf cudweed, *Gnaphalium supinum* or dwarf willow, *Salix herbacea)* are content with just about two months; mosses, lichens and algae are, incidentally, still less demanding.

The vegetation period in the Alps is mostly limited by the long duration of the snow cover. Snow obviously protects plants from frost and desiccation throughout the coldest time of the year; on the other hand, it blocks the growth of plants because of limitation of light and heat at times when external temperatures would permit growth for a long time. Alpine plants must produce flowers and fruits within a short vegetation period, but these processes are very complex. For instance, flowering in many high altitude plants is stimulated by high temperatures but ist is often preceded by an obligatory cool period, lest the flowers appear in autumn or winter when insects are absent and the general conditions unfavourable. Flower-buds for a given season are mostly formed already during the previous summer or autumn so that favourable conditions of the new vegetation period can be used as soon as possible. Glacier crowfoot *(Ranunculus glacialis)* actually forms its flowering structures two years before blooming *(4.p.)*. Some plants do not flower before the days become longer in late spring or summer (long-day flowers). For this reason only a few species e.g. common heath *(Erica carnea)* or shrubby milkwort *(Polygala chamaebuxus)* can be seen in bloom during warm winters. Growth, too, requires both a higher temperature as well as a certain length of the daylight or an undergone cool period. For instance, rhizomes of false hellebore *(Veratrum)* collected in autumn and subsequently put in a warm

52

greenhouse do not grow; but if they are first kept in a cold frame, for about three months, growth occurs at once when the temperature is raised. Seed germination is frequently regulated by quite complex factors in order to preclude premature germination and the subsequent death of seedlings. Seeds of many alpine plants must pass some weeks in a cold place prior to germination; should an immediate germination be desired, they must be pretreated by various methods (e.g. scarification of the seed-coat, treatment with diluted acid, etc.). Seeds usually do not germinate before the temperature of the soil rises to ca. 20°C and remains warm for a longer time *(4.c.)*. This physiological mechanism protects them from germination at an unsuitable time when frost might cause the death of young seedlings. On the whole, germinating behaviour is quite diversified and varies from one species to another. Seeds of Alpine plants are generally larger than those of closely related lowland species; on the other hand, plants of high altitudes usually produce fewer seeds. They are frequently dependent on vegetative reproduction because the harsh climate may often result in destruction of flowers by frost, lack of pollination, or incomplete seed development.

On the whole, alpine species live longer than their lowland relatives, annuals e.g. blackish stonecrop *(Sedum atratum)*, dwarf eye-bright *(Euphrasia minima)*, tender gentian *(Gentiana tenella)* being very rare. Many plants inhabiting alpine grassland or scree have overwintering leaves; they are thus able to assimilate at once after the snow has melted.

The short vegetation period requires the fastest possible pollination of flowering alpine plants. In arctic areas, wind-pollinated plants e.g. grasses, sedges, or rushes, are frequent; in the Alps, however, they are less important (38% of the species in Island and Greenland vs. 16% in the Alps). Wind pollination is advantageous because plants are not dependent on insects; on the other hand, wind-pollinated plants must produce large amounts of pollen to ensure pollination. Alpine plants growing under harsh conditions cannot afford too much waste of resources. In the Alps, insects occur in larger numbers and represent more species than in the Arctic. Unlike the inconspicuous wind-pollinated flowers, Alpine flowers are particularly showy and can be found rapidly by insects. They are brightly coloured and rather large in comparison to other plant parts; they also produce a strong scent and large amounts of nectar. Similarly to flowers in steppes and deserts, the intensity of colours (esp. red and blue) is particularly impressing in the Alps. Insects often being absent (e.g. during a spell of bad weather), self-pollination occurs more frequently than in the lowlands. Alpine plants are usually not specialized as far as pollinators are concerned and can be pollinated by various insects. Simple flowers prevail; complicated, odd forms e.g. columbine *(Aquilegia)*, aconite *(Aconitum)*, or larkspur *(Delphinium)* depending on specialized pollinators are rare in the Alpine flora.

4.4. Plant-soil relationships

Plants and soil have a complex relationship. Plants must be anchored in the soil with their roots and underground organs; they must respire as well as take up water and nutrients.

The deeper and looser the soil, the better the chance of a good *anchorage*. On cliffs, roots must encircle the rock, reach deeply into crevices and enlarge them. Plants growing on unstable scree must develop a particularly widespread system of roots and underground organs in order to stabilize the mobile scree at least locally, so that they can survive damage from rockfall or from being covered by debris, by sprouting elsewhere. Typical scree plants therefore creep over or under the ground and may sometimes spread over large distances as e.g. distichous oat-grass *(Trisetum distichophyllum)*, round-leaved pennycress *(Thlaspi rotundifolium)*, bellflower of Mt. Cenis *(Campanula cenisia)* or dwarf valerian *(Valeriana supina)*.

Aeration in *wet soils* (mires, flushes) is mostly reduced, the oxygen available for respiration being exceedingly limited. Only very specialized plants e.g. marsh marigold *(Caltha palustris)*, cottongrass *(Eriophorum)*, Davall's sedge *(Carex davalliana)*, swampy horsetail *(Equisetum palustre)* are able to grow there. *Water content* of the soil is only seldom a limiting factor in the Alps, water supply usually being good (precipitation, snowmelt, groundwater). Only on south-facing slopes or in lower sites of the Central or Southern Alps may the water be temporarily limiting for some plants.

The *nutrient content* of the soil largely determines the composition of the plant cover; influence of calcium and nitrogen is particularly strong.

Soils rich in nitrogen occur in the Alps above all in the vicinity of alp-huts and in places where animals rest; they can also be found under alder thicket (alder is able to fix nitrogen because it lives in symbiosis with root bacteria), at the foot of cliffs, or in gullies and hollows where nutrients accumulate. Such places have a characteristic luxurious flora consisting of tall, large-leaved herbs called megaforbs. Fertilized meadows, too, consist mostly of nitrogen-indicating plants. Nitrogen indicators e.g. alpine meadow-grass *(Poa alpina)*, alpine timothy *(Phleum alpinum)*, may occur even in meagre meadows, in places where cow dung lay some time before. Typical nitrogen-requiring (nitrophilous)[8] plants are common nettle *(Urtica dioeca)* which, incidentally, does not occur much higher than 1500 m, monk's rhubarb *(Rumex alpinus)*, all-good *(Chenopodium bonus-henricus)*, alpine groundsel *(Senecio alpinus)*, common monkshood *(Aconitum napellus)*. Species belonging to the heath family *(Ericaceae)* e.g. blueberry *(Vaccinium myrtillus)* alpine bilberry *(Vaccinium gaultherioides)*, ling heather *(Calluna vulgaris)*, trailing azalea *(Loiseleuria procumbens)*, orchids *(Orchidaceae)*, clubmoss *(Lycopodium)*, northern twinflower *(Linnaea borealis)*, etc. practically never occur in

---

The suffix *«-philous»* originates from Greek and means «loving» or «liking»; «nitrophilous» means thus «nitrogen-loving», «calciphilous» – «calcium-loving», «acidiphilous» – «acidloving». The suffix *«-phobe»* means «avoiding».

54

sites rich in nitrogen; these plants are confined to soils very poor in nutrients where competition is limited. Owing to the mycorrhiza-fungi (fungi that live around and inside roots) they are able to take up nutrients from the surrounding humus which would not be available otherwise.

Many plants occur only in calcium-rich soils or, conversely, only in soils containing no calcium. For this reason they were formerly called calcium-loving (calciphilous)[8] and calcium-avoiding (calcifuge), respectively. However, this terminology is not correct in most cases: the soil conditions are very complex, behaviour of a given species being virtually never quite the same as that of another taxon. Plants occurring as a rule on calciferous soils may often inhabit sites poor in calcium if no competition occurs and vice versa. It should also be remembered that a species inhabiting a large area may have varied requirements as to the composition of the soil; within the central part of its distribution area it may be not very specialized as to the substratum, but in a peripheral area it is confined to calcium-rich soils because it is more competitive under these conditions. Some species undergo racial differentiation resulting in the formation of races which are physiologically specialized but morphologically rather alike (ecological races) and grow, respectively, only in calcium-rich and calcium-poor soils (e.g. evergreen sedge, *Carex sempervirens*).

Soils poor in calcium e.g. podsol or peat soils in bogs are mostly acidic and poor in nutrients too (esp. soluble compounds containing phosphorus and nitrogen). Calcium-avoiding (calcifuge) plants were for this reason formerly called acidity indicators (acidiphilous). Soils poor in calcium usually contain a sufficient quantity of heavy metals soluble in acid medium. Calcium-rich soils are basic (alkalic) or neutral; they usually contain more nitrogen because of the occurrence of legumes *(Papilionaceae)* able to fix atmospheric nitrogen in their root nodules. Root bacteria do not occur in very acid soils. Heavy metals e.g. iron or mangan are less soluble in a basic medium and remain unavailable to many plants; this deficiency may cause a yellowish colour of leaves (chlorosis). High calcium content is not the sole decisive factor in the life of the calcium-indicating plants, the presence of other bases and other factors (e.g. good aeration of the soil, tolerance of water-stress) being equally important; it is therefore advisable to employ the word «base-indicating» (basiphilous) instead of «calciphilous». Alpine serpentine soils, poor in nutrients, typically have a low content of calcium accompanied by a high content of magnesium; they are neutral to basic. The areas of their occurrence e.g. the Totalp near Davos are characterized by an exceedingly sparse vegetation. Plants occurring there are partly typical of calcium-rich soils (e.g. common heath, *Erica carnea* or broad-leaved mouse-ear, *Cerastium latifolium);* partly, however, they are representative of acidic soils (e.g. alpine bilberry, *Vaccinium gaultherioides* or Koch's gentian, *Gentiana kochiana*). The calcium indicators mentioned suggest a high base content of the soil whereas the occurrence of the acidity indicators reflects a low calcium content; last but not least, all serpentine plants are

55

specifically adapted to soils poor in nutrients. Numerous calcium-indicating plants and also some acidity-indicating ones grow also upon dolomite which contains little calcium but much magnesium; acidity indicators root into the upper horizon of humus where nutrients are scarce and bases have been washed out as a result of high precipitation.

If the calcium and acidity indicators behave uniformly, it can be recognized whether a given soil is rich or poor in bases. The corresponding indicative values of particular Alpine plants are given with the description of species in Chapter 7. They are codified with a capital «R» followed by a cipher; 5 is a good calcium indicator, 4 – a moderate one, whereas 1 and 2 correspond respectively to a good and a moderate indicator of acidity. Other indicative values are also given. Edaphic conditions are better reflected in the occurrence of whole plant combinations or associations than by the presence of a single species.

Selected indicators of calcium: blue sesleria *(Sesleria coerulea)*, cushion sedge *(Carex firma)*, net-leaved willow *(Salix reticulata)*, gypsophila *(Gypsophila repens)*, round-leaved pennycress *(Thlaspi rotundifolium)*, rock kernera *(Kernera saxatilis)*, blue saxifrage *(Saxifrage caesia)*, stalky cinquefoil *(Potentilla caulescens)*, yellow oxytropis *(Oxytropis campestris)*, alpine rockrose *(Helianthemum alpestre)*, Swiss rock-jasmine *(Androsace helvetica)*, leafless speedwell *(Veronica aphylla)*, heart-leaved globularia *(Globularia cordifolia)*, black yarrow *(Achillea atrata)*.

Selected indicators of acidity: two-lined sesleria *(Sesleria disticha)*, hare's tail cottongrass *(Eriophorum vaginatum)*, alpine sedge *(Carex curvula)*, curved sand-wort *(Minuartia recurva)*, annual stonecrop *(Sedum annuum)*, blueberry *(Vaccinium myrtillus)*, stinking primrose *(Primula hirsuta)*, hemispherical rampion *(Phyteuma hemisphaericum)*, musk yarrow *(Achillea moschata)*, alpine marguerite *(Chrysanthemum alpinum)*, whitish hawkweed *(Hieracium intybaceum)*.

Two closely related species that exclude one another from their respective ecological niches or geographical areas and are able to hybridize are called *vicariants*. For instance, the two species of alpenrose are ecologically vicariant because either of them occurs only in acidic soils or only in base-rich ones. Vicariant plant species can be distinguished not only in relation to the base content of the soil; their occurrence may also be influenced by differences in soil moisture, nutrient content, or climatic conditions. Species replacing one another in various areas of occurrence are called geographical vicariants.

Examples of pairs of vicariant species:

a/ base content of the soil

base-rich	base-poor
broad-leaved mouse-ear *(Cerastium latifolium)*	one-flowered mouse-ear *(Cerastium uniflorum)*
fringed sandwort *(Arenaria ciliata)*	two-flowered sandwort *(Arenaria biflora)*
white alpine pasqueflower *(Pulsatilla alpina)*	yellow alpine pasqueflower *(Pulsatilla sulphurea)*
blackish stonecrop *(Sedum atratum)*	annual stonecrop *(Sedum annuum)*

androsace-like saxifrage
   (*Saxifraga androsacea*)
alpine kidney-vetch
   (*Anthyllis alpestris*)
hairy alpenrose
   (*Rhododendron hirsutum*)
Clusius's gentian (*Gentiana clusii*)
Hoppe's cudweed
   (*Gnaphalium hoppeanum*)
black yarrow (*Achillea atrata*)

Seguier's saxifrage
   (*Saxifraga seguieri*)
Cherler's kidney-vetch
   (*Anthyllis cherleri*)
rust-leaved alpenrose
   (*Rhododendron ferrugineum*)
Koch's gentian (*Gentiana kochiana*)
dwarf cudweed
   (*Gnaphalium supinum*)
musk yarrow (*Achillea moschata*)

b/ water content of the soil

wet

aconite-leaved buttercup
   (*Ranunculus aconitifolius*)

moist

large white buttercup
   (*Ranunculus platanifolius*)

c/ air temperature (4.1.)

meadow plants of lower altitudes

red clover (*Trifolium pratense*)
sainfoin (*Onobrychis viciifolia*)

common kidney-vetch
   (*Anthyllis vulgaris*)
ribwort plantain
   (*Plantago lanceolata*)
common scabious
   (*Scabiosa columbaria*)
scabious knapweed
   (*Centaurea scabiosa*)

meadow plants of high altitudes

snow clover (*Trifolium nivale*)
mountain sainfoin
   (*Onobrychis montana*)
alpine kidney-vetch
   Anthyllis alpestris)
black plantain (*Plantago atrata*)

bright scabious (*Scabiosa lucida*)

alpine knapweed
   Centaurea alpestris

In nearly all species occurring in the subalpine and suprasubalpine zone intermediary forms or gradual transitions can be found. Such species-groups may very often undergo a further differentiation resulting in the formation of specialized races in warm valleys of the Southern and Central Alps, upon various substrata, or in other Alpine ranges (e.g. SW Alps).

Forest at lower altitudes

lady-fern (*Athyrium filix-femina*)
spiked rampion
   (*Phyteuma spicatum*)
goldenrod (*Solidago virga-aurea*)

Forest and brush at higher altitudes

alpine lady-fern (*Athyrium alpestris*)
oval-headed rampion
   (*Phyteuma ovatum*)
alpine goldenrod (*Solidago alpestris*)

Rocks and scree below the timberline

stiff-haired saxifrage
   (*Saxifraga aspera*)

Rocks and scree above the timberline

moss saxifrage (*Saxifraga bryoides*)

d/ situation in the Alps

western Alps

mountain pine (*Pinus montana*)

eastern Alps

dwarf mountain pine (*Pinus mugo*)

purple gentian *(Gentiana purpurea)*	pannonic gentian *(Gentiana pannonica)*
erbarotta yarrow *(Achillea erba-rotta)*	musk yarrow *(Achillea moschata)*
hoary groundsel *(Senecio incanus)*	Carniol groundsel *(Senecio carniolicus)*
outer Alpine ranges	*inner Alpine ranges*

alpine hutchinsia
  (Hutchinsia alpina)
	short-stalked hutchinsia
	  (Hutchinsia brevicaulis)

evergreen draba *(Draba aizoides)*	Hoppe's draba *(Draba hoppeana)*

round-leaved pennycress
  (Thlaspi rotundifolium)
	corymbose pennycress
	  (Thlaspi corymbosum)

Plants occurring in the inner Alpine ranges often require finer soils than species inhabiting the outer ranges (in the latter areas plants frequently grow upon hard calciferous substrata, clay-rich calciferous soils being available in the former regions).

4.5. Summary: important factors limiting plant growth in the Alps

1. *Low temperatures:* life functions proceed too slowly (esp. in shadowy gullies, snow-patches, and at high altitudes).
2. *Extreme temperatures:* danger of frost and desiccation (esp. in exposed places, upon cliffs, ridges, south-facing slopes).
3. *Dry air and strong winds:* danger of desiccation (esp. in exposed sites, upon cliffs, ridges, south-facing slopes).
4. *Short vegetation period:* too little time for important life processes (esp. in shadowy gullies, hollows, snow-patches, avalanche paths, and at high altitudes).
5. *Soil movement:* damage by rockfall, covering by debris, denudation (esp. on steep slopes, in avalanche paths, talus and scree, alluvial areas).
6. *Unbalanced soil conditions:* owing to the limited soil development, water and nutrient capacity is low; it brings about the danger of desiccation, nutrient deficiency, frequently also an unbalanced mineral composition (esp. in raw soils, at high altitudes, upon specific substrata e.g. dolomite, serpentine, quartzite).

5. Vegetation of the Alps

Plants inhabiting a given place, viewed as a whole, are called vegetation or plant cover. Appearance and composition of a vegetation are largely determined by life conditions (climate, soil, competition) and also by the geographical situation. Similar life conditions result in vegetation types similar in appearance. Also, plants which are not closely related but grow in similar places may look alike because in every area only those plants are successful which have a growth-form adapted to a given climate. In African deserts one thus finds column-like, thorny plants («cacti») of the spurge family *(Euphorbiaceae)*, very similar to the genuine cacti *(Cactaceae)* native of American deserts; however, the two families are not at all related. Similar forms may occur in other families too. Such a parallel development within different systematical groups is called *convergence*. In the Alps, for instance, plants belonging to most different families (pink, saxifrage, primrose, etc.) form flat cushions because this particular growth-form is advantageous under high-mountain conditions. According to the appearance of the vegetation, various types can be distinguished in various climatic zones. In the Arctic, it is the *tundra* (treeless vegetation consisting of dwarf shrubs, grasses and graminoids, lichens and mosses); in the boreal zone – the *taiga* (coniferous forest); in the cool moderate zone – *summer-green foliage woods;* in the Mediterranean zone – *hard-leaved woods*. In dry moderate, subtropical or tropical zones occur *deserts* (areas that on account of their extreme aridity remain bare or only partially covered by a scanty treeless vegetation), *steppes* (treeless, rather closed vegetation rich in grasses) and/or *savannas* (steppes with loose stands of trees or brush). Last but not least, vegetation in moist and warm tropical zones is principally represented by *tropical rain forests*. Similarly to the North-South gradient, vegetation changes as well with increasing altitude. As in any mountain chain, one can recognize in the Alps different altitudinal zones or belts characterized by specific plants and corresponding partly to the vegetation zones. These altitudinal belts are characterized by specific vegetation types (e.g. particular forests) and different growth-forms.

A more detailed classification of vegetation leads to a system of plant communities with their characteristic appearance, composition of species, and clearly recognizable requirements in climatic and edaphic conditions.

5.1. Altitudinal belts

During any excursion in the Alps, a quite impressive change in vegetation can be noticed with increasing altitude. Boundaries between particular altitudinal belts are mostly not very sharp but obscured by broad transitions or an inherent overlapping of various vegetation types. Human influence also contributed to the complex situation in places where the natural vegetation has been driven away. Notwithstanding these difficulties, change of vegetation accompanying the changing altitude is easy to recognize because temperature differences influence the occurrence and competitive abilities of given species. Lowland plants have their uppermost limit of occurrence in the Alps; Alpine species have both an uppermost and a downwards limit. Most plants are able to grow and to remain competitive within several altitudinal belts; others, however, are confined to particular belts and are a characteristic component there.

In addition to temperature, continentality of a given climate plays a rôle in the altitudinal distribution of plants. Continentality generally increases from the outer Alpine ranges towards the central Alpine massifs; this change can be recognized downwards and upwards from middle altitudes too. Continentality signifies great temperature extremes, much frost and sunshine, weak cloudiness and low moisture of the air. Middle heights, influenced by higher precipitation and a more pronounced cloudiness (the limit of the cloud cover often corresponds to middle altitudes) have a more oceanic climate than the lowlands. Higher altitudes have much precipitation, but frequently less cloudiness, and a more limited humidity of the air is easily recognizable there; absence of cold air also plays a certain rôle.

The boundary that is best visible is the treeline; the timberline viz. limit of the occurrence of compact tree stands lies mostly 50–300 m lower. The belt between timberline and treeline (or krummholz-line which lies frequently a little higher) was formerly considered as a combat zone of the forest. The tree silhouettes marked by weather and wind (sometimes also by grazing) are often very impressive indeed; however, it is largely accepted nowadays that the «combat zone» is not natural but Man-influenced. As a result of forest clearing and grazing, woods gradually became less compact at their uppermost limit and the timberline sank within the last 600 years. In mountain areas which are not much influenced by human activity the timberline is rather compact even if the trees gradually become smaller. Snow can occasionally result in the formation of ascending shrubs that build a characteristic krummholz belt (above all dwarf mountain pine). This vegetation type is widely distributed in the eastern Alps; in Switzerland it occurs only in places endangered by avalanches and unstable rocky soils. Under natural conditions, the timberline in our country would therefore mostly correspond to the treeline and it should lie, without exception, at higher altitudes than nowadays (Fig. 15, p. 40). On the other hand, the timberline does not form a strictly horizontal line everywhere; compared to more moderate sites, it lies lower e.g. in the bottom of valleys because of cold-air currents, in hollows and gullies owing to late-lying snow, and on windy ridges because of exposure. Also, tree stands do not occur consistently on cliffs, slopes with shallow soil, mobile scree, and in avalanche-exposed places; as a result, the timberline appears frayed.

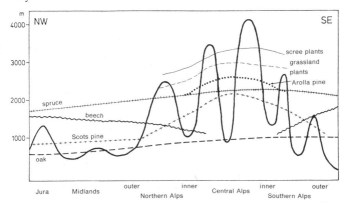

Fig. 20. The uppermost limits of some important trees and high-alpine plant groups (from 5.*n.*).

The treeline is primarily influenced by heat deficiency. While most trees are able to endure very low temperatures during their dormancy period, a minimum amount of heat during the vegetation period is vital, not only for metabolic balance but also for the formation of new shoots and the ripening of buds. Should the heat be insufficient, the plant is unable to build structures protecting it form frost (thick external cell walls with wax layer, energy reserves) and may become severely damaged in winter *(4.u.)*. Plants growing above the timberline depend on air layers that are close to the ground because they warm up well and are more humid; low-growing plants are thus well-protected against frost and desiccation and covered by the insulating snow in winter. Plants taller than 20 cm are hardly seen above the timberline except for places with a favourable microclimate (e.g. rocky niches, sheltered cliff ledges).

The natural timberline in continental zones lies higher than in areas with an atlantic climate because of higher diurnal summer temperatures. In the Central Alps it corresponds to 2100–2500 m, in the outer Alpine ranges to 1800 – 2100 m (fig. 15, p. 40). In southwestern sites trees are able to grow at most about 100 m higher than in northeastern ones. In the Mediterranean area the timberline lies partly lower than in the Alps on account of too great aridity. In tropical and subtropical areas with sufficient sunshine and precipitation (e.g. the Himalayas, Mexico) some trees may grow far above 4000 m.

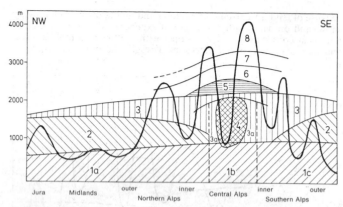

Fig. 21. Altitudinal belts in the Swiss Alps (from *5.n.*):

1. Colline belt (oak-beech belt). 1a. The variant occurring in the Northern Alps which includes pedunculate oak *(Quercus robur)*, sessile oak *(Q. petraea)* and much beech *Fagus silvatica)*. 1b. The variant occurring in the Central Alps which includes white oak *(Quercus pubescens)* but no beech. 1c. The variant occurring in the Southern Alps which includes white oak *(Quercus pubescens)* as well as beech *(Fagus silvatica)*.
2. Montane belt (beech-silver fir belt) including *Fagus silvatica* and *Abies alba*.
3. Subalpine belt of spruce *(Picea excelsa)*. 3a. The variant occurring in the Central Alps which includes spruce *(Picea excelsa)* and Scots pine *(Pinus silvestris)*.
4. Continental mountain belt of Scots pine *(Pinus silvestris)*.
5. Suprasubalpine belt of Arolla pine *(Pinus cembra)*.
6. Alpine belt (low grassland belt).
7. Subnival belt of stabilized scree vegetation (mostly flat cushions).
8. Nival belt (no flowering plants except for local, sheltered places).

According to the uppermost limit of occurrence of important trees as well as the appearance of particular forms of growth, the altitudinal belts in the Alps (Figs 20–21) can be described as follows:

5.1.1. Colline belt (oak-beech belt)

The upper boundary of the colline belt is defined by the uppermost occurrence of oak *(Quercus)*. The natural vegetation of this belt consists of summer-green foliage woods. Coniferous forests are either confined to a few special sites or planted. Natural occurrence of fir *(Abies)* or spruce *(Picea)* is rare.

Distinct vegetation variants within the colline belt are observed in the Northern, Central, and Southern Alps, respectively.

North of the Alps prevails beech *(Fagus)* mixed with other deciduous trees viz. oak *(Quercus)*, hornbeam *(Carpinus)*, lime *(Tilia)*, cherry *(Prunus)*. Large areas of the Midlands formerly inhabited by beech are nowadays covered by oak-hornbeam woods

(*«Querco-Carpinetum»*) as a result of forest management. The upper-most limit of oak lies in the Jura, the Midlands and in the northern Alpine foreland between 600 and 800 m.

The colline belt in the continental Central Alps is typically inhabited by white oak *(Quercus pubescens)*. However, forests of this type have been largely destroyed by intensive farming and form only small stands nowadays. Beech *(Fagus)* is almost missing on account of the climate which is too continental for this species. The vegetation includes many submediterranean and subcontinental steppe plants. The uppermost occurrence of oak *(Quercus)* lies in the Central Alps between ca. 600 and 1000 m depending on exposure and solar radiation.

The colline belt in the Southern Alps includes mixed forests of white oak *(Quercus pubescens)*, mixed forests of lime *(Tilia)*, forests of manna-ash *(Fraxinus ornus)* and hop-hornbeam *(Ostrya)*, sweet chest-nut *(Castanea sativa)*, birch *(Betula)* as well as mixed forests of beech *(Fagus)*. This belt is characterized by a pronounced diversity of species. Submediterranean and suboceanic forest plants occur frequently and in a large number of species. The uppermost occurrence of oak lies in the Southern Alps between 800 and 1000 m.

The uppermost occurrence of oak depends on the sum of tem-perature. The colline belt is characterized by warm summer tem-peratures and strong solar radiation (mean July value over 16°C). Mean temperatures at the same altitude in the Northern Alps are about 2°C lower than those in the Southern Alps and about 1°C lower than those in the Central Alps. Owing to these differences the uppermost limit of oak rises from north to south by about 300 m; stronger solar radiation occurring in south-facing slopes of the Central and Southern Alps permits still higher altitudes.

As far as cultivated plants are concerned, grape *(Vitis)*, walnut *(Juglans)* and maize *(Zea mais)* are able to grow up to the oak limit. Grain and fruit are also grown in the Northern and Southern Alps up to the oak limit.

5.1.2. Montane belt (silver fir-beech belt)

The uppermost boundary of the montane belt is delimited by the uppermost occurrence of beech *(Fagus)*. The natural vegetation of this belt consists primarily of beechwoods and includes also a mixed forest of beech and coniferous trees. Regional classification of these forests does not seem necessary as they are largely uniform.

Spruce and silver fir are very competitive in this belt; silver fir *(Abies alba)* even has its ecological optimum here. Coniferous woods prevail in places where beech does not occur on account of edaphic conditions (e.g. very wet or very dry soils), but the uppermost limit of beech is usually rather distinct. Plants representative of a suboceanic climate typically accompanying beech in the montane belt are very numerous indeed; woods are rich in ferns and tall herbs or have many acidity-indicating species in stands mixed with spruce and silver fir.

In the Jura the uppermost limit of beech lies barely below the highest summit (the Reculet, at ca. 1700 m); at the very summit only treeless grassland or dwarf mountain pine stands occur on account of the harsh local climate. In the outer Alpine ranges, beech occurs up to 1400–1500 m; in the inner ranges it still reaches 1100–1300 m, but is virtually missing in the continental Central Alps. In the outer Southern Alps, in grows above 1700 m but disappears soon northwards and is practically absent in the Ticino north of Giornico.

The uppermost limit of beech is not at all, or only to a limited extent, determined by a simple temperature limit. Beech is generally unable to endure low winter temperatures; moreover, its leaves are frost-sensitive and may be severely damaged by a snowfall occurring during the growing season. No beech is therefore seen in areas where frost occurs during the growing period.

The montane belt is characterized by high precipitation, high air humidity, rather balanced temperatures, and virtually no frost during the vegetation period. On the other hand, the sunshine is usually not very strong.

The uppermost limit of sycamore *(Acer pseudoplatanus)*, scabrous elm *(Ulmus scabra)* and partly also of ash *(Fraxinus excelsior)* is comparable to that of beech; silver fir *(Abies alba)* enters farther into the continental areas and is also able to survive a little higher. As far as the agriculture in the montane belt is concerned, no management other than stock-farming is possible.

5.1.3. Subalpine belt (spruce belt)

The uppermost boundary of the subalpine belt is defined by the uppermost limit of spruce *(Picea)*. The natural vegetation here consists of coniferous woods with spruce nearly always prevailing. In areas with more humid air silver fir *(Abies alba)* may also occur, whereas in continental areas larch *(Larix)* forms mixed stands with spruce.

Subalpine coniferous woods are rather uniform in large Alpine areas except for the inner Alpine valleys where a continental variant occurs: it is characterized by numerous warmth-indicating plants and above all by a frequent occurrence of Scots pine *(Pinus silvestris)* in spruce forests. Typical woods upon special substrata (dolomite, serpentine, quartzite, etc.) include mountain pine *(Pinus montana)* whereas Scots pine *(P. silvestris)* is representative of the continental variant. This difference can be very well seen in the area of Davos: Scots pine is well-distributed upon dolomite and limestone slopes towards Filisur, whereas mountain pine prevails upon serpentine at the side of the valley towards Klosters.

The herb layer of spruce forests is rather uniform over the whole Alpine area as long as no grazing occurs. Woods are either rich in tall herbs on more humid slopes or have a prevailing layer of blueberry *(Vaccinium myrtillus)* with shaggy woodreed *(Calamagrostis villosa)* growing in open places. In the Central Alps, spruce forest descends to ca. 800 m but differs there floristically only a little from the stands at higher altitudes. Great temperature extremes and the dry air typical of the continental climate are very suitable to spruce, the only difference being a little higher mean temperatures.

The uppermost limit of spruce lies in the outer Alpine ranges at ca. 1800 m; in the inner ranges, it corresponds to 2000–2100 m depending of the exposure. Bar the inner ranges, spruce forms the timberline nearly everywhere in the Alps.

The altitudinal limit of spruce corresponds to a temperature limit which lies in the Alps at a little higher altitude than the 10°C-isotherm of July viz. ca. 9.5°C. The climate of the subalpine belt is characterized by great differences in temperature, strong sunshine, and frequently also by drier air than the climate of the montane belt.

A typically developed subalpine belt is suited solely to stock-farming; as far as the outer ranges are concerned, only alp-farming (summer management) is possible. In the inner Alpine ranges, on the other hand, year-round farming can be done, limited crop growing being possible too, in the continental Central Alps.

5.1.4. Continental mountain belt (Scots pine belt)

The continental mountain belt occurs only in the innermost part of the Central Alps, in areas where summer precipitation in general does not exceed 250 mm. The lowest boundary of this belt is adjacent to the colline (white oak) belt, its uppermost limit corresponds to the limit of Scots pine. Scots pine *(Pinus silvestris)* in the colline and montane belts is usually confined to special places where no other trees are able to grow (steep rocky slopes, marl or sandy soils, serpentine, dolomite, quartzite, etc.); in the continental Central Alps, however, it forms large forests upon any substratum. These sites are too dry and frost-endangered for beech and generally too dry for spruce. The latter tree grows only in climatically more favourable places (locally moister and cooler sites, less shallow soils) where it forms small isolated stands, or occurs in mixed stands with Scots pine. Pure Scots pine forests that are not limited to special places and influenced by hundreds of years of management occur presumably only in the driest areas of the Central Alps (in Switzerland only in the Wallis).

The herb layer of Scots pine forest includes many steppe plants, in general base-indicating species.

The uppermost limit of Scots pine does not always represent a climatic limit but corresponds, with increasing precipitation, to a limit of competition against spruce. It lies between ca. 1600 and 2100 m and is recognizable in places where Scots pine gives way to spruce upon siliceous substrata. The continental mountain belt is broad; it may comprise more than 1000 m of difference in altitude and in a sense it is azonal. In the outer Alpine ranges, on the other hand, Scots pine does not occur higher than up to some 1000 m a.s.l. The continental mountain belt is climatically characterized by low precipitation, great temperature extremes, and very strong solar radiation.

Juniper *(Juniperus communis)* has a similar uppermost limit as that of Scots pine.

As far as the agriculture is concerned, the continental mountain belt is very well-suited to arable farming even at higher altitudes. Fertilized meadows, on the other hand, must generally be irrigated.

5.1.5. Suprasubalpine belt (Arolla pine belt)

The suprasubalpine belt occurs in the Central Alps above the spruce belt; it reaches about 100–400 m higher than the subalpine belt, its uppermost limit being defined by the limit of Arolla pine *(Pinus cembra)*. Suprasubalpine belt in its fully-developed phase is represented by nearly pure forests of Arolla pine; larch *(Larix)* occurs particularly as a first colonizer on more shallow soils nearly always rich in clay. In the Central Alps larch occurs in the subalpine and (less frequently) in the continental mountain belt too; on the other hand, Arolla pine does not descend more than a few hundred meters below the uppermost limit of spruce. Alpine bilberry *(Vaccinium gaultherioides)* has its occurrence center within the uppermost boundary of the suprasubalpine belt. Similarly to the uppermost limit of the subalpine belt, the uppermost boundary of the suprasubalpine belt is marked nowadays by a consistent occurrence of at least 20–30 cm tall dwarf shrubs (esp. the rust-leaved alpenrose, *(Rhododendron ferrugineum)*.

The uppermost limit of Arolla pine is a temperature limit also influenced by solar radiation. Arolla pine can grow higher than spruce in places where the sunshine is strong (annual precipitation remaining below 150 cm). In the most continental areas (Upper Engadine), Arolla pine reaches altitudes with a mean July temperature of 7.5°C.

The suprasubalpine belt is suitable solely for summer stock-farming (alp management).

5.1.6. Alpine belt (low grassland belt)

The uppermost limit of the alpine belt is determined by the limit of closed patches of low grassland. Characteristic species are evergreen sedge *(Carex sempervirens)* growing upon calciferous and also calcium-poor substrata; further species include alpine sedge *(Carex curvula)* and mousetail-like elyna *(Elyna myosuroides)*. The alpine belt is characterized by low grassland as long as the soil conditions remain rather stable and no late-lying snowdrift accumulates locally. Plants taller than 30 cm viz. shrubs and tall meadow plants or tall herbs occur only locally above the natural treeline in rocky niches, between boulders, etc.

The uppermost limit of the alpine belt in the outer Alpine ranges lies between 2400 and 2500 m, in the inner ranges between 2700 and 3000 m. It represents a heat boundary line and corresponds roughly to a mean July temperature of 5°C.

The alpine belt is used by Man as grazing-land for cattle and sheep in the lower parts, the upper parts being grazed exclusively by sheep.

5.1.7. Subnival belt (flat cushion belt)

The uppermost limit of the subnival belt corresponds to the uppermost limit of flowering plants that still grow well albeit scattered, primarily on stabilized scree. Typical plants include king of the Alps *(Eritrichium nanum)*, alpine rock-jasmine *(Androsace alpina)*, glacier crowfoot *(Ranunculus glacialis)*, mossy cyphal sandwort *(Minuartia sedoides)*, purple saxifrage *(Saxifraga oppositifolia)*; the isolated plants frequently form flat cushions. The subnival belt is characterized by a virtually nil development of the soil.

The uppermost limit of the subnival belt lies about 300–500 m above the alpine belt and is determined by a mean length of the snow-free period (ca. 2 months).

5.1.8. Nival belt (snow belt)

This belt occurs only in the inner Alpine ranges at about 3000–3400 m; flowering plants no longer occur except in local warm rock niches. On the other hand, algae and lichens grow upon cliffs, boulders, and firn-fields up to the highest summits.

5.2. Plant communities

Plants inhabiting the same site[9] and thus exposed to the same life conditions (climate, soil, influence of animals and Man, competition) form a community. Similar communities occur in similar sites; if a given plant community is known, an opinion can be reached as to environmental factors operating at a given site.

First colonizers of a given site form a *pioneer community*. The first species to appear in ponds silting up or slow waters, cliffs, boulder fields, or scree are pioneer plants. Competition between pioneer plants is not strong at first; they must simply be able to grow and function under conditions offered by a given site. For instance, scree plants must anchor themselves to the mobile scree and withstand mechanical damage or cover by debris; they therefore develop widely spread underground organs and may form buds and shoots anew. If the scree vegetation is not repeatedly covered by rock debris, it may stabilize the scree; the subsequent local accumulation of humus and fine soil prepares ground for more demanding plants. The vegetation, still open at the beginning, will gradually become more closed; at a more advanced stage grassland appears and with it strong competition. As time goes on, scree plants are mostly overgrown by other species and eventually ousted from their original site. The strength of scree plants lies in their potential for rapid dispersal (mostly by wind, small seeds having pappus, hairs, wings, etc.) and also in their ability to grow upon a mobile, bare scree. Below the timberline dwarf shrubs and trees begin to appear in formerly open places as soon as some humus and fine soil

---

[9] *Site* is an ecological term and denotes environmental factors operating in a given place; *locality* has a geographical meaning. Both terms may be used arbitrarily.

is accumulated; grassland plants shadowed by taller species cannot withstand the light deficiency and also cannot support the increasing soil acidity. The community formed at the end of the plant succesion is called *climax community,* transitions between the pioneer and the climax community being referred to as *seres* or *seral stages.* Since the development leading from pioneer communities to climax is in the Alps every so often perturbed by avalanches, landslips, flooding, etc., there

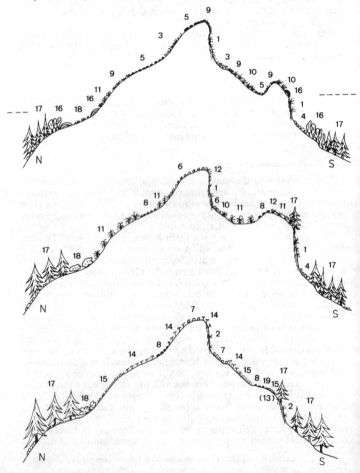

is no danger that Alpine pioneer plants become extinct; on the other hand, nearly all pioneer sites have disappeared in the Midlands as a result of human activity (construction, regulation of the flow of streams and rivers, etc.) and pioneer plants are exceedingly rare in this area.

According to *Braun-Blanquet,* an *association* is a basic unit of plant communities. It can be characterized by its own species which do not occur in other neighbouring associations. Associations are given Latin names which include one or two characteristic species and the suffix *«-etum».* For instance, the heath-pine forest is named the *Erico-Pinetum* from *Erica* (= heath) and *Pinus* (= pine). Closely related associations form an *alliance;* its Latin name has the suffix *«-ion».*

Some species are confined to a single community or occur in a few precisely defined ones, whereas others are widely distributed and form a part of numerous communities. Recognition of particular communities in the field is not always easy as their boundaries may be obscured by human influence, gradual transitions, or a mosaic-like distribution pattern. Notwithstanding these problems (more than 100 associations have already been described for the Alps) it seems very interesting to find out which plants occur together more frequently than others. It is easier to learn about plants and to find them in the wild when one already knows their environment.

Forest is the typical natural community below the timberline. In the outer Alpine ranges and at lower altitudes one finds mostly spruce forest (Fig. 23); on the other hand, forest of Arolla pine is represen-

Fig. 22.   Natural vegetation types from the upper subalpine belt to the subnival belt – an overview (after *4.m.*).

Communities on rocks and cliffs	1: Vegetation on calciferous substrata *(Potentillion caulescentis)* 2: Vegetation on siliceous substrata *(Androsacion vandellii)*
Communities on talus, stabilized scree, and snow-patches	3: Alpine vegetation on calcareous talus *(Thlaspion rotundifolii)* 4: Subalpine vegetation on calcareous talus *(Petasition paradoxi)* 5: Snow-patch vegetation on calciferous substrata *(Arabidion coeruleae)* 6: Scree vegetation on base-rich silicate *(Drabion hoppeanae)* 7: Scree vegetation on siliceous substrata *(Androsacion alpinae)* 8: Snow-patch vegetation *(Salicion herbaceae)*
Grassland	9: Cushion sedge grassland *(Caricion firmae)* 10: Blue sesleria steppe *(Seslerion coeruleae)* 11: Rust-coloured sedge grassland, and violet fescue grassland *(Caricion ferrugineae)* 12: Elyna-dominated grassland *(Elynion)* 13: Coloured fescue grassland *(Festucion variae,* only the Southern Alps) 14: Alpine sedge grassland *(Caricion curvulae)* 15: Mat-grass pasture *(Nardion)*
Forests, bush	16: Mountain pine forests and shrubs *(Erico-Pinion)* 17: Blueberry-coniferous forests *(Vaccinio-Piceion)* (the outermost Alpine ranges: spruce forests; the inner ranges: spruce forests with larch, and Arolla pine forests at higher altitudes) 18: Tall-herb stands and green alder thicket *(Adenostylion;* the green alder is absent on calciferous substrata poor in clay). 19: Trailing azalea stands *(Loiseleurio-Vaccinion)*

tative of higher altitudes within the inner ranges. Beech forest rises up to the timberline on the calciferous slopes of the Southern Alps and the Jura. Silver fir occurs in the outer Alpine ranges, particularly on clayey soils; it forms mixed stands with beech or spruce. Mountain pine, erect or trailing, grows upon calciferous scree, on exposed cliffs, boulder fields and in shallow soils. Dwarf shrub communities mainly occur on higher subalpine sites where human influence (forest clearing, grazing) has reduced or destroyed the typical forest vegetation. Thickets of green alder and willow grow on shadowy, humid, and often unstable slopes (esp. avalanche paths). Tall herbs seek moist hollows and gullies; they may also grow well in moist forests, upon slopes rich in nutrients, and enter the green alder stands as well. Natural vegetation free of trees and shrubs occurs otherwise below the timberline only upon rocky outcrops and cliffs or on unstable slopes and mires. Meadows and pastures are formed in places where forest and brush have disappeared under human influence. In places very rich in nutrients (e.g. resting-places of animals, vicinity of alp-huts) stands of monk's rhubarb are quite conspicuous.

The alpine belt is characterized by natural grassland. The most widely distributed community in the inner Alpine ranges is that of *alpine sedge* which grows in all not too extreme sites upon siliceous substrata. In steep, sunny, not excessively moist slopes upon calciferous substrata grows *blue sesleria grassland,* in a little more humid places – grassland *dominated by rust-coloured sedge;* upon substrata a little poorer in bases on sunny slopes grassland *dominated by coloured fescue* occurs; on ridges, vegetation *dominated by mouse-tail-like elyna* is a transition towards the alpine sedge grassland. Gullies and north-facing slopes that remain for a long time under snow are inhabited by *snow-patch vegetation;* upon calciferous substrata the vegetation is dominated by blunt-leaved willow and net-leaved willow, whereas dwarf willow prevails upon substrata poor in calcium. At very high altitudes where closed grassland patches no longer occur pioneer *scree vegetation* colonizes unstable raw soils, while *cliff plants* grow upon rocky faces and may reach altitudes well above 4000 m in sunny sheltered places (Fig. 22).

The following part of this book deals with the most important plant communities occurring in the Alps. They are grouped according to growth-form, base and water content of the soil, as well as management type.

5.2.1. Forest at higher altitudes

Forest is the most complex form of plant coexistence. In our country it occurs everywhere below the timberline, bar the sites constantly perturbed by e.g. landslips, avalanches, grazing, or mowing. The value of Alpine forests does not relate to the yield of timber only as trees grow slowly in the harsh climate; for instance, some Arolla pine trees may be 40–50 years old but remain only about 2 m tall. Transport of timber is difficult, too. The principal importance of the mountain forest relates to its protective function, for it keeps landslides and avalanches in check. Unfortunately, the vital rôle of forest has not been sufficiently recognized in some areas in the past; forest has been cleared for timber or severely abused by grazing, even on steep slopes; its rejuvenation has been seriously hampered. As a result avalanches and landslides occurred and the areas became unhabitable in winter. Reforestation of mountain slopes is difficult, expensive, and time-consuming; what has been destroyed by carelessness and ignorance within a few years frequently takes many generations to be successfully repaired. Forest is also essential for human recreation. A healthy forest ensures a natural balance of climate and harmony of the landscape; it well deserves our especial respect and care. Unfortunately, the forest dieback («Waldsterben») has already reached higher Alpine areas and may yet have serious consequences for the stability of steep slopes.

The pattern of occurrence of particular forest communities in relation to humidity and base content of the soil is presented in Fig. 23. Not included are larch-Arolla pine forests, and dry pine forests occurring in the continental Central Alps as well as the beechwoods inhabiting the oceanic outer ranges and the Jura.

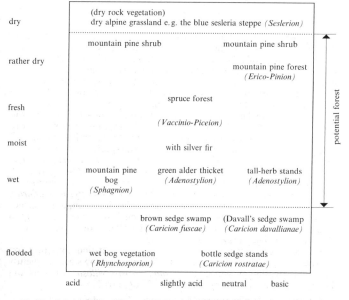

Fig. 23. Subalpine belt of the Swiss Alps: natural vegetation in relation to moisture and base content of the soil (after *4.m.*). Not included are vegetation types developed under influence of special factors (e.g. soilslips, avalanches, strong winds, locally strong solar radiation, late-lying snow).

a. Beechwoods. Beech *(Fagus silvatica)* is typical of the montane vegetation belt. It forms large, tall, and mostly closed woods upon calciferous substrata of the outer Alpine ranges and the Jura. Beech grows nearly to the timberline (1500–1900 m). Together with sycamore *(Acer pseudoplatanus)* and silver fir *(Abies alba)* it forms characteristic light sycamore-beech forest *(Acero-Fagetum)*. Owing to strong sidelight (steep slopes), high precipitation, and rather nutrient rich soils the herb layer of these forests includes tall herbs e.g. mountain dock *(Rumex arifolius)*, large white buttercup *(Ranunculus platanifolius)*, wolly buttercup *(Ranunculus lanuginosus)*, round-leaved saxifrage *(Saxifraga rotundifolia)*, wood cranesbill *(Geranium silvaticum)*, adenostyle *(Adenostyles alliariae)*, alpine sow-thistle *(Cicerbita alpina)*, large-leaved ferns, etc.

b. Silver fir forests. Similarly to beech, silver fir *(Abies alba)* is mostly confined to the montane belt where it forms large woods alone, or together with beech. It grows higher up only exceptionally e.g. on clayey, fresh soils on steep slopes forming mixed stands with spruce *(Picea excelsa)*. Luxurious tall herbs in the herb layer are mostly the same as those growing in sycamore-beech forests. Adenostyle being particularly frequent, the association is named adenostyle-silver fir forest *(Adenostylo-Abietetum)*.

c. Spruce forests. Spruce *(Picea excelsa)* is indeed the most widely distributed tree within the subalpine belt of the Alps; it only avoids exceedingly dry soils. On account of its rapid growth and the all-round use of its timber, spruce is frequently planted also in sites where it would not be naturally competitive against other trees (e.g. in the lowlands).

Of the numerous variants, the subalpine spruce forest *(Piceetum subalpinum)* is by far the most common. It grows on not too steep slopes of the Northern and Central Alps up to 1800–2000 m. The soil in its upper layer is acid, rich in humus, and poor in nutrients (podsol). Tall, dark spruce forests do not include many shrubs and herbs, the soil being partly covered with moss. Characteristic species of spruce forests are numerous acidity-loving plants e.g. blueberry *(Vaccinium myrtillus)*, cowberry *(V. vitis-idaea)*, wood cow-wheat *(Melampyrum silvaticum)*, interrupted clubmoss *(Lycopodium annotinum)*, coral-root *(Corallorrhiza trifida)* and one-flowered wintergreen *(Pyrola uniflora)*.

In the inner and southern Alpine ranges larch accompanies spruce *(Larici-Piceetum)*: it can prevail in not much developed soils upon siliceous substrata, on steep, rather unstable slopes, or in places where the forest has been grazed for a long time.

Spruce forests occurring in moist and nutrient-rich soils (esp. on northern slopes) include numerous tall herbs. Hollows are frequently inhabited by shaggy woodreed *(Calamagrostis villosa)* whereas wet boggy soils are covered by a blanket of bog moss.

d. Larch-Arolla pine forests. Arolla pine *(Pinus cembra)* occurs nearly exclusively in the Central Alps within the uppermost forest belt (above 1600 m). Stands of Arolla pine are greatly reduced nowadays by excessive use of timber. The Arolla pine forest is not suited for grazing because herbs do not grow well under the trees; larch *(Larix)* with its easily-decaying needles which are shed every year, does not influence the ground much and its light forests grow well when grazed; for this reason larch is given preference over Arolla pine. Also, larch is able to grow on scree and in boulder fields and is often planted in the lowlands as well. Arolla pine and larch form light woods in the Central Alps between ca. 1800 and 2400 m, mostly upon siliceous substrata. Similarly to the subalpine spruce forest, the soil in these woods is leached and characterized by a thick humus layer. Many plants of the herb layer are thus the same as those growing in spruce forests; on the other hand, forests of larch-Arolla pine include more shrubs (esp. dwarf shrubs) and herbs (esp. grasses) than spruce woods. Characteristic of the larch-Arolla pine forests are rust-leaved alpenrose *(Rhododendron ferrugineum)*, blue-fruited honeysuckle *(Lonicera coerulea)*, cowberry *(Vaccinium vitis-idaea)*, blueberry *(V. myrtillus)* and alpine bilberry *(V. gaultherioides)*. Northern twinflower *(Linnaea borealis)* which becomes very rare westward i.e. already in the Wallis occurs occasionally amongst dwarf shrubs. Further species include various taxa of clubmoss *(Lycopodium)*, cow-wheat *(Melampyrum)*, woodrush *(Luzula)*, alpine coltsfoot *(Homogyne alpina)* as well as shaggy woodreed *(Calamagrostis villosa)*; the latter species frequently forms large stands.

e. Mountain pine forests. The mountain pine *(Pinus montana)* is a tree with few demands: it is able to grow even in very dry and exposed places upon unbalanced substrata poor in nutrients (limestone, dolomite, serpentine, quartzite). Like all pines, it requires much light. At lower altitudes viz. from the lower subalpine belt downwards mountain pine is replaced by Scots pine *(Pinus silvestris)*. Mountain pine woods are most frequently represented in the Alps by heath-mountain pine association *(Erico-Pinetum montanae)*; this light forest with no true shrub layer is widely distributed on calciferous soils within landslide areas and upon steep slopes. Common heath *(Erica carnea)* occurs very frequently whereas shrubby milkwort *(Polygala chamaebuxus)*, striated mezereon *(Daphne striata)*, cowberry *(Vaccinium vitis-idaea)*, blue sesleria *(Sesleria coerulea)* and birdsfoot-trefoil *(Lotus corniculatus)* are less common. While the heath-mountain pine forest grows primarily on sunny slopes, shadowy places are inhabited by a mountain pine forest including hairy alpenrose *(Rhododendron hirsutum)* as well as various taxa of whortleberry *(Vaccinium)* and also false medlar *(Sorbus chamaemespilus)*. In contrast to the heath-mountain pine forest, the humus layer in the alpenrose-mountain pine forest is thick and decomposes very slowly.

f. River-valley woodlands. Grey alder *(Alnus incana)* forms woods in wet river valleys in the Alps up to ca. 1200–1600 m. Higher up, bay willow *(Salix pentandra)* and other willow species that are barely taller than 10 m prevail in wet woods that occur only as scattered fragments in high valleys of the inner Alpine ranges. The herb layer of these woods include meadow-like vegetation. German tamarisk *(Myricaria ger-*

manica) grows near the water flow in sand rich in fine-soil particles whereas bare gravel and sand are mostly inhabited by scree plants which have their main occurrence at higher altitudes.

g. Birch groves. Groves of silver birch *(Betula pendula)* occur as pioneer woods in shallow, often stony, siliceous soils; they form small stands on rather flat slopes with locally late-lying snow.

5.2.2. Dwarf shrub, bush, and tall-herb communities

The communities described in this chapter are well-distributed below the timberline in places where particular factors preclude the formation of forest. The occurrence of green alder thicket is influenced by intermittently wet soils and avalanches; dwarf mountain pine bush occurs on unstable slopes or in shallow soils; willow thicket grows in places continuously irrigated by springs, mountain streams, or snowmelt. Tall-herb communities mostly occur on calciferous soils which are nutrient-rich and occasionally very wet. Dwarf shrubs grow consistently in places where forest has been cleared and cannot return on account of extensive grazing. Dwarf shrubs often being poisonous (alpenroses), prickly (junipers), or leathery, they are avoided by cattle and able to expand rather fast. Should the dwarf shrubs be cleared, a pasture is formed and the return of dwarf shrubs may be prevented by intensive grazing. Fig. 24 shows that various dwarf shrub communities are dependent on solar radiation, duration of the snow cover, and exposure to wind.

a. Green alder thickets. Green alder *(Alnus viridis)* occurs on humid, mineral-rich soils in places with humid air; in dry valleys of the Central Alps it is confined to north-facing slopes. Green alder is widely

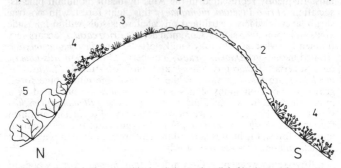

Fig. 24.   Dwarf shrub communities in relation to the relief of landscape (after *A.m.*):
1. Trailing azalea stands *(Loiseleurio-Cetrarietum)*
2. Dwarf juniper stands *(Junipero-Arctostaphyletum)*
3. Mountain crowberry stands *(Empetro-Vaccinietum)*
4. Alpenrose bush *(Rhododendro-Vaccinietum)*
5. Green alder thicket *(Alnetum viridis)*

distributed in the subalpine and suprasubalpine belt where it forms 1–3 m tall thickets *(Alnetum viridis)* on somewhat unstable humid slopes and in avalanche paths; avalanches glide over the elastic bush causing no damage. Green alder is not grazed by cattle and can expand in humid abandoned pastures. Incidentally, goats feed on the plant rather willingly. Similarly to legumes, green alder forms root nodules containing nitrogen-fixing bacteria; it is thus accompanied by nitrophilous, mostly large-leaved plants which are also characteristic of places where animals rest and of tall-herb communities. In addition to some willows (e.g. *Salix appendiculata, S. hastata)* one finds here adenostyle *(Adenostyles alliariae)*, masterwort *(Peucedanum ostruthium)*, various species of aconite *(Aconitum napellus, A. paniculatum, A. lycoctonum)*, round-leaved saxifrage *(Saxifraga rotundifolia)*, mountain chervil *(Chaerophyllum cicutaria)*, large-leaved yarrow *(Achillea macrophylla)*, two-flowered violet *(Viola biflora)* as well as alpine lady-fern *(Athyrium alpestre)* and broad buckler-fern *(Dryopteris dilatata)*.

b. Tall-herb communities and vegetation in resting places of animals. Natural tall-herb comunities are confined to gullies and hollows on calciferous substrata that remain covered by snow for a long time. Soil in such sites is rich in nutrients and humus. The vegetation being particularly thick and more than 1 m tall, no shrubs or trees are able to establish themselves there. The tall-herb association *Adenostylo-Cicerbitetum* includes mostly the same species as the green alder thicket; particularly frequent, too, are blue sow-thistle *(Cicerbita alpina)*, alpine willowherb *(Epilobium alpestre)*, species of lady's mantle *(Alchemilla)*; on the other hand, alpine larkspur *(Delphinium elatum)*, alpine tozzia *(Tozzia alpina)* and glabrous cerinthe *(Cerinthe glabra)* are rather rare.

Tall-herbs frequently also form the herb layer in forests and bushes. Last but not least, they typically occur in places which are rich in nutrients and not regularly managed (e.g. round rock-piles, on banks of streams, at roadsides, in depressions in meadows). The community occurring in the resting places of cattle *(Rumicetum alpini)* also represents the tall-herb vegetation; it grows in over-manured soils that are no longer managed, in particular near stables, alp-huts, in resting places of animals. The stands, mostly dominated by monk's rhubarb *(Rumex alpinus)* are unpalatable to cattle unless sprinkled with salt; the plentiful nutrients are thus unused and the vegetation can expand well. Leaves of the monk's rhubarb were in former times cooked and used as feed for pigs; goats feed on the plant as well. Additional species in this type of vegetation are mountain dock *(Rumex arifolius)*, alpine groundsel *(Senecio alpinus)*, all-good *(Chenopodium bonus-henricus)*, common monkshood *(Aconitum napellus)* and tender speedwell *(Veronica tenella)*. The common nettle *(Urtica dioeca)* occurs too, but is restricted to lower altitudes.

c. Willow thickets. Willow thickets occur mostly along streams and in flushes. Willow being generally difficult to determine, no specific names are given here. Among willows grow mostly tall herbs and also some swamp plants. A particular community dominated by Swiss willow *(Salix helvetica)* occurs as a pioneer vegetation in siliceous scree slopes that are covered by snow for a long time.

d. Dwarf mountain pine stands. Dwarf mountain pine *(Pinus mugo)* grows in unstable or shallow and intermittently dry soils where snow does not lie too late in the year; it can be found, too, in avalanche paths on sunny slopes. In our country the species occurs mostly within the subalpine and suprasubalpine belt and does not grow much higher; in this respect the Swiss Alps differ from the eastern part of the Alpine chain. Dwarf mountain pine occurs frequently upon limestone and dolomite but is able to grow upon serpentine, quartzite, and granite as well. The herb layer of dwarf mountain pine stands may include the same species as the mountain pine forest; pioneer plants appear very often, too, particularly in stands growing upon scree or rock. These plants are listed in the chapter dealing with scree and rock vegetation (p.   ).

e. Alpenrose bushes. In places where the forest at higher altitudes has been destroyed and grazing is not very intensive alpenrose bushes grow in sites which remain snow-covered in winter. The alpenrose with its evergreen leaves is not very frost-resistant and avoids south-facing slopes or hilltops that are snow-free in winter (see Fig. 24). Large stands of rust-leaved alpenrose *(Rhododendron ferruginei-Vaccinietum)* frequently occur on soils poor in calcium and indicate a past occurrence of forest. The herb layer in this vegetation includes blueberry *(Vaccinium myrtillus)*, alpine bilberry *(V. gaultherioides)*, and other species of the forest of larch-Arolla pine; they form a mosaic with fragments of the mat-grass pasture. Similar yet much smaller stands are formed by hairy alpenrose *(Rhododendron hirsutum)* east of the Aare and the massif of Gotthard in calcium-rich soils; they include species of the mountain pine forest and of the meadow-grass pasture.

f. Dwarf juniper stands. In south-facing slopes where snow may often slip off dwarf juniper *(Juniperus nana)* replaces the alpenrose; it forms dwarf shrub stands *(Junipero-Arctostaphyletum,* Fig. 24) together with bearberry *(Arctostaphylos uva-ursi)*, ling heather *(Calluna vulgaris)*, cowberry *(Vaccinium vitis-idaea)* and blueberry *(V. myrtillus)*. Species of the matgrass pasture are sometimes seen here too.

g. Mountain crowberry stands. Similarly to dwarf juniper and alpine bilberry, mountain crowberry *(Empetrum hermaphroditum)* has its main distribution upon substrata poor in calcium in the vicinity of a former timberline. Shorter than the alpenrose, it is able to inhabit places which have a rather thin snow cover; it occurs below hilltops, ridges, etc. in spite of the fact that it is not very frost-resistant (Fig. 24). Stands of mountain crowberry *(Empetro-Vaccinietum)* represent a transition between the frost-resistant carpets of trailing azalea which occur in windswept sites and the alpenrose bushes requiring rather sheltered conditions. Species accompanying mountain crowberry are

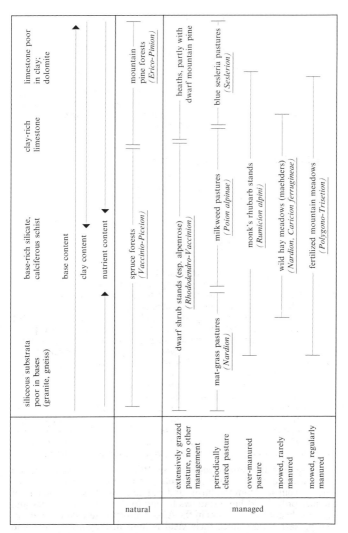

Fig. 25. Subalpine belt of the Swiss Alps: human influence upon vegetation. Not included are vegetation types developed under influence of special factors (e.g. landslips, avalanches, etc.).

the same as those growing in the alpenrose stands but they remain shorter.

h. Trailing azalea stands. Trailing azalea *(Loiseleuria procumbens)* forms flat carpets on the ground. Owing to its prostrate growth the species is able to grow a little over the natural timberline because it endures exposure to wind and a scanty snow cover. It occurs upon substrata poor in calcium, mainly on hilltops and ridges (Fig. 24). Stands of trailing azalea *(Loiseleurio-Cetrarietum)* are interspersed with numerous fruticose lichens e.g. Iceland moss *(Cetraria islandica)* or species of reindeer moss *(Cladonia)*.

5.2.3. Meadows, pastures and grasslands

Except for very dry sites, meadows and pastures below the natural timberline are dependent on human management. An outline of communities is given in Fig. 25. Grassland communities, occurring in the lower alpine belt in relation to humidity and base content of the soil are presented in Fig. 26. These vegetation types are still regularly grazed but would look alike without the influence of grazing. Of the many communities known, only some more important ones can be presented here.

a. Fertilized mountain meadows. Fertilized mountain meadows require regular mowing and manuring. They are mown twice a year in sunny places and at lower altitudes (up to ca. 600 m below the timberline), shadowy and higher localized sites being mown once a year only. Fertilized mountain meadows are nowadays mostly confined to the surroundings of farm settlements where the ground is not too steep and mowing can be done with machines. Vegetation in these places is called yellow oat-grass meadows *(Polygono-Trisetion)* after the yellow oatgrass *(Trisetum flavescens)* which is a characteristic component. In early spring masses of white crocus *(Crocus albiflorus)* appear in fertilized mountain meadows. Further representative species include mountain chervil *(Chaerophyllum cicutaria)*, common bistort *(Polygonum bistorta)*, oval-headed rampion *(Phyteuma ovatum)* in more humid meadows, whereas Villar's chervil *(Chaerophyllum villarsii)*, Scheuchzer's bellflower *(Campanula scheuchzeri)* and wild pansy *(Viola tricolor)* are frequently seen on drier sites. Many of these meadows comprise 40–70 different species within a small area.

b. Wild hay meadows or «maehders». Wild hay meadows are mown only once a year or just once in a while, and hardly ever manured. They mostly occur far from the farms and can be mown towards the end of summer only. Wild hay meadows belong to the richest in species and the most beautiful meadows in the Alps. Unfortunately they are disappearing rather fast; since their yield is limited, they are remote and frequently unsuited to the use of machines, farmers do not manage them anymore. The abandoned maehders situated on steep slopes are subjected to erosion because the snow freezes on the unmown plants in winter; while slipping down, it tears away whole plants making a rent in the vegetation cover. Wild hay meadows can be classified according to the soil content in bases, nutrients, and moisture. In places where soil contains more nutrients, vegetation includes e.g. alpine lovage *(Ligusticum mutellina)*, wood cranesbill *(Geranium silvaticum)*, mountain dock *(Rumex arifolius)* and many species typical of fertilized meadows. Acidic meadows are inhabited amongst others by yellow alpine pasqueflower *(Pulsatilla sulphurea)*, bearded bellflower *(Campanula barbata)*, giant cat's-ear *(Hypochoeris uniflora)* and further species of mat-grass pasture; on the other hand, meadows on base-rich soils include rust-coloured sedge *(Carex ferruginea)*, narcissus-flowered anemone *(Anemone narcissiflora)* and other species of the rust-coloured sedge grassland.

c. Pastures below the timberline. In places where nutrients, bases and moisture abound the sap-green, very productive milkweed pasture *(Poion alpinae)* which is occasionally manured a little occurs as the representative vegetation. Typical species here include meadow-grass *(Poa alpina)*, alpine lovage *(Ligusticum mutellina)*, rough hawkbit *(Leontodon hispidus)*, golden hawk's-beard *(Crepis aurea)* and various species of clover *(Trifolium)*. «Milkweed» is a collective name for plants of the composite family which have a milky sap e.g. hawkbit *(Leontodon)* or hawk's-beard *(Crepis)*. Pastures below the timberline include few grasses, herbs being much more frequent.

Acidic soils are inhabited by **mat-grass pastures** *(Nardion)*, widely distributed in the Alps since even base-containing soils are subject to leaching as a result of the high precipitation level. Mat-grass *(Nardus stricta)* is grazed by cattle only when its leaves are very young; it is therefore able to expand and forms a dull-green, thick grassland. Characteristic species include mountain arnica *(Arnica montana)*, alpine clover *(Trifolium alpinum)*, Koch's gentian *(Gentiana kochiana)*, common pussytoes *(Antennaria dioeca)*, bearded bellflower *(Campanula barbata)* and pyramidal bugle *(Ajuga pyramidalis)*.

If meadows on base-rich, meagre, dry, or humid soils are grazed, **the blue sesleria grassland** *(Seslerion)* of a similar type as that in the alpine belt is formed.

d. Grassland above the timberline (see Fig. 26). Base-poor alpine soils at lower altitudes are covered by **vegetation dominated by mat-grass** *(Nardion)* already including various species typical of the alpine sedge grassland of higher altitudes e.g. hemispherical rampion *(Phyteuma hemisphaericum)* or daisy-leaved speedwell *(Veronica bellidioides)*.

In soils a little richer in bases, and particularly on south-facing slopes occurs **grassland dominated by violet fescue** *(Festuco violaceae-Trifolietum thalii)*. Typical species of this vegetation include Thal's clover *(Trifolium thalii)*, snow clover *(T. nivale)*, black plantain *(Plantago atrata)* and various plants representing the milkweed pasture to which the community is similar in its composition. The milkweed pasture can (under influence of grazing) develop as well on lower sites of the alpine belt where it may cover less steep slopes. Transitions between the violet fescue grassland and the vegetation dominated by mat-grass as well as those between both grassland types and snow-patch communities are numerous and depend on the relief of the landscape.

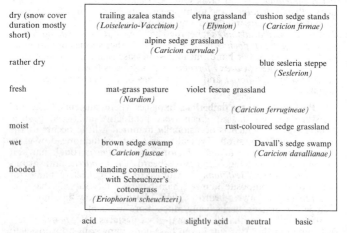

dry (snow cover duration mostly short)	trailing azalea stands (*Loiseleurio-Vaccinion*)	elyna grassland (*Elynion*)	cushion sedge stands (*Caricion firmae*)
	alpine sedge grassland (*Caricion curvulae*)		
rather dry			blue sesleria steppe (*Seslerion*)
fresh	mat-grass pasture (*Nardion*)	violet fescue grassland	
			(*Caricion ferrugineae*)
moist			rust-coloured sedge grassland
wet	brown sedge swamp *Caricion fuscae*		Davall's sedge swamp (*Caricion davallianae*)
flooded	«landing communities» with Scheuchzer's cottongrass (*Eriophorion scheuchzeri*)		
	acid	slightly acid neutral	basic

Fig. 26. Alpine belt of the Swiss Alps: Grassland communities in relation to moisture and base content of the soil. Not included are communities on rocks, cliffs, scree, as well as the snow-patch vegetation (After *4.m.*).

Alpine sedge grassland *(Caricion curvulae)* is an important high alpine vegetation growing on acid soils. This grassland is easily recognizable by its yellowish-green colour resulting from early dieback of tips of the outer, mostly backward-curved leaves of alpine sedge *(Carex curvula);* the thick tussocks of this species are clearly the main vegetation component. Typical species here include two-lined sesleria *(Sesleria disticha)*, Carniol groundsel *(Senecio carniolicus)*, shaggy groundsel *(S. incanus)*, alpine marguerite *(Chrysanthemum alpinum)*, daisy-leaved speedwell *(Veronica bellidioides)*, dwarf eye-bright *(Euphrasia minima)*, hemispherical rampion *(Phyteuma hemisphaericum)* and Kerner's lousewort *(Pedicularis kerneri)*. Dwarf cudweed *(Gnaphalium supinum)* and ear-like woodrush *(Luzula spadicea)* can be seen on more humid sites whereas vegetation in dry wind-exposed places includes many lichens in addition to the typical plants.

Calcareous soils in the alpine belt on south-facing slopes are inhabited by **blue sesleria grassland** *(Seslerio-Caricetum sempervirentis)* whereas vegetation in north-facing places is **dominated by rust-coloured sedge** *(Caricetum ferrugineae)*. Soil development in the alpine belt being not much advanced on northern sites, the rust-coloured sedge grassland does not occur very high and is soon replaced by scree vegetation. Contrary to this pattern, the blue sesleria grassland and the alpine sedge grassland both are able to reach altitudes 300–500 m above the natural timberline.

Typical species of the **blue sesleria grassland** include, apart from blue sesleria *(Sesleria coerulea)*, evergreen sedge *(Carex sempervirens)*, yellow oxytropis *(Oxytropis campestris)*, Jacquin's oxytropis *(Oxytropis jacquinii)*, alpine milk-vetch *(Astragalus alpinus)*, bald-stemmed globularia *(Globularia nudicaulis)*, alpine aster *(Aster alpinus)* and edelweiss *(Leontopodium alpinum)*.

Vegetation dominated by blue sesleria is frequently rich in flowers and may inhabit some rocky ledges. Blue sesleria *(Sesleria coerulea)* forms thick tussocks and can thus stabilize the soil on steep slopes. Owing to the constant soil movement (esp. under frost influence) the vegetation forms horizontal girdles so that the blue sesleria grassland is distinctly terraced. The terraces are not caused by grazing as is the case with those appearing in the acid alpine grassland.

The **rust-coloured sedge grassland** *(Caricetum ferrugineae)* is confined to north-facing sites or more humid hollows that contain a large amount of fine soil and thus have a high water capacity. Rust-coloured sedge *(Carex ferruginea)* is accompanied by globose orchid *(Orchis globosa)*, white alpine pasqueflower *(Pulsatilla alpina)*, mountain sainfoin *(Onobrychis montana)*, glacial milk-vetch *(Astragalus frigidus)* and narcissus-flowered anemone *(Anemone narcissiflora)*. The rust-coloured sedge grassland occurring at lower altitudes was formerly used as wild hay meadows.

In the southern part of the Central Alps and in the adjacent part of the Southern Alps terraced **grassland dominated by coloured fescue** *(Festucetum variae)* occurs in sunny places upon substrata not too poor in bases. Coloured fescue *(Festuca varia)* forms thick large tussocks with stiff, bristly young leaves. Species typical of this vegetation include rock speedwell *(Veronica fruticans)*, stellar hare's ear *(Bupleurum stellatum)* and betony-leaved rampion *(Phyteuma betonicifolium)*.

Windswept ridges, hilltops, and passes that are frequently free of snow in winter are inhabited by specialized grassland types: **the cushion sedge grassland** *(Caricetum firmae)* occurs upon hard limestone and dolomite whereas the **grassland dominated by mouse-tail-like elyna** *(Elynetum)* grows in base-rich soils which contain more fine particles; substrata poor in bases are inhabited by the above discussed variant of the alpine sedge grassland rich in lichens (in the lower alpine belt still occur some stands of the trailing azalea which were presented in the part dealing with dwarf shrub communities).

The **cushion sedge grassland** *(Caricetum firmae)* consists of scattered clumps of cushion sedge *(Carex firma)* and other species which often have a similar growth form. Plants representative of calciferous scree are frequent, too (e.g. mountain avens, *Dryas octopetala)*. Further typical species include bluish saxifrage *(Saxifraga caesia)*, alpine rock-rose *(Helianthemum alpestre)*, Clusius's gentian *(Gentiana clusii)* and dwarf orchid *(Chamorchis alpina)*.

Mouse-tail-like elyna *(Elyna myosuroides)* forms thick tufts which support desiccation and strong solar radiation well. **Grassland dominated by this species** *(Elynetum)* is often interspersed with lichens. Characteristic herbs include one-flowered fleabane *(Erigeron uniflorus)*, Carpathian pussytoes *(Antennaria carpatica)*, small-flowered sedge (Carex parviflora) and, rarely, glacial pink *(Dianthus glacialis)*.

5.2.4. Flushes and mires

Soils that are intermittently or permanently wet are inhabited by special plant communities. Plant litter is often not fully decomposed because of the oxygen deficiency, and humus or peat accumulates. Communities occurring over a peat layer of a particular depth (at least ca. 15 cm) are called mires.

Mires which are still influenced by ground-water are called fens. On the other hand, plants forming part of bogs cannot reach the water table with their roots because the peat layer is too thick; they are fed by rainwater or melting snow only.

Water along streams and springs is mostly rich in oxygen. If a good supply of calcium also occurs, **vegetation dominated by Jacquin's rock-cress** viz. the *Cratoneuro-Arabidetum* is formed; typical species include, in addition to Jacquin's rockcress *(Arabis jacquinii)*, starry saxifrage *(Saxifraga stellaris)*, yellow mountain saxifrage *(Saxifraga aizoides)* and numerous moss species; according to the occurrence of particular mosses, numerous small local associations can be distinguished. Places with water poor in calcium are inhabited by **vegetation dominated by large bittercress** *(Cardamine amara)* which also includes marsh marigold *(Caltha palustris)*, starry saxifrage *(Saxifraga stellaris)* as well as nodding willowherb *(Epilobium nutans)* and chickweed willowherb *(Epilobium alsinifolium)*. Both communities described above are distributed within the alpine and subalpine belt.

At lower altitudes, the common reed *(Phragmites communis)* forms together with various sedges specialized communities in silting-up ponds and slowly flowing waters. These «**landing communities**» *(Caricion rostratae)* are **dominated at higher altitudes by bottle sedge** *(Carex rostrata)* which occurs nearly up to the timberline. At higher altitudes, in ponds with water poor in calcium occurs another vegetation type called *Eriophorion scheuchzeri* and **dominated by Scheuchzer's cottongrass** *(Eriophorum scheuchzeri)* which is accompanied in firmer soil by brown sedge *(Carex fusca)* and alpine willowherb *(Epilobium alpinum)*. Calcium-rich ponds are hardly inhabited by «landing communities» because the fluctuations of the water level are too extreme. **Brown sedge swamp** *(Caricion fuscae)* can be seen at lower altitudes too, if the swamps are meagre and poor in calcium; turfy deergrass *(Trichophorum caespitosum)* and rivulet bittercress *(Cardamine rivularis)* occur there frequently. These communities may occur as well in potential forest sites below the timberline if they are regularly cut for litter in the autumn. Similar vegetation which belongs to the mire category on account of its thick peat layer occur as well upon calcareous substrata; the communities dominated by Davall's sedge *(Carex davalliana)* form **Davall's sedge swamps** *(Caricion davallianae)* there. Plants characteristic of this vegetation include broad-leaved cottongrass *(Eriophorum latifolium)*, marsh helleborine *(Epipactis palustris)*, bird's-eye primrose *(Primula farinosa)*, Traunsteiner's orchid *(Orchis traunsteineri)*, common butterwort *(Pinguicula vulgaris)* and marsh felwort *(Swertia perennis)*.

Bogs which contain still less nutrients than fens are inhabited above all by various species of bog moss *(Sphagnum)* able to store water. Typical plants are hare's tail cottongrass *(Eriophorum vaginatum)*, turfy deergrass *(Trichophorum caespitosum)*, and also species not described in this book viz. round-leaved sundew *(Drosera rotundifolia)*, cranberry *(Oxycoccus quadripetala, O. microcarpa)* and bog rosemary *(Andromeda polifolia)*. Bogs occur in the Alps nearly up to the timberline and the layer of peat may sometimes reach a considerable depth (several m).

5.2.5. Snow-patch and scree communities (see Fig. 22)

No closed grassland can be formed in places influenced by late-lying snow, low temperatures, or soil movement and rockfall. Snow-patch vegetation occurs on sites where snow lies longer than 9 months. As soon as the duration of the snow cover becomes shorter, transition communities towards the neighbouring grassland are formed. An open grassland community may appear in snow-patches upon siliceous substrata in places with a continuous layer of humus; on the other hand, grassland patches upon limestone or dolomite remain rather small and scattered because of the deficient soil development (humus may accumulate only in small pockets); the plant cover thus reminds one rather of a scree vegetation. In the subnival belt only scree communities are formed as development of humus is virtually nil upon *any* substratum.

a. Snow-patch vegetation. Snow-patch vegetation upon siliceous substrata in the alpine belt is dominated by dwarf willow *(Salix herbacea)* and accordingly called the **dwarf willow carpet** *(Salicetum herbaceae)*. Typical species include dwarf cudweed *(Gnaphalium supinum)*, dwarf snowbell *(Soldanella pusilla)*, two-flowered sandwort *(Arenaria biflora)*, five-fingered lady's mantle *(Alchemilla pentaphyllea)*, starwort mouse-ear *(Cerastium trigynum)*; amongst these plants there are patches of snowbed moss *(Polytrichum sexangulare)* which may be the only survivor if the snow does not melt for a long time. Dwarf buttercup *(Ranunculus pygmaeus)* is a rarity here.

Similar sites upon calciferous substrata are inhabited by **carpet-forming willows** *(Salicetum retuso-reticulatae)* or a **vegetation dominated by bluish rockcress** *(Arabis coerulea)* and accordingly called *Arabidetum coeruleae*. The latter community forms a rather discontinuous plant cover and represents a pure scree vegetation remaining under snow for

9–10 months, whereas the former is rather continuous and is snow covered for about 9 months. Typical species of the **carpet-forming willow community** include net-leaved willow *(Salix reticulata)*, blunt-leaved willow *(Salix retusa)*, Bavarian gentian *(Gentiana bavarica)*, alpine crowfoot *(Ranunculus alpester)*. Representative species of the **bluish rockcress community** are bluish rockcress *(Arabis coerulea)*, snow dock *(Rumex nivalis)*, androsace-like saxifrage *(Saxifraga androsacea)* and Hoppe's cudweed *(Gnaphalium hoppeanum)*.

b. Subnival communities on stabilized scree. Stabilized scree communities occurring on high-alpine sites are generally not assigned to snow-patch vegetation in spite of the fact that the duration of snow is more or less the same. Given the high altitude, hollows and gullies in the subnival belt are hardly inhabited by any flowering plants. Typical vegetation in the subnival siliceous scree is represented by an association **dominated by alpine rock-jasmine** *(Androsacetum alpinae)*. Typical plants include, in addition to alpine rock-jasmine *(Androsace alpina)*, other cushion plants viz. king of the Alps *(Erytrichium nanum)*, moss saxifrage *(Saxifraga bryoides)*; glacier crowfoot *(Ranunculus glacialis)* also is very characteristic. Nearly all these species may climb individually up to 4000 m under favourable conditions.

Base-rich siliceous scree in the subnival belt is inhabited by an association **dominated by Hoppe's draba** *(Drabetum hoppeanae)*. Typical species of this association include Hoppe's draba *(Draba hoppeana)*, genipi wormwood *Artemisia genipi)*, corymbose pennycress *(Thlaspi corymbosum)*, short-stemmed hutchinsia *(Hutchinsia brevicaulis)*, alpine toadflax *(Linaria alpina)*, two-flowered saxifrage *(Saxifraga biflora)*, Mt. Cenis bellflower *(Campanula cenisia)*, and, as a rarity, fern-leaved lousewort *(Pedicularis aspleniifolia)*.

Stabilized scree upon hard calciferous rock in the subnival belt is virtually no longer inhabited, the water supply being insufficient on account of the low fine soil content. Fragments of the bluish rockcress association may sporadically occur here.

c. Communities on mobile scree and moraines. Scree slopes in the alpine belt are mostly characterized by a mobile scree, for the stabilized scree weathered very long ago and became colonized by grassland. Limestone and dolomite scree slopes are particularly frequent, not only in the alpine belt but also on lower sites because these rocks weather very slowly and an occasional rockfall further precludes stabilization. On the other hand, siliceous scree below the timberline undergoes a rather rapid further development and forest appears even if the scree does not become fully stabilized or rockfall occurs regularly. Owing to ski-run grading scree slopes have largely expanded in the vicinity of big winter resorts; they are primarily colonized by a very impoverished vegetation.

The pioneer community occurring on still slightly mobile siliceous scree is **dominated by mountain sorrel** and accordingly called *Oxyrietum digynae*. Typical species of this plant cover which also occurs frequently on moraines include mountain sorrel *(Oxyria digyna)*, one-flowered

84

mouse-ear *(Cerastium uniflorum)*, white-leaved adenostyle *(Adenostyles leucophylla)*, creeping avens *(Geum reptans)*, Clusius's leopard's-bane *(Doronicum clusii)*; ear-like woodrush *(Luzula spadicea)* is characteristic of mobile siliceous scree slopes that are shadowy and remain covered by snow for a long time.

The vegetation on mobile limestone or dolomite scree in the alpine belt is **dominated by round-leaved pennycress** and thus called *Thlaspeetum rotundifolii*. Typical species of this association include round-leaved pennycress *(Thlaspi rotundifolium)*, alpine poppy *(Papaver alpinum* s.l.), broad-leaved mouse-ear *(Cerastium latifolium)*, ciliated moehringia *(Moehringia ciliata)*, small bellflower *(Campanula cochleariifolia)*, black yarrow *(Achillea atrata)* and alpine hutchinsia *(Hutchinsia alpina)*.

Mobile calciferous scree rich in fine soil is inhabited by an association called *Leontodontetum montani* which is **dominated by mountain hawkbit** *(Leontodon montanus)* occurring in the company of yellow mountain saxifrage *(Saxifraga aizoides)*, grass-of-Parnassus-leaved buttercup *(Ranunculus parnassifolius)*, purple saxifrage *(Saxifraga oppositifolia)* and dwarf valerian *(Valeriana supina)*.

Below the timberline, calciferous scree is characteristically inhabited by the **butterbur-dominated association** *Petasitetum paradoxi*; typical species include, apart from paradoxial butterbur *(Petasites paradoxus)*, mountain valerian *(Valeriana montana)*, athamantha *(Athamanta cretensis)*, smooth-stemmed thistle *(Carduus defloratus)*, alpine rockcress *(Arabis alpina)* and glabrous adenostyle *(Adenostyles glabra)*.

In the colline and montane belt narrow-leaved hemp-nettle *(Galeopsis angustifolia)* typically occurs. Montane and subalpine calciferous scree slopes in the southern Alpine ranges (e.g. the Bergamo Alps) are particularly rich in various plant species. They contain many endemic taxa e.g. yellow fumitory *(Corydalis lutea)* which nowadays is much wider distributed because of planting. At the southern foot of the Jura also occur numerous species of calciferous scree; they do not grow in the Alps and otherwise have a southern distribution. Good examples are narrow-leaved centhranthus (Centranthus angustifolius), hyssop-leaved ironwort *(Sideritis hyssopifolia)* and also rocky toadflax *(Linaria petraea)* which occurs nearly exclusively in the Jura.

5.2.6. Vegetation on rocks and cliffs (Fig. 22)

Specialized plants forming part of the vegetation on rocks and cliffs take root in rock crevices. On the other hand, vegetation occurring upon rocky ledges and at the foot of cliffs consists of grassland fragments.

Communities inhabiting rocks and cliffs can be classified according to the calcium content of their respective substrata as well as the altitude (below or above the timberline).

Substrata rich in calcium above the timberline are inhabited by an association **dominated by Swiss rock-jasmine** and called *Androsacetum* *helveticae*. Typical species here include Swiss rock-jasmine *(Androsace helvetica)*, auricula *(Primula auricula)* and white mountain saxifrage *(Saxifraga aizoon)*. At lower altitudes an association **dominated by stalky cinquefoil** *(Potentillo-Hieracietum)* occurs typically; characteristic species include, apart from stalky cinquefoil *(Potentilla caulescens)*, rock kernera *(Kernera saxatilis)*, dwarf rockcress *(Arabis pumila)*, heart-leaved globularia *(Globularia cordiifolia)* and various species of hawkweed *(Hieracium)*. The dolomite cliffs of the Bergamo Alps are particularly rich in species, some taxa being quite spectacular and endemic e.g. tassel rampion *(Synotoma comosum)*. Mountain pennycress *(Thlaspi montanum)* is in Switzerland confined to calciferous rocks of the Jura.

Siliceous substrata above the timberline are inhabited by an association **dominated by Vandelli's rock-jasmine** *(Androsacetum vandellii)*. Characteristic species include Vandelli's rock-jasmine *(Androsace vandellii)*, king of the Alps *(Erytrichium nanum)*, Rhaetic rampion *(Phyteuma hedraianthifolia)*, dwarf rampion *(P. humile)*, broad-leaved primrose *(Primula latifolia)* and noble wormwood *(Artemisia mutellina)*. Siliceous rocks below the timberline are inhabited by an association **dominated by stinking primrose** *(Asplenio-Primuletum hirsutae)*. In addition to stinking primrose *(Primula hirsuta)*, representative species of this association include various taxa of spleenwort *(Asplenium)*, scabrous saxifrage *(Saxifraga aspera)*, pyramidal saxifrage *(S. cotyledon)*, Scheuchzer's rampion *(Phyteuma scheuchzeri)* and Swiss treacle mustard *(Erysimum helveticum)*.

6. Key to determination of the most important Alpine plants

6.1. Introduction and instructions for use

The key works basically on the dichotomous principle, by which at each step the reader is confronted with a choice between two contrasting characteristics 1., 1*. or 2., 2*.), more than two characteristics viz. 1., 1*., 1**., 1***., etc. being rare. The reader has to choose one of the offered alternatives by comparing the description with the plant studied; this choice leads to a further figure on the left, lower down in the key, and new alternatives are to be considered. After further choices the reader should eventually reach an entry which has no further figure and which gives the name of a plant.

The key leads mostly to the determination of a genus only. The species may then be determined by comparison of various drawings, colour plates, and descriptions of the species. Such a verification of determination is always advisable.

Plants to be determined should be in bloom and if possible fresh. The present key deals, as a rule, only with plants which occur frequently at altitudes higher than 1500 m. Not included are lowland plants which may occasionally occur higher on south-facing slopes or have been introduced.

Because some plant characteristics are so variable, the choice of alternatives may sometimes be rather difficult; in this case, one should arbitrarily choose one possibility. Should the plant «key out», another alternative is to be chosen. Determination of plants with inflorescences that simulate a single flower is often difficult. For instance, flowers of marguerite, thistle, or dandelion are in fact inflorescences which consist of numerous florets. Each of these florets has a tube-like or tongue-like corolla, 5 stamens which form a tube, and one pistil with ovary, style, and stigma. The flower of the edelweiss even consists of several heads, the white petals being only very pilose cauline leaves which subtend the flower-heads. It should be thus decided before determination is started whether a given flower is truly a *single flower* (the innermost ovary, then stamens, and the perianth as the outermost part – the latter either uniform or differentiated into sepals and petals) or an *inflorescence* comprising numerous, mostly small and tightly clustered florets surrounded by bracts (not tepals).

6.2. Glossary of some botanical terms

actinomorphic: divisible into similar parts in many planes (opposite to zygomorphic; see Fig. 28, flower symmetry).

adenotrichous: covered with glandular hairs which secrete a, usually sticky, fluid.

alternate: placed singly at different levels on an axis; usually said of leaves or leaflets (see Fig. 27, leaf arrangement).

basal: situated at, or pertaining to, the base of the stem.

bush: see shrub.

calyx: the outer, mostly green part, of a differentiated perianth.

catkin: deciduous spike of tiny flowers, falling off as a whole.

cauline: usually said of leaves; borne on the aerial part of the stem, esp. the upper part, but not subtending a flower or inflorescence.

compound: consisting of smaller parts (e.g. a compound leaf consists of leaflets that are completely separated form each other; see Fig. 27, compound leaves).

compound umbel: umbel consisting of smaller umbels.

cordate: heart-shaped.

corolla: the inner, mostly coloured part of a differentiated perianth (see Fig. 28, single flower).

corolla appendage: scale-like structure on a petal, above all in the pink family (see Fig. 28, petals).

divided: leaf margin cut deeply into lobes, sometimes nearly to the leaf midrib or mid-vein. Twice divided are leaves with divided lobes; if the lobes of the second rank are divided themselves, the leaf is triple divided etc.

ear: inflorescence with sessile individual flowers grouped along an axis (fig. 28, inflorescences). See also: spike.

entire: undivided i.e. without deep incisions (see Fig. 27, leaf).

epicalyx: calyx-like structure outside the genuine calyx esp. in the rose family.

flower: see Fig. 28.

hastate: shaped like an arrowhead (see Fig. 28, leaf forms).

head: a dense cluster of sessile or nearly sessile flowers on a very short axis or receptacle (see Fig. 28, inflorescence).

inferior ovary: an ovary situated below the point of origin of the calyx, corolla, and stamens (see Fig. 28, ovary).

inflorescence: the flower cluster of a plant (see Fig. 28, inflorescence).

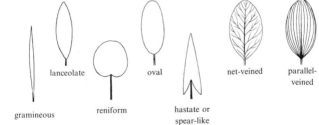

Leaf parts:

leaf-blade
leaf stalk or petiole
stipules

Leaf arrangement:

alternate   opposite   verticillate   basal rosette

entire   lobed   palmately divided (nearly to the base)   pinnately divided (nearly to the mirib)

Compound leaves:

smooth-edged   serrated margins   clover leaf-like   pinnate   leaflet   terminal leaflet

Leaf forms:

gramineous   lanceolate   reniform   oval   hastate or spear-like   net-veined   parallel-veined

Fig. 27. Morphology and position of leaves (compare the corresponding terminology in the glossary).

89

Inflorescences:

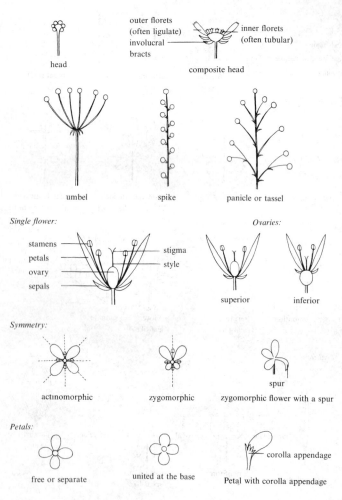

head

outer florets
(often ligulate)
involucral
bracts

inner florets
(often tubular)

composite head

umbel

spike

panicle or tassel

Single flower:

stamens
petals
ovary
sepals

stigma
style

Ovaries:

superior

inferior

Symmetry:

actinomorphic

zygomorphic

zygomorphic flower with a spur

spur

Petals:

free or separate

united at the base

corolla appendage

Petal with corolla appendage

Fig. 28. Morphology of flowers and inflorescences (compare the corresponding terminology in the glossary).

involucral bracts: bracts subtending a flower cluster, as e.g. in the heads of the composite family.

lanceolate: lance-shaped i.e. slightly wider below, gradually tapering to the tip (see Fig. 27, leaf forms).

leaf, leaf blade, leaf stalk or *petiole:* see Fig. 27.

leaflet: one of the segments of a compound leaf: in contrast to lobes, leaflets are completely separated from each other (see Fig. 27, compound leaves). Unlike leaves, leaflets have no buds in their axils.

leaf sheath: see sheath.

multilateral: many-sided orientation of organs (leaves or flowers) on the stem.

net-veined: leaf veins form a net pattern, only the main veins being occasionally parallel.

opposite: arising in pairs, one element facing the other on either side of the stem (see Fig. 27, leaf arrangement).

oval: broadly elliptic (see Fig. 27, leaf forms).

ovary: female organ inside of flower which carries ovules and will develop into fruit after the seeds are formed (see Fig. 28, single flower).

panicle or *tassel:* strictly branched racemose inflorescence, though often applied to *any* branched inflorescence. Flowers pedicellate. Simple panicle consists of flowers growing directly from the main axis whereas the branched panicle has lateral axes (see Fig. 28, inflorescences).

pappus: the modified calyx limb in the composite family, forming a crown of bristles or scales at the tip of the achene.

parallel-veined: all leaf veins run parallel (see Fig. 27, leaf forms).

pedicel: stalk of a flower in a flower cluster.

pedicellate: having a pedicel.

pentamerous: having the parts in fives.

perianth: flower leaves (tepals) often coloured, which surround the inner organs of the flower viz. stamens and ovaries: in most plants differentiated into calyx and corolla; not identical with involucral bracts.

petals: parts of corolla, usually coloured (see Fig. 28, single flower).

pinnate: compound leaf consisting of more than three leaflets, with leaflets arranged on both sides of a common axis (see Fig. 27, leaf division); double pinnate means that particular leaflets are pinnatisect themselves; in triple or compound pinnate leaves the leaflets of the second and further rank are also sectioned.

raceme: an unbranched, elongated, indeterminate inflorescence with each flower subequally pedicellate. Corresponds to a simple panicle.

reniform: kidney-shaped (see Fig. 27, leaf forms).

rosette: a crowded cluster of leaves, appearing to rise from the ground (see Fig. 27, leaf arrangement).

scales: very small, strongly reduced, oval to lanceolate leaves.

scarious: thin and membraneous.

sepals: parts of the calyx, usually green.

-serial: said of leaves or flowers (e.g. bi-serial or tri-serial means arranged along the stem by twos or threes).

sheath: membraneous, green or pale tubular stem envelope formed by the base of the petiole.

shrub: a woody perennial plant, smaller than a tree, usually with several stems branched at the base. Dwarf shrubs remain short (under 1 m), semi-shrubs are woody at the base only.

smooth-edged: leaf without serrated edges (see Fig. 27, leaf division).

spike: see ear.

spur: a hollow, sac-like, conical or slender projection of some part of a flower (see Fig. 28, flower symmetry).

squarrose: with stiff spreading branches.

stamens: male organs of the flower bearing the pollen (see Fig. 28, single flower).

stigma: the apical part of a pistil or style through which the pollination is effected (see Fig. 28, single flower). A style may have one or several stigmas.

stipule: an appendage at the base of a petiole or leaf or on each side of its insertion (see Fig. 27, compound leaves).

style: the contracted portion of a pistil or carpel between the ovary and the stigma (see Fig. 28, single flower).

superior ovary: an ovary situated above the point of origin of the calyx corolla, and stamens (see Fig. 28, ovary).

tendril: thread-like part of a pinnate leaf replacing the terminal leaflet.

tepals: perianth segments.

terminal: situated at the uppermost point.

terminal leaflet: the uppermost leaflet in a compound leaf (see Fig. 27, compound leaves).

tetramerous: having the parts in fours.

toothed or *dentate:* leaf margin cut into teeth (see Fig. 27, leaf division).

umbel: a flower cluster in which the pedicels arise from a common point, like the ribs of an umbrella (see Fig. 28, inflorescence).

unilateral: one-sided orientation of organs (leaves or flowers) on the stem.

verticillate: leaves whorled i.e. arising three or more from the stem at the same level or point (see Fig. 27, leaf arrangement).

villous: shaggy.

zygomorphic: divisible into similar halves in only one plane (bilaterally symmetric, opposite to actinomorphic).

6.3. Key

Spore-bearing plants (e.g. ferns, clubmosses, horsetails) are not included in this key.

°in case of multi-coloured flowers, the prevailing colour is valid.

1.	Plant without green leaves	**Group 1** (p. 93)
1.*	Plant with green leaves or needles	2
2.	Stem woody (trees, shrubs or bushes, dwarf shrubs, semi-shrubs)	**Group 2** (p. 94)
2.*	Stem not woody	3
3.	Leaves gramineous, single flowers small and rather inconspicuous but often in close inflorescences	**Group 3** (p. 96)
3.*	Leaves not gramineous or flowers conspicuous	4
4.	Flowers white°	**Group 4** (p. 97)
4.*	Flowers red, orange-red, brown-red, pink, purple, or red-violet°	**Group 5** (p. 101)
4.**	Flowers blue, lilac or violet°	**Group 6** (p. 106)
4.***	Flowers yellow, yellowish, orange-yellow, greenish, or brownish°	**Group 7** (p. 109)

Group 1: plants without green leaves

1.	Plant with thin, winding stem only: **dodder** *(Cuscuta)*	
1.*	Plant with straight, upright stem	2
2.	Flowers in heads	3
2.*	Flowers arranged along an axis (ear-like)	4
3.	Heads in a panicle: **butterbur** *(Petasites)*	
3.*	Heads single, yellow: **coltsfoot** *(Tussilago)*	
4.	Forest plant; flowers with 6 free (separate) tepals: **coralroot** *(Corallorrhiza)*	
4.*	Plant of treeless areas; flowers with 5 united tepals and one calyx: **broomrape** *(Orobanche)*	

93

Group 2: stem woody (trees, shrubs or bushes, dwarf shrubs, semi-shrubs)

1.	Plant with needles or small, narrow, rigid leaves (narrower than 2.5 mm)	2
1.*	Plant with leaves (wider than 2.5 mm)	12
2.	Trees or large shrubs (taller than 50 cm); needles mostly longer than 2 cm	3
2.*	Small shrubs (mostly shorter than 50 cm); needles (or leaves) mostly much shorter than 2 cm	7
3.	Needles singly on branches	4
3.*	Needles in bunches of two or more	5
4.	Needles flat, with 2 whitish stripes underneath, mostly arranged in one plane on the branch: **silver fir** *(Abies)*	
4.*	Needles angular, without white stripes, arranged in all planes on the branch: **spruce** *(Picea)*	
5.	Needles bright green, in bunches of 20–60, soft, shorter than 3 cm: **larch** *(Larix)*	
5.*	Needles dark green, in bunches of 2 or 5, rigid, mostly longer than 3 cm	6
6.	Needles in bunches of 2: **pine** *(Pinus montana and P. silvestris)*	
6.*	Needles in bunches of 5: **Arolla pine** *(Pinus cembra)*	
7.	Plant with prickly needles 0.8–1.8 cm long: **juniper** *(Juniperus)*	
7.*	Plant with narrow, rigid leaves or needles (shorter than 0.8 cm)	8
8.	Plant with scale-like leaves (shorter than 0.3 cm)	10
8.*	Plant with needles or narrow leaves (0.5–0.8 cm long) .	9
9.	Plant strongly smelling when crushed, with berry-like fruits: **savin** *(Juniperus sabina)*	
9.*	Plant virtually odourless when crushed, with inconspicuous fruits and reddish-violet flowers: **ling heather** *(Calluna vulgaris)*	
10.	Branches of the plant prostrate; flowers small, pink, bell-shaped: **trailing azalea** *(Loiseleuria procumbens)*	
10.*	Branches of the plant rising	11
11.	Flowers ascidiform (pitcher-like), red; plant without berries: **heath** *(Erica)*	
11.*	Flowers inconspicuous, red to purple; plant with black berries: **crowberry** *(Empetrum)*	
12.	Leaves opposite: **honeysuckle family** *(Caprifoliaceae)* . .	13
12.*	Leaves alternate	15
13.	Plant creeping over the ground, shorter than 20 cm: **northern twinflower** *(Linnaea borealis)*	
13.*	Plant upright, shrub-like	14
14.	Leaves entire, smooth-edged: **honeysuckle** *(Lonicera)*	
14.*	Leaves pinnate (with leaflets): **elder** *(Sambucus)*	
15.	Trees or large bushes (taller than 25 cm)	16

94

15.*	Small bushes, dwarf shrubs, and semi-shrubs (mostly shorter than 25 cm)	32
16.	Leaves pinnate (with leaflets) or divided nearly to mid-vein	17
16.*	Leaves entire or divided at most to the middle	18
17.	Flowers blue, large, single: **alpine clematis** (*Clematis alpina*)	
17.*	Flowers red or white, large, single; plant prickly: **rose** (*Rosa*)	
17.**	Flowers white, small, grouped umbel-like; plant without prickles: **rowan** (*Sorbus aucuparia*)	
18.	Leaves palmately divided nearly to the middle, with 3–5 broad tips	19
18.*	Leaves entire, without tips	20
19.	Tree, taller than 2 m: **maple** (*Acer*)	
19.*	Bush, at most 2 m tall: **currant** (*Ribes*)	
20.	Leaves, smooth-edged, without stipules	21
20.*	Leaves dentate or with stipules at the base	24
21.	Leaves rounded to oval, whitely tomentose underneath: **cotoneaster** (*Cotoneaster*)	
21.*	Leaves not whitely tomentose underneath	22
22.	Leaves large, wider than 3 cm; tree taller than 2 m: **beech** (*Fagus silvatica*)	
22.*	Leaves narrower than 3 cm, bush at most 1 m tall . . .	23
23.	Flowers red; plant without berries: **alpenrose** (*Rhododendron*)	
23.*	Flowers white or red; plant with red berries: **spurge-laurel** (*Daphne*)	
24.	Leaves coarsely toothed	25
24.*	Leaves very finely toothed or nearly smooth-edged, with stipules	30
25.	Flowers and fruits in catkins	26
25.*	Flowers white or pink, grouped umbel-like	29
26.	Leaves rounded, with long stalks (petiole mostly longer than the leaf), with undefined tip: **aspen** (*Populus tremula*)	
26.*	Leaves oblong or elongated and sharp-tipped	27
27.	Tree or tall bush with white bark: **birch** (*Betula*)	
27.*	Bush or tree with dark-coloured bark	28
28.	Leaves mostly wider than 3 cm, without stipules: **alder** (*Alnus*)	
28.*	Leaves mostly narrower than 3 cm, with (often falling off) stipules at the base: **willow** (*Salix*)	
29.	Leaves white underneath; flowers white: **whitebeam** (*Sorbus aria*)	
29.*	Leaves green underneath; flowers pink: **false medlar** (*Sorbus chamaemespilus*)	
30.	Leaves rounded; flowers greenish or white, pedicellate	31
30.*	Leaves oblong; flowers in catkins: **willow** (*Salix*)	
31.	Petals greenish, shorter than 0.5 cm: **buckthorn** (*Rhamnus*)	

95

31.* Petals white, 1.5–2 cm long: **June-berry** *(Amelanchier)*
32. Flowers grouped spherically, blue: **globularia** *(Globularia)*
32.* Flowers not grouped spherically, their colour other than
blue 33
33. Flowers inconspicuous, whitish, greenish, or yellowish,
smaller than 3 mm 34
33.* Flowers larger than 3 mm 35
34. Flowers in multi-flowered catkins: **willow** *(Salix)*
34.* Flowers pedicellate, in bunches with few flowers: **buckthorn**
(Rhamnus)
35. Flowers zygomorphic, yellow and white, or yellow and red:
shrubby milkwort *(Polygala chamaebuxus)*
35.* Flowers actinomorphic 36
36. Petals free 37
36.* Petals (or coloured tepals) united 38
37. Petals white, mostly 8: **mountain avens** *(Dryas octopetala)*
37.* Petals yellow (rarely white), mostly 5: **rockrose**
(Helianthemum)
38. Leaves more than four times as long as wide; flowers pink:
striated mezereon *(Daphne striata)*
38.* Leaves at most four times as long as wide: **heath family**
(Ericaceae) 39
39. Leaves overwintering, leathery 40
39.* Leaves shed in autumn, not leathery 41
40. Leaves speckled underneath, edges curved down a little:
cowberry *(Vaccinium vitis-idaea)*
40.* Leaves not speckled, flat: **common bearberry** *(Arcto-*
staphylos uva-ursi)
41. Leaves mostly longer than 2 cm, with fringed margins:
alpine bearberry *(Arctostaphylos alpina)*
41.* Leaves smaller than 2 cm, bare 42
42. Leaves green, slightly dentate: **blueberry** *(Vaccinium myr-*
tillus)
42.* Leaves bluish-green, smooth-edged: **alpine bilberry** *(Vac-*
cinium gaultherioides)

**Group 3: leaves gramineous, single flowers small and rather
inconspicuous**

1. Stem with nodes: **genuine grasses** *(Gramineae)*
1.* Stem without nodes 2
2. Leaves tri-serial; stem mostly triangular: **sedge family**
(Cyperaceae)
2.* Leaves not tri-serial; stem not triangular 3
3. Stem without leaves; leaves in a basal rosette: **plantain**
(Plantago)
3.* Stem with leaves, at least in the lower part 4
4. Leaves bi-serial; flowers white to yellowish: **tofieldia**
(Tofieldia)

96

4.*	Leaves not bi-serial	5
5.	Leaves completely bare: **rush** *(Juncus)*	
5.*	Leaves hairy at least underneath at the margin: **woodrush** *(Luzula)*	

Group 4: flowers white

1.	Leaves (at least lower ones) opposite (occasionally verticillate)	2
1.*	Leaves alternate, verticillate, or in a basal rosette . . .	11
2.	Petals separate: **pink family** *(Caryophyllaceae)*	3
2.*	Petals united	8
3.	Sepals united	4
3.*	Sepals free	6
4.	Styles 2; 5 scarious, pale stripes on calyx: **gypsophila** *(Gypsophila)*	
4.*	Styles 3 or 5; whole calyx red or reddish: **campion** *(Silene)*	
6.	Sepals with white scarious margin: **mouse-ear** *(Cerastium)*	
6.*	Sepals without white margin	7
7.	Leaves rounded, at most twice as long as wide: **sandwort** *(Arenaria)*	
7.*	Leaves at least twice as long as wide: **sandwort** and **moehringia** *(Minuartia* and *Moehringia)*	
8.	Leaves small, leathery, at least four times as long as wide: **mountain germander** *(Teucrium montanum)*	
8.*	Leaves at most four times as long as wide	9
9.	Flowers 1–2 on a 5–10 cm long shoot: **northern twinflower** *(Linnaea borealis)*	
9.*	Flowers numerous, in a dense group	10
10.	Calyx very small, hardly visible; stamens 3: **valerian** *(Valeriana)*	
10.*	Calyx bell-shaped, 4-toothed; stamens 4: **eye-bright** *(Euphrasia)*	
11.	Flowers numerous (pedicellate or not), grouped in umbel or head	12
11.*	Flowers forming spike or panicle, single or in pairs . .	35
12.	Leaves consisting of three leaflets (clover-like leaf): **clover** *(Trifolium)*	
12.*	Other leaf types	13
13.	Flowers not pedicellate, grouped in compact heads enveloped in bracts: **composite family** *(Compositae)* . . .	14
13.*	Flowers pedicellate (pedicles sometimes very short) . .	21
14.	Plant with prickles: **silver thistle** *(Carlina simplex)*	
14.*	Plant without prickles	15
15.	Leaves entire, smooth-edged	16
15.*	Leaves divided or dentate	18
16.	Leaves not whitely tomentose: **fleabane** *(Erigeron)*	
16.*	Leaves whitely tomentose on both sides	17

17. Heads radially enveloped in whitely tomentose leaves: **edelweiss** *(Leontopodium alpinum)*
17.* Heads not radially enveloped in leaves: **pussytoes** *(Antennaria)*
18. Leaves large, rounded, or triangular: **butterbur** *(Petasites)*
18.* Leaves oblong 19
19. Heads measuring less than 1 cm in diameter: **yarrow** *(Achillea)*
19.* Heads measuring more than 1 cm in diameter 20
20. Stem without leaves (sometimes leaves only at the base): **Micheli's daisy** *(Bellidiastrum michelii)*
20.* Stem with leaves: **marguerite** *(Chrysanthemum)*
21. Petals united in front forming a dark-violet bill: **rampion** *(Synotoma)*
21.* Petals with free tips, at least in front 22
22. Flowers measuring more than 1 cm in diameter: **narcissus-flowered anemone** *(Anemone narcissiflora)*
22.* Flowers measuring less than 1 cm in diameter 23
23. Petals united: **rock-jasmine** *(Androsace)*
23.* Petals (or petal-like involucral bracts) free 24
24. Leaves parallel-veined, smooth-edged; plant smelling like a leek: **alpine leek** *(Allium victorialis)*
24.* Leaves divided, net-veined: **carrot family** *(Umbelliferae)* 25
25. Umbel wrapped in whitish leaves forming a star-shaped envelope: **astrantia** *(Astrantia)*
25.* Umbel not enveloped in whitish leaves 26
26. Leaf sections and tips fine, nearly hairlike (narrower than 1 mm) 27
26.* Leaf sections or tips rather rough, not hairlike (wider than 1 mm) 31
27. Plant with a strong odour of fennel: **spignel** *(Meum athamanticum)*
27.* Plant without the fennel odour but with a spicy flavour 28
28. Petals hairy on the outside: **athamantha** *(Athamanta cretensis)*
28.* Petals naked on the outside 29
29. Compound umbel consisting of 20–30 smaller umbels: **Haller's laser** *(Laserpitium halleri)*
29.* Compound umbel consisting of less than 20 small umbels 30
30. Plant mostly taller than 30 cm, squarrosely branched: **caraway** *(Carum carvi)*
30.* Plant mostly shorter than 30 cm, little branched: **lovage** *(Ligusticum)*
31. Leaves double trifid, with oval, dentate sections: **masterwort** *(Peucedanum ostruthium)*
31.* Leaves pinnatisect (seldom nearly undivided) 32
32. Leaves divided once (seldom nearly undivided) 33
32.* Leaves divided twice or several times 34
33. Leaves shaggy: **hogweed** *(Heracleum)*

33.* Leaves not shaggy: **burnet-saxifrage** *(Pimpinella)*
34. Petals fringed; compound umbel consisting at most of 20 small umbels: **chervil** *(Chaerophyllum)*
34.* Petals naked; compound umbel consisting mostly of more than 20 small umbels: **laser** *(Laserpitium)*
35. Flowers zygomorphic 36
35.* Flowers actinomorphic 42
36. Leaves entire, smooth-edged 37
36.* Leaves compound, consisting of numerous small leaflets 40
37. Flowers single, on stem without leaves: **butterwort** *(Pinguicula)*
37.* Flowers numerous, on stem with leaves at least on the lower part 38
38. Flowers with spurs 39
38.* Flowers without spurs: **helleborine** *(Epipactis)*
39. Flowers with long (ca. 2 cm) spurs: **lesser butterfly orchid** *(Platanthera)*
39.* Flowers with only short spurs: **small white orchid** *(Leucorchis)*
40. Less than 10 leaflets per leaf: **glacial milk-vetch** *(Astragalus frigidus)*
40.* More than 10 leaflets per leaf 41
41. Flowers partly bluish: **milk-vetch** *(Astragalus)*
41.* Flowers entirely white or partly yellowish: **oxytropis** *(Oxytropis)*
42. Petals united 43
42.* Petals (or coloured tepals) free 50
43. Plant forming flat cushions or basal rosette: **rock-jasmine** *(Androsace)*
43.* Plant forming neither flat cushions nor basal rosette . . 44
44. Corolla longer than 1.3 cm 45
44.* Corolla shorter than 1 cm 47
45. Corolla bell-shaped: **bellflower** *(Campanula)*
45.* Corolla cup- or star-shaped 46
46. Leaves opposite: **felwort** *(Lomatogonium)*
46.* Leaves alternate to verticillate: **chickweed wintergreen** *(Trientalis)*
47. Leaves verticillate 48
47.* Leaves alternate 49
48. Flowers about 1 cm long, hanging: **Solomon's seal** *(Polygonatum)*
48.* Flowers measuring less than 0.5 cm in diameter: **bedstraw** *(Galium)*
49. Leaves wider than 0.5 cm: **vincetoxicum** *(Vincetoxicum)*
49.* Leaves narrower than 0.5 cm: **bastard toadflax** *(Thesium)*
50. Petals 4 51
50.* Petals (or coloured tepals) 5 or more 57
51. Flowers measuring more than 1.5 cm in diameter: **alpine poppy** *(Papaver alpinum)*

51.*	Flowers measuring less than 1.5 cm in diameter: **mustard family** *(Cruciferae)*	52
52.	Fruits at most four times as long as wide	53
52.*	Fruits at least four times as long as wide	56
53.	Leaves deeply divided: **hutchinsia** *(Hutchinsia)*	
53.*	Leaves entire	54
54.	Fruits spherical: **rock kernera** *(Kernera saxatilis)*	
54.*	Fruits flat	55
55.	Fruits with wing-shaped margin; petals longer than 0.5 mm: **pennycress** *(Thlaspi)*	
55.*	Fruits without margin; petals shorter than 0.5 cm: **draba** *(Draba)*	
56.	Fruits with two sutures, without veins: **bittercress** *(Cardamine)*	
56.*	Fruits with two sutures and two distinct veins: **rockcress** *(Arabis)*	
57.	Leaves gramineous, at least 8 times as long as wide . .	58
57.*	Leaves not gramineous, 1–5 times as long as wide . . .	64
58.	Flowers measuring less than 0.5 cm in diameter: **tofieldia** *(Tofieldia)*	
58.*	Flowers measuring more than 0.5 cm in diameter . . .	59
59.	Flowers with yellow corolla appendage: **daffodil** *(Narcissus)*	
59.*	Flowers without corolla appendage	60
60.	Plant 3–8 cm tall; flowers growing directly from the ground: **crocus** *(Crocus)*	
60.*	Plant mostly taller than 8 cm; flowers on a stem	61
61.	Perianth segments (tepals) with green tips: **snowflake** *(Leucojum)*	
61.*	Perianth segments without green tips	62
62.	Perianth segments longer than 2 cm: **St. Bruno's lily** *(Paradisia)*	
62.*	Perianth segments shorter than 2 cm	63
63.	Flowers single: **snowdon lily** *(Lloydia serotina)*	
63.*	Flowers numerous, in simple close panicle: **asphodel** *(Asphodelus albus)*	
64.	Petals mostly 8; plant slightly woody: **mountain avens** *(Dryas octopetala)*	
64.*	Petals 5, rarely more; plant not woody	65
65.	Flowers smaller than 0.5 cm: **knotgrass** *(Polygonum)*	
65.*	Flowers larger than 0.5 cm	66
66.	Ovary single; stamens 5 or 10	67
66.*	Ovaries numerous; stamens more than 10	70
67.	Ovary superior with 1 long style	68
67.*	Ovary inferior, rarely superior; styles 2 or missing . . .	69
68.	Leaves entire, at most dentate: **wintergreen** *(Pyrola)*	
68.*	Leaves palmate, divided up to the middle: **cranesbill** *(Geranium)*	
69.	Flowers measuring more than 1.5 cm in diameter: **grass of Parnassus** *(Parnassia palustris)*	

69.*   Flowers measuring less than 1.5 cm in diameter: **saxifrage** *(Saxifraga)*
70.   Ovaries mostly 5; leaves thick, fleshy: **stonecrop** *(Sedum)*
70.*   Ovaries not numerous; leaves not fleshy   71
71.   Epicalyx surrounding the calyx; leaves palmate: **cinquefoil** *(Potentilla)*
71.*   Perianth not differentiated, or consisting of calyx and corolla; no epicalyx   72
72.   Perianth consisting of calyx and corolla   73
72.*   Perianth not differentiated, only corolla-like   74
73.   Petals 1–5; leaves entire or palmate: **buttercup** *(Ranunculus)*
73.*   Petals 6–12; leaves pinnate or double-pinnate: **callianthemum** *(Callianthemum)*
74.   Leaves with 7–9 digitate leaflets arising from a central point: **Christmas rose** *(Helleborus niger)*
74.*   Leaves palmate or pinnate, with narrow tips: **anemone, pasqueflower** *(Anemone, Pulsatilla)*

Group 5: flowers red, orange-red, brown-red, pink, purple, or red-violet
       (see also Group 6)

1.   Leaves opposite (often situated cross-wise at the base)   2
1.*   Leaves alternate, verticillate or in a basal rosette . . .   24
2.   Petals united (often only at the very base)   3
2.*   Petals free   14
3.   Flowers longer than 1.5 cm: **gentian** *(Gentiana)*
3.*   Flowers shorter than 1.5 cm   4
4.   Flowers forming a compact head which is flat underneath and enveloped in bracts   5
4.*   Flowers not forming a flat head   6
5.   Flowers with distinct black calyx bristles: **bright scabious** *(Scabiosa lucida)*
5.*   Flowers with light bristles only: **wood scabious** *(Knautia silvatica)*
6.   Corolla wheel-shaped, with tetramerous margin: **speedwell** *(Veronica)*
6.*   Corolla tubular or bell-shaped in the lower half   7
7.   Flowers bell-shaped, about 1 cm long: **northern twinflower** *(Linnaea borealis)*
7.*   Flowers tubular in the lower part   8
8.   Flowers only with very short, hardly visible calyx: **valerian** *(Valeriana)*
8.*   Flowers with distinct, tubular, 5-toothed or 2-lobed calyx: **mint family** *(Labiatae)*   9
9.   Plant taller than 20 cm; leaves longer than 1.5 cm . . .   10
9.*   Plant at most 20 cm tall; leaves shorter than 1.5 cm . .   13

104

61.* Leaves repeatedly divided, pinnate: **lousewort** *(Pedicularis)*

62. Leaves large, smooth-edged, lanceolate: **lungwort** *(Pulmonaria)*

62.* Leaves small, oval to ligulate, often with some teeth: **balsam** *(Erinus)*

63. Flowers zygomorphic 64

63.* Flowers actinomorphic 67

64. Leaves divided but with no separate leaflets; plant with a tuber in the ground: **fumitory** *(Corydalis)*

64.* Leaves pinnate with rounded to oval leaflets; plant with no tuber: **pea family** *(Papilionaceae)* 65

65. Fruits (loments) flat; flowers nodding: **alpine French honeysuckle** *(Hedysarum obscurum)*

65.* Fruits not in form of loments; flowers mostly upright or spreading 66

66. Flowers purple; fruit short, one-seeded, wrinkled: **sainfoin** *(Onobrychis)*

66.* Flowers bright red or reddish-blue; fruit (pod) inflated, many-seeded: **oxytropis** *(Oxytropis)*

67. Leaves thick, fleshy 68

67.* Leaves flat 69

68. Flowers measuring less than 1 cm in diameter: **stonecrop** *(Sedum)*

68.* Flowers measuring more than 1 cm in diameter: **houseleek** *(Sempervivum)*

69. Flowers measuring less than 0.4 cm in diameter 70

69.* Flowers measuring more than 0.4 cm in diameter . . . 73

70. Leaves pinnate, with rounded to oval leaflets: **burnet** *(Sanguisorba)*

70.* Leaves entire 71

71. Leaves lanceolate: **knotgrass** *(Polygonum)*

71.* Leaves rounded, oval or hastate 72

72. Leaves rounded, reniform: **mountain sorrel** *(Oxyria digyna)*

72.* Leaves oval or hastate: **dock** *(Rumex)*

73. Petals 4 74

73.* Petals (or coloured tepals) 5 or more 75

74. Leaves finely divided: **Pyrenean petrocallis** *(Petrocallis pyrenaica)*

74.* Leaves entire: **willowherb** *(Epilobium)*

75. Leaves with 3 (rarely 4–5) digitate leaflets: **glossy cinquefoil** *(Potentilla nitida)*

75.* Leaves divided in another way 76

76. Plant at most 20 cm tall; flowers pink to white: **glacier crowfoot** *(Ranunculus glacialis)*

76.* Plant taller than 20 cm; flowers purple-violet: **cranesbill** *(Geranium)*

Group 6: flowers blue, lilac, or violet

1. Leaves opposite (often situated cross-wise at the base)   2
1.* Leaves alternate, verticillate, or in a basal rosette   . . .   17
2. Flowers not pedicellate, grouped in heads enveloped in bracts   3
2.* Flowers pedicellate, arranged along an axis or single   . .   4
3. Flowers with distinct black calyx bristles: **bright scabious** *(Scabiosa lucida)*
3.* Flowers with light bristles only: **wood scabious** *(Knautia silvatica)*
4. Petals free: **saxifrage** *(Saxifraga)*
4.* Petals united, at least at the base   5
5. Corolla wheel-shaped or star-shaped, petals free nearly to the base   6
5.* Corolla funnel-shaped, or tubular in the lower part   . .   8
6. Corolla measuring more than 1 cm in diameter; petals 5   7
6.* Corolla measuring less than 1 cm in diameter; petals 4: **speedwell** *(Veronica)*
7. Corolla dark violet: **marsh felwort** *(Swertia perennis)*
7.* Corolla pale blue: **felwort** *(Lomatogonium)*
8. Flowers actinomorphic: **gentian** *(Gentiana)*
8.* Flowers zygomorphic   9
9. Flowers dark brown-violet: **alpine bartsia** *(Bartsia alpina)*
9.* Flowers violet, lilac, or blue   10
10. Calyx tetramerous; fruit jutting out from the calyx: **eyebright** *(Euphrasia)*
10.* Calyx pentamerous or two-lipped; fruit concealed in the calyx: **mint family** *(Labiatae)*   11
11. Flowers shorter than 1 cm   12
11.* Flowers longer than 1 cm   14
12. Plant with no mint fragrance; inflorescence mostly with red leaves: **pyramidal bugle** *(Ajuga pyramidalis)*
12.* Plant with mint-like fragrance; inflorescence without red leaves   13
13. Leaves hardly 2 cm long; plant hardly 20 cm tall: **thyme** *(Thymus)*
13.* Leaves longer than 2 cm; plant taller than 30 cm: **mint** *(Mentha)*
14. Leaves or leaf segments more than 7 times as long as wide: **dragonhead** *(Dracocephalum)*
14.* Leaves at most 7 times as long as wide   15
15. Flowers bi-coloured (white-violet): **alpine scullcap** *(Scutellaria alpina)*
15.* Flowers monochrome, violet to blue   16
16. Inflorescence at least 4 cm long, mostly unilateral: **horminum** *(Horminum pyrenaicum)*
16.* Inflorescence at most 4 cm long, multilateral: **selfheal** *(Prunella)*

50. Leaves cordate, dentate: **perennial honesty** *(Lunaria rediviva)*
50.* Leaves very narrowly lanceolate, smooth-edged, with stellate hairs: **alpine stock** *(Matthiola vallesiaca)*
51. Petals free 52
51.* Petals united 54
52. Flowers without spurs: **aconite** *(Aconitum)*
52.* Flowers with spurs 53
53. Plant taller than 30 cm: **alpine larkspur** *(Delphinium elatum)*
53.* Plant shorter than 30 cm: **violet, pansy** *(Viola)*
54. All leaves in a basal rosette, sticky: **butterwort** *(Pinguicula)*
54.* Leaves not sticky 55
55. Leaves blue-green, slightly fleshy, the lower leaves verticillate: **alpine toadflax** *(Linaria alpina)*
55.* Leaves green, not fleshy 56
56. Leaves naked: **milkwort** *(Polygala)*
56.* Leaves shaggy: **viper's bugloss** *(Echium vulgare)*

Group 7: flowers yellow, yellowish, orange-yellow, greenish, or brownish

1. Leaves opposite (often situated cross-wise at the base) 2
1.* Leaves alternate, verticillate, or in a basal rosette . . . 16
2. Flowers in compact heads, not pedicellate 3
2.* Flowers along an axis or single, mostly pedicellate . . . 4
3. Plant taller than 50 cm, strongly branched: **alpine cephalaria** *(Cephalaria alpina)*
3.* Plant hardly 50 cm tall, with 1–3 flower-heads: **mountain arnica** *(Arnica montana)*
4. Flowers smaller than 0.4 cm, greenish, actinomorphic . 5
4.* Flowers larger than 0.4 cm 7
5. Leaves very small and narrow; cushion-forming plant: **mossy cyphal sandwort** *(Minuarita sedoides)*
5.* Leaves longer than 2 cm; plant taller than 5 cm 6
6. Leaves narrowly lanceolate; plant up to 20 cm tall: **spikenard** *(Valeriana celtica)*
6.* Leaves large, hastate; plant taller than 20 cm: **all-good** *(Chenopodium bonus-henricus)*
7. Petals free or missing 8
7.* Petals united 10
8. Flower zygomorphic: **twayblade** *(Listera)*
8.* Flower actinomorphic 9
9. Leaves leathery; plant hardly 30 cm tall, slightly woody: **rockrose** *(Helianthemum)*
9.* Leaves not leathery; plant mostly taller than 30 cm, not woody: **St. John's wort** *(Hypericum)*

10.	Flowers longer than 2.5 cm, actinomorphic: **gentian** *(Gentiana)*	
10.*	Flowers shorter than 2.5 cm, mostly zygomorphic . . .	11
11.	Sepals 5, sharply pointed like an awn	12
11.*	Sepals 4, not sharply pointed like an awn	13
12.	Flowers longer than 2 cm, lower lip variegated: **hemp-nettle** *(Galeopsis)*	
12.*	Flowers shorter than 1.5 cm, light-yellow: fox-tail betony *(Betonica alopecuros)*	
13.	Calyx inflated and laterally compressed: **yellow-rattle** *(Rhinanthus)*	
13.*	Calyx attached to the corolla	14
14.	Cauline leaves mostly without teeth, 3–10 times as long as wide: **cow-wheat** *(Melampyrum)*	
14.*	Cauline leaves mostly dentate, at most 3 times as long as wide	15
15.	Plant mostly taller than 20 cm; corolla indistinctly two-lipped: **alpine tozzia** *(Tozzia alpina)*	
15.*	Plant mostly shorter than 20 cm; corolla distinctly two-lipped: **eye-bright** *(Euphrasia)*	
16.	Flowers not pedicellate, forming a compact head enveloped in numerous bracts: **composite family** *(Compositae)*	17
16.*	Flowers not in a head enveloped in numerous bracts, mostly pedicellate	27
17.	Plant with prickles: **thorny thistle** *(Cirsium spinosissimum)*	
17.*	Plant without prickles	18
18.	Plant with milky sap; flower heads with only ligulate flowers	19
18.*	Plant without milky sap; flower heads with tubular flowers, at least in the centre	20
19.	Stem under the head thicker than 0.5 cm, villous: **one-headed cat's ear** *(Hypochoeris uniflora)*	
19.*	Stem under the head narrower than 0.5 cm: **hawkbit** *(Leontodon)*, **dandelion** *(Taraxacum)*, **hawk's-beard** *(Crepis)*, or **hawkweed** *(Hieracium)*	
20.	Flowers deep yellow, the outer ones ligulate	21
20.*	Flowers yellowish or brownish, all tubular	26
21.	Heads measuring less than 3.5 cm in diameter	22
21.*	Heads measuring more than 3.5 cm in diameter	24
22.	No leaves at the bottom at the time of flowering: **coltsfoot** *(Tussilago)*	
22.*	Leaves present at the bottom at the time of flowering .	23
23.	Involucral bracts in several rows, like tiles on a roof, obtuse: **goldenrod** *(Solidago)*	
23.*	Involucral bracts in 1–2 rows, acuminate: **groundsel** *(Senecio)*	
24.	Plant cobwebby white: **leopard's-bane groundsel** *(Senecio doronicum)*	

110

24.*	Plant pilose but not cobwebby white	25
25.	Cauline leaves narrowly lanceolate, more than 4 times as long as wide: **ox-eye** *(Buphthalmum)*	
25.*	Cauline leaves oval, at most 4 times as long as wide: **leopard's-bane** *(Doronicum)*	
26.	Leaves smooth-edged: **cudweed** *(Gnaphalium)*	
26.*	Leaves divided into fine segments: **wormwood** *(Artemisia)*	
27.	Plant with much milky sap; upper leaves in the inflorescence opposite: **spurge** *(Euphorbia)*	
27.*	Plant without or with only a little milky sap, without opposite leaves	28
28.	Flowers zygomorphic	29
28.*	Flowers actinomorphic	50
29.	Plant prickly: **whin** *(Genista)*	
29.*	Plant not prickly	30
30.	Leaves compound (cloverleaf-like or pinnate): **pea family** *(Papilionaceae)*	31
30.*	Leaves entire, palmately or pinnately divided but without leaflets	39
31.	Leaves with 3 or 5 leaflets (rarely more, but then the terminal leaflet larger)	32
31.*	Leaves with more than 5 leaflets (all leaflets more or less equal in size)	35
32.	1–8 flowers in a head-like or umbel-like inflorescence: **common bird's-foot trefoil** *(Lotus corniculatus)*	
32.*	Mostly more than 8 flowers in the inflorescence	33
33.	Leaf clover-like; leaflets approximately of the same size	34
33.*	Leaf pinnately compound, terminal leaflet much larger: **kidney-vetch** *(Anthyllis)*	
34.	Flowers shorter than 1 cm: **clover** *(Trifolium)*	
34.*	Flowers longer than 1 cm: **yellow goatroot** *(Ononis natrix)*	
35.	Flowers arranged umbel-like	36
35.*	Flowers arranged spike-like	37
36.	Leaves with small stipules fruits with horseshoe-shaped segments: **horseshoe vetch** *(Hippocrepis comosa)*	
36.*	Leaves with large stipules; fruits with narrow oval segments: **crown vetch** *(Coronilla)*	
37.	Leaves pinnate with tendrils or prickly tips: **pea, vetchling** *(Lathyrus)*	
37.*	Leaves pinnate with terminal leaflets	38
38.	Sharply pointed tip set upon the keel: **oxytropis** *(Oxytropis)*	
38.*	Keel blunt: **milk-vetch** *(Astragalus)*	
39.	Leaves entire, smooth-edged, naked	40
39.*	Leaves divided or dentate, often pilose	46
40.	Plant with branched stems, prostrate: **shrubby milkwort** *(Polygala chamaebuxus)*	
40.*	Plant with unbranched, upright stems, leaves parallel-veined: **orchid family** *(Orchidaceae)*	41

41.	Flowers yellow: **orchid** *(Orchis)*	
41.*	Flowers greenish, brownish, or multi-coloured	42
42.	Flowers with a slipper-shaped yellow lower lip and 4 brown-red, extended perianth segments: **lady's slipper** *(Cypripedium)*	
42.*	Flowers with lower lip not slipper-shaped	43
43.	Flowers narrower than 0.5 cm: **dwarf orchid** *(Chamorchis alpina)*	
43.*	Flowers wider than 0.5 cm	44
44.	Flowers with long deep brown lower lip: **fly orchid** *(Ophrys insectifera)*	
44.*	Flowers with yellow-green to red-brown lower lip	45
45.	Lower lip longer than 0.5 cm: **frog orchid** *(Coeloglossum viride)*	
45.*	Lower lip shorter than 0.5 cm: **musk orchid** *(Herminium monorchis)*	
46.	Flowers with spurs; leaves with stipules at the base of the petiole: **violets, pansies** *(Viola)*	
46.*	Flowers without spurs; leaves without stipules	47
47.	Leaves very deeply divided	48
47.*	Leaves dentate	49
48.	Leaves palmately divided; petals free: **aconite** *(Aconitum)*	
48.*	Leaves pinnately divided (like a fern leaf): **lousewort** *(Pedicularis)*	
49.	Corolla wheel-shaped or funnel-shaped: **mullein** *(Verbascum)*	
49.*	Corolla tubular to bell-shaped: **foxglove** *(Digitalis)*	
50.	Petals united	51
50.*	Petals free or missing	58
51.	Flowers gold-yellow	52
51.*	Flowers yellowish-white or greenish	54
52.	Flowers in an umbel; stem without leaves: **auricula** *(Primula auricula)*	
52.*	Flowers not in an umbel; stem with leaves or no stem	53
53.	Leaves small, nearly needle-shaped; no stem visible: **yellow rock-jasmine** *(Androsace vitaliana)*	
53.*	Leaves large, stem over 30 cm tall: **mullein** *(Verbascum)*	
54.	Stem leafy only in the lower third; inflorescence unilateral: **serrated wintergreen** *(Pyrola secunda)*	
54.*	Stem leafy up to more than the middle; inflorescence multilateral	55
55.	Leaves opposite: **vincetoxicum** *(Vincetoxicum officinale)*	
55.*	Leaves alternate	56
56.	Flowers longer than 2 cm; leaves narrower than 1 cm: **tufted bellflower** *(Campanula thyrsoides)*	
56.*	Flowers shorter than 2 cm; leaves wider than 1 cm	57
57.	Leaves sessile, cordate (heart-shaped), and embracing: **glabrous cerinthe** *(Cerinthe glabra)*	
57.*	Leaves petiolate or sessile with narrowed base: **spiked rampion** *(Phyteuma spicatum)*	

113

74.*	Flowers measuring 1–3 cm in diameter	75
75.	Plant shorter than 15 cm: **yellow star-of-Bethlehem** *(Gagea)*	
75.*	Plant taller than 15 cm: **false hellebore** *(Veratrum)*	
76.	Tepals coloured, 10–15, forming a globular flower: **globe flower** *(Trollius europaeus)*	
76.*	Tepals coloured, less than 10	77
77.	Epicalyx on the outside of the calyx	78
77.*	No epicalyx	80
78.	Flowers measuring less than 0.8 cm in diameter; petals shorter than sepals: **sibbaldia** *(Sibbaldia procumbens)*	
78.*	Petals longer than calyx	79
79.	Leaf palmate; fruits inconspicuous: **cinquefoil** *(Potentilla)*	
79.*	Leaf pinnate; fruits with feather-like elongated style: **avens** *(Geum)*	
80.	Stamens 10	81
80.*	Stamens more than 10	83
81.	Flowers slightly nodding, with 1 style: **wintergreen** *(Pyrola)*	
81.*	Flowers hardly nodding, with 2 or more styles	82
82.	Ovary with 2 styles: **saxifrage** *(Saxifraga)*	
82.*	Ovary with 4–20 styles: **stonecrop** *(Sedum)*	
83.	One ovary per flower: **rockrose** *(Helianthemum)*	
83.*	Numerous ovaries per flower	84
84.	Basal leaves fleshy, in a spherical rosette: **houseleek** *(Sempervivum)*	
84.*	Basal leaves not fleshy	85
85.	Basal leaves kidney-shaped, entire: **marsh-marigold** *(Caltha palustris)*	
85.*	Basal leaves not kidney-shaped, divided or missing at the time of flowering	86
86.	Flowers with calyx and corolla: **buttercup** *(Ranunculus)*	
86.*	Flowers only with corolla-like, coloured perianth (no calyx): **yellow alpine pasqueflower** *(Pulsatilla sulphurea)*	

7. Description of important Alpine species

7.1. Explications and abbreviations

The following pages deal with the most important flowering plants inhabiting the Swiss Alps. The brief descriptions of flowering plants are preceded by some remarks on selected spore-bearing plants occurring in the Alps.

The most important unit of systematics[10] is the *species*. Plants belonging to the same species are mostly able to hybridize and produce fertile offspring; they closely resemble each other in their principal characteristics. Two species differ from one another in important characteristics and are but seldom able to hybridize (plants resulting from such crosses are called *hybrids*). Taxa[11] which differ from each other in few, rather cryptic, morphological[12] characters but otherwise are rather well separated are frequently called *microspecies*. Numerous plant groups which to date are considered as one species could be in fact splitted into microspecies with help of more sophisticated research. For instance, modern cytological[13] methods permit quick counting of *chromosomes* (components of the cell nucleus which transmit the genetic information to further generations); in this way, taxa with different chromosome numbers may be found. The chromosome number is not infrequently correlated with definite morphological characteristics. Microspecies may have different ecological requirements, too; they are often rather good site indicators, as their occurrence may be limited to a few precise sites (e.g. a fine calciferous scree or a swampy soil poor in calcium). Two taxa not very different from one another in morphological characteristics and connected by more or less continuous series of intermediate forms are called *subspecies*.

Related species form a *genus* and related genera are grouped into *families*. The Latin description of a given species is always headed by its generic name (e.g. *Rhododendron* for alpenroses); it is followed by its specific name (e.g. *hirsutum* for the hairy alpenrose, *Rhododendron hirsutum*). The Latin binomial is followed by a capital letter or an abbreviated word referring to the name of author who described a given species for the first time. For instance, «L.» is the abbreviation of the

---

[10] *Systematics* deals with classification of living organisms.

[11] *Taxon* (in German: «Sippe») corresponds to a group of plants which has been given no definite taxonomical rank.

[12] *Morphology* deals with plant construction: it describes and compares characters relating to form and appearance of a given plant.

[13] *Cytology* deals with cells and their components.

name of the famous Swedish botanist and naturalist Carl v. Linné. Latin names which are sometimes given in parentheses are synonyms; this means that a given species may be given different names in different books.

English names presented in our book mainly follow various British publications; some names have been translated directly from the Latin. There may be differences both in spelling as well as in the actual nomenclature as far as British and American sources are concerned; for reasons of space it unfortunately proved impossible to deal comprehensively with this problem in the present book.

A glossary of some botanical terms is given on pp.

Description of species

For each plant described a brief morphological diagnosis is given followed by data on its sites and general distribution, as well as its occurrence in the Swiss Alps. All data on altitudes refer to the Swiss Alps and indicate the uppermost and lowermost limits of occurrence; in some particularly favourable places (south-facing slopes etc.) plants may grow higher whereas one finds them considerably lower on shadowy sites as well as along streams, avalanche paths, etc. The terminology used in the geographical data is explained in Chapter 2 dealing with phytogeographic regions. The time of flowering is codified with ciphers corresponding to given months (e.g. 7 for July) and refers to altitudes higher than 1200 m a.s.l.

Indicative values

For a better assessment of ecological requirements, each species described is given a code referring to its indicative values *(6.1.n.)*; the code indicates life conditions at natural sites inhabited by a given species. Particular numbers should be considered as guidelines rather than as an absolute classification, for the competition may sometimes alter the conditions of the site. The following aspects are included:

F *humidity number*

The humidity number denotes mean soil humidity during the vegetation period. Lower numbers correspond to less humid soil whereas higher ones codify a more pronounced soil humidity.

1: the species occurs principally on very dry soils; it is absent on wet soils and not competitive enough on dry soils. Typical indicator of dryness.
2: the species mainly occurs on dry soils; it avoids very dry and very wet soils and is not competitive enough in humid soils. Indicator of medium aridity.
3: the species occurs on medium-dry to humid soils, its ecological amplitude being rather broad; dry and wet soils are avoided. Indicates a medium humidity.
4: the species principally occurs on humid to very humid soils; it may occasionally inhabit wet soils; dry soils are avoided. Indicator of humidity.
5: the species occurs on wet soils soaked with water; medium-humid and dry soils are avoided. Indicator of wetness.

116

Apart from these numbers, additional marks are used to characterize complex soil humidity conditions:

↑: plants grow in places influenced by flowing water (e.g. stream or river banks, wet river valleys, or habitats with downslope water flow).

w: plants occur mostly on intermittently humid soils; the F cipher shows mean soil humidity whereas the «w» indicates that the soil is much more humid after precipitation and also much drier during periods of drought.

R *reaction number*

The reaction number indicates the content of free hydrogen ions in the soil. Lower numbers show acid soils poor in bases whereas high numbers correspond to a higher base content of the soil (neutral to basic soils).

1: the species occurs principally on very acid soils (pH 3–4.5); it is never to be found on neutral to basic soils. Typical indicator of acidity.

2: the species occurs mainly on acid soils (pH 3.5–5.5); it is hardly seen on neutral to basic soils. Acidity indicator.

3: the species occurs mainly in weakly-acid soils (pH 4.5–7.5); it is never seen on very acid soils, but occasionally may appear on neutral or weakly-basic ones.

4: the species occurs mostly on base-rich soils (pH 5.5–8): it avoids very acid soils. Base indicator.

5: the species nearly always occurs on base-rich soils (pH over 6.5); acid soils are avoided. Typical base indicator (usually calcium indicator).

x: the plants occur on very acid to basic soils; they avoid medium quality soils where they are not competitive enough.

N *nutrient number*

The nutrient number denotes the nutrient (esp. nitrogen) content of the soil. Lower numbers codify a low nutrient content, higher ones – soils rich in nutrients.

1: the species occurs principally on soils very poor in nutrients; it is absent from nutrient-rich soils. Typical indicator of nutrient deficiency.

2: the species occurs mainly on soils poor in nutrients; it is generally absent from or not competitive enough on soils with good to excessive nutrient supply. Nutrient insufficiency indicator.

3: the species occurs mainly on moderately meagre to moderately nutrient-rich soils; it is absent from very meagre and excessively manured soils.

4: the species occurs mostly on nutrient-rich soils; it is hardly seen on soils poor in nutrients. Nutrient indicator.

5: the species occurs principally on soils with excessive nutrient (mostly nitrogen) supply; it never appears on meagre soils. Indicator of overmanuring; pollution indicator in waters.

x: plants occurring both on nutrient-rich as well as meagre soils.

H *humus number*

The humus number indicates the humus content of the soil at a given site. High numbers correspond to a high humus content within the root horizon, low numbers denote scarce or missing humus components.

1: the species occurs principally on raw soils (no humus); soils with thick humus layers are avoided. Raw soil indicator.

2: the species occurs mainly on raw soils with scanty humus layers; it is absent from peat and mold soils. Mineral soil indicator.
3: the species occurs mostly on soils with a medium humus content (usually in the form of mull); it may be seen only occasionally on raw or peat soils.
4: the plants occur mainly on humus-rich soils (mull or mold soils, often also raw humus), but their roots reach partly to the mineral soil. Humus indicators.
5: species nearly exclusive to humus-rich soils; mineral soils avoided. Raw humus or peat indicator.
x: plants growing both on raw as well as on humus-rich soils.

D *size of soil particle number (and aeration deficiency number)*

The size of soil particle number indicates the soil structure and aeration (above all with oxygen) at a given site. Low numbers correspond to very coarse soils whereas high numbers denote soils with very fine particles and oxygen deficiency.

1: the species occurs principally on cliffs, boulders, and stone-walls. Cliff plant.
2: the species occurs mainly on medium coarse to coarse scree, talus, or gravel, skeleton components in the root horizon measuring over 2 mm in diameter. Plant of talus, gravel, and scree.
3: the species occurs mainly on permeable, skeleton-rich, or sandy soils which are very well-aerated, skeleton components in the root horizon measuring on an average 0.05–2 mm. Light soil indicator.
4: the species occurs mainly on fine sandy or dusty soils poor in skeleton; soil aeration is rather good, mean diameter of fine soil particles often being 0.002–0.05 mm. Coarse scree and cliffs are avoided. Heavy soil indicator.
5: the species occurs principally on very fine-grained, clayey, or peaty soils which are mostly impermeable or at least insufficiently aerated (poor in oxygen). Mean diameter of fine soil particles is mostly less than 0.002 mm. Sandy, gravelly, or rocky soils are avoided. Frequent clay indicator (when the H number is less than 5) or peat indicator (when the H number is equivalent to 5); in general, indicator of oxygen deficiency.
x: plants occurring both on rocky as well as peaty or clayey soils.
↑: plants growing on unstable soils. Indicators of a mobile scree.

L *light number*

The light number denotes the mean light intensity still sufficient to ensure good plant growth during the vegetation period. Low numbers correspond to modest light demands, high ones indicate plants requiring much light.

1: the species is able to grow even in very shady places (less than 3% of relative light intensity); it occurs at half-shady and at light sites only when competition is weak. Typical shade indicator.
2: the species occurs mainly on shady sites (hardly below 3% but often less than 10% relative light intensity); seen on light sites only when competition is weak. Shade indicator.
3: the species frequently occurs in half-shade (mostly, however, not below 10% relative light intensity); it is less frequent in full light.
4: the species occurs mainly in full light, but temporarily tolerates limited shade. Light indicator.
5: the species occurs only in full light and does not tolerate any shade whatsoever. Typical light indicator.

T *temperature number*

The temperature number indicates the mean temperature of a given site during the vegetation period; it is largely dependent on altitude. Low numbers correspond to sites at high altitudes, high numbers denote plants of lower altitudes.

1: the species occurs principally in the alpine vegetation belt (above the timber-line); it may also occur in cool or slightly competition-influenced places at lower altitudes. Typical high alpine and arctic plant. Indicator of cold at lower altitudes.
2: the species occurs mainly in the subalpine and suprasubalpine belt; it may grow above the timberline in sunny places and also descends to lower altitudes on cooler and less competition-influenced sites. Mountain and boreal plant.
3: the species occurrs mainly in the montane belt, often also at lower and higher altitudes. It is mostly widely distributed.
4: the species occurs mainly in the colline belt; it may grow higher in sunny places. Well distributed at lower altitudes in Europe.
5: the species occurs exclusively in the warmest places, its main distribution area being southern Europe. Indicator of warmth.

K *continentality number*

The continentality number denotes diurnal and annual temperature differences as well as air humidity. Low numbers correspond to minor temperature differences and a high air humidity, whereas high numbers indicate pronounced temperature differences and frequently very dry air.

1: the species occurs principally in areas with oceanic climate; mild winters and high air humidity are indispensable. Plants given high temperature numbers are frost-sensitive, plants with lower numbers require a longer duration of snow cover. They can be found only in insubric areas and in the westernmost part of the Alps as well as in snow-patches and bogs.
2: the species occurs mainly in areas with sub-oceanic climate; it does not support late frost and great temperature extremes, being absent or appearing only locally in Alpine areas with a continental climate (e.g. lower sites in the Central Alps).
3: the species occurs outside the areas with a strongly continental climate. It can be found virtually everywhere in the Alps.
4: the species occurs mainly in areas with a rather continental climate. Great differences in temperature, low winter temperatures and limited air humidity are well tolerated, sites with late-lying snow being avoided. It is distributed principally in continental Alpine areas with low precipitation, otherwise it may be found only on exposed sites.
5: species exclusive to areas with continental climate, mostly inhabiting sites exposed to sun and wind. Occurs only in the most continental Alpine areas.

Data on plant protection

The ever-decreasing diversity of species observed nowadays has its main cause in the destruction of living space which results from human activities: all the same, the endangering effect that flower-picking and the digging out of whole plants has upon rare and beautiful species should not be underestimated. Protection of these plants is today regulated by various official measures. Apart from the nature reserves in which all flower-picking or digging out is prohibited, numerous plants are under a total or partial protection. The rules for the protection of species vary from country to country and also from one area to another (in Switzerland, for instance, from one Canton to another); they may be not easily comprehensible to the layman. On the whole, massive flower-picking or digging out is prohibited virtually everywhere, and the same rule applies to collecting out for commercial purposes.

In our book, data on the protection of Alpine plants are given after the description of the species; the abbreviations refer to the areas in which a given species is protected. It should be kept in mind, however, that the present data may no longer be valid after a few years, as the nature conservancy regulations are subject to alterations. Total protection is codified with italic letters; it means that *any* flower-picking or digging out is prohibited. Partial protection is indicated only when picking of more than 3–5 stems is prohibited, as well as digging out. All or many further plants are partly protected in numerous Cantons, provinces, or countries, picking of more than 10 stems and digging out being prohibited. All Alpine plants are partially protected in AI, AR, BE, GR/Bz. Not only Switzerland *(6.6. b)* but also adjacent countries and provinces are listed; they include Bavaria *(6.6. f)*; Liechtenstein *(6.6. h)*; Austria *(6.6. g)*: Vorarlberg, Tyrol; Italy *(6.6. b)*: Bolzano, Trento, Lombardy (Bergamo, Brescia, Como, Sondrio, Varese), the valley of Aosta, Piedmont (Novarra, Vercelli); France *(6.6. i)*.

A number of Alpine plants are included in the «Red Lists» which present particularly endangered or vulnerable species on the edge of extinction in a given area. Such plants are endangered by *any* intervention, not only by flower-picking. The grading of ski runs, construction work, flooding, altered management may lead to the total disappearance of the species. The present book takes into consideration only the «Red Lists» of Switzerland *(6.6. d)* and Europe *(6.6. e)*. Plants appearing in the «Red Lists» should be viewed with particular care; actual or planned interventions which may further endanger these species should be reported to the responsible nature conservancy office of a given Canton.

Abbreviations

Switzerland (CH)

AG	Aargau	NW	Nidwalden
AI	Appenzell Innerrhoden	OW	Obwalden
AR	Appenzell Ausserrhoden	SG	St. Gall
BE	Berne	SH	Schaffhausen
BE$_n$	Berne (Alpine foreland, the Midlands and the Jura)	SO	Solothurn
BL	Basel-Landschaft	SZ	Schwyz
BS	Basel-Stadt	TG	Thurgau
FR	Fribourg	TI	Ticino
GE	Geneva	UR	Uri
GL	Glarus	VD	Vaud
GR	Grisons	VD$_j$	Vaud (Jura)
JU	Jura	VS	Wallis
LU	Lucerne	ZG	Zug
NE	Neuchâtel	ZH	Zurich

Adjacent areas

A	Austria	Li	Liechtenstein
Ao	valley of Aosta	No	Novarra
B	Bavaria	P	Piedmont
Bg	Bergamo	So	Sondrio
Bs	Brescia	Ti	Tyrol
Bz	Bolzano	Tn	Trento
Co	Como	Va	Varese
F	France	Vc	Vercelli
L	Lombardy	Vo	Vorarlberg

Red List

E	greatly endangered
V	vulnerable
R	rare
*	at European level

7.2. Spore-bearing or cryptogamous plants

Spores are reproductive cells formed on the surface of the plant or within the plant. They are mostly very resistant, often mobile, and able to grow into new plants under suitable conditions. Spore-bearing plants include algae, lichens, mosses, ferns, horsetails, and clubmosses. Many of these plants are very small and can be determined only under microscope. They are mostly difficult to distinguish from each other and thus generally not included in «floras», their classification being dealt with in specialized works. Other organisms viz. bacteria and fungi, formerly assigned to plants, play an important rôle in every ecosystem.[14]

---

[14] *Ecosystem* includes all organism living in a given place, their life conditions, relationships, cycles, and energy flux pathways.

Algae

Algae are small, green-, red-, or blue-coloured plants; they grow principally in waters (lakes, streams) but may also occur on humid earth or rock surfaces (e.g. blue algae forming the «ink stripes» on cliffs) or on the snow e.g. «red snow» resulting from the occurrence of the **glacial algae**, *Chlamydomonas nivalis;* curiously enough, this species belongs to the green algae group.

Lichens

Lichens represent a community formed by fungi and green or blue algae, the fungus enclosing the algae completely with its tissues. Lichens belong to the least demanding plants and thus play an important rôle in the Alpine flora. They colonize bare rocks and soils or grasslands and forest; they also grow on branches and stems of shrubs and trees but are not parasites. Lichens living mostly at extreme sites, their growth may be very limited indeed; for instance, a year's growth found in some encrusting lichens corresponded to only 0.1 mm.

Some particularly conspicuous lichens include:

a. **Usnea,** *Usnea* Dill.
Usnea forms long, beard-like structures; it occurs mostly upon coniferous trees, in areas with rather humid air.

b. **Reindeer moss,** *Cladonia* Hill. (Plate 1.1)
Reindeer moss, particularly frequent in cool areas, is easily recognizable by its club-shaped limbs. Many species of this group occur in alpine grassland as well as in woods or dwarf shrub stands. In Lapland they constitute the main source of food for reindeer (esp. in winter).

c. **Iceland moss,** *Cetraria* Ach. (Plate 1.1)
Iceland moss, which is not a moss from the botanical point of view, was in former times often used as food in Scandinavia. It has a bitter taste and is still used as a medicine against chronic catarrh. Many species of this group occur in alpine grasslands all over the world. In contrast to the reindeer moss, Iceland moss has flat limbs.

d. **Geographical lichen,** *Rhizocarpon* Ramond (Plate 1.2)
Species of this genus form the characteristic yellow, flat crust upon rock poor in calcium. Further encrusting lichens are typical of various substrata, either poor or rich in calcium.

The photograph shows a fragment of a gneiss boulder with numerous encrusting lichens: in addition to the yellow geographical lichen *(Rhizocarpon geographicum* DC.), the grey-coloured *Aspicilia gibbosa* (Ach.) Krb. (upper left) as well as further species of *Aspicilia* and the light-yellow *Lecanora polytropa* (Ehrh.) Schaer (lower left). Kindly determined by Dr. E. Frey, Münchenbuchsee.

122

Mosses, *Bryophyta*

Mosses resemble phanerogams but have no genuine roots, only root-like rhizoids. They grow preferably in humid places e.g. forest soil, about flushes, in snow-patches, near streams, etc. The numerous, common Alpine mosses are difficult to determine; only one species characteristic of snow-patches is thus dealt with in this book.

Hexagonal haircap-moss, *Polytrichum sexangulare* Floerke *(P. nor-vegicum* Hedwig) (Plate 2.1)
Leaves filiform, curved, in rows of six on shoots; spore-cases narrow, pointed, on thin stalks. Snow-patches; soils poor in bases, with late-lying snow; 1500–3000 m; rather common. Arctic-Alpine plant. F4, R2, N3, H3, D4, L4, T1, K1. Spores ripe: 7–10.

Ferns, *Pteridophyta*

Like phanerogams, ferns are differentiated into shoot, leaves, and roots; however, they bear spores and thus have no flowers and fruits.

1st family: **clubmoss family,** *Lycopodiaceae*

Leaves very narrowly lanceolate, needle-like or scale-like, distributed along an axis; sporangia in terminal cone-like groups or in leaf axils. The family is represented in the Alps by 8 species.

a. **Clubmoss,** *Lycopodium* L.
Interrupted clubmoss, *Lycopodium annotinum* L. (Plate 1.3)
Stem creeping over the ground, up to 1 m long; leaves 5–10 mm long, spreading or turned backwards; fertile branches up to 15 cm tall; sporangia in terminal cone-like groups. Woods; acid, humous soils; 1200–2000 m; rather common. Eurosibirian-North American plant. F3, R1, N2, H5, D5, L1, T2, K3. Spores ripe: 6–9.

Fir clubmoss, *Lycopodium selago* L. *(Huperzia selago* [L.] Bernh.)
(Plate 1.4)
5–15 cm tall; leaves directed forwards; spores in round sporangia in leaf axils; 1000–2900 m; not common. Cosmopolitan plant (cool regions). F3, R2, N2, H4, D3, L3, T2, K3. Spores ripe: 7–10.

Fig. 29. Spike moss
(Selaginella selaginoides),
⅓ × (from *6.1.k.*).

2nd family: **spike moss family,** *Selaginellaceae*

The family is related to clubmosses and represented in the Alps by two species.

Spike moss, *Selaginella* Pal.
Lesser clubmoos, *Selaginella selaginoides* (L.) Link. (Fig. 29)
3–8 cm tall; moss-like; sporangia in leaf axils. Pastures, light woods; humid soils; 1000–2600 m; rather common but often overlooked. Eurosibirian-North American plant. F3, R3, N2, H4, D4, L3, T2, K3. Spores ripe: 6–8.

3rd family: **horsetail family,** *Equisetaceae*

Stem segmented, with dentate sheaths; sporangia in terminal cone-like groups. Stems rigid because of the high silicic acid content. The family is represented in the Alps by about 8 species.

a. **Horsetail,** *Equisetum* L.
Wood horsetail, *Equisetum silvaticum* L. (Plate 2.3)
10–50 cm tall; stem with whorls of branched lateral shoots; sheaths with 3–5 teeth. Forests, swampy meadows; wet soils; 800–1800 m; rather common. Eurosibirian-North American plant. F4w, R2, N3, H3, D5, L2, T3, K3. Spores ripe: 4–5.

Marsh horsetail, *Equisetum palustre* L. (Plate 2.4)
20–70 cm tall; stem with few simple lateral shoots; sheaths with 6–10 teeth. Swamps, banks of streams; wet soils; 400–2000 m; rather common. Eurosibirian-North American plant. F4w, R3, N2, H4, D5, L4, T3, K3. Spores ripe: 6–9.

124

4th family: **adder's tongue family,** *Ophioglossaceae*

Leaf differentiated into a vegetative and a spore-bearing part. Spores in rounded sporangia. The family is represented in the Alps by only five, mostly rare, species.

a. **Moonwort,** *Botrychium* Sw.
   Moonwort, *Botrychium lunaria* (L.) Sw.   (Plate 2.2)
   3–12 cm tall; only a single leaf present; vegetative part pinnate, with half-moon-shaped segments; spore-bearing part also pinnate, with spherical segments. Meadows, pastures, scree slopes; 600–2800 m; not common. Cosmopolitan plant (cool regions). F3, R3, N2, H3, D4, L4, T2, K3. Spores ripe: 6–9.
   Protected: *SH*.

5th family: **licorice fern family,** *Polypodiaceae*

Leaves rolled snail-like when young; spores in rounded or oblong sporangia on the under surface of the leaf or on special leaves. There are more than 30 various species of the family in the Alps, esp. in areas with humid air.

a. **Saw fern,** *Blechnum* L.
   Hard fern, *(Blechnum spicant* (L.) Sm   (Plate 3.2)
   10–25 cm tall; leaves simply pinnate; the outer ones without sporangia, in a flat rosette, with triangular segments; the inner ones upright, with very narrow, well separated, spore-bearing segments. Forests, pastures; acid, humous soils; 800–1800 m; rather common. Eurosibirian-North American plant. F3, R2, N2, H4, D4, L2, T2, K3. Spores ripe: 7–9.

b. **Buckler-fern,** *Dryopteris* Adanson
   Broad buckler-fern, *Dryopteris dilatata* (Hoffm.) A. Gray
                                                          (Plate 3.1; Fig. 30C)
   30–120 cm tall; leaves broadly oval in outline, 2–3-pinnate; segments with awned teeth. Woods, tall-herb stands; humid, acid soils; 500–2200 m; common. Eurosibirian plant. F4, R2, N3, H5, D4, L2, T2, K2. Spores ripe: 7–9.

   Male fern, *Dryopteris filix-mas* (L.) Schott   (Plate 3.4; Fig. 30B)
   30–120 cm tall; leaves narrowly lanceolate in outline, 1-pinnate; pinnae pinnately divided to the base, with dentate segments. Forests, tall-herb stands; humid soils; 200–2400 m; common. Eurosibirian-North American plant. F3, R3, N3, H4, D4, L2, T3, K3. Spores ripe: 6–9.

   Rigid buckler-fern, *Dryopteris villarsii* (Bell.) Woynar   (Fig. 30D)
   15–60 cm tall; leaves lanceolate in outline, rigid, 2-pinnate, with small, spherical glands visible only with a magnifying glass. Talus slopes; limestone; 1700–2200 m; rather rare. Mountain plant of Central and Southern Europe. F3, R5, N3, H4, D2, L3, T2, K2. Spores ripe: 7–8.

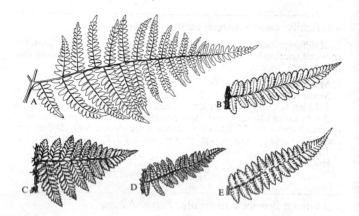

Fig. 30. Ferns. A: bracken *(Pteridium aquilinum)*. B: male fern *(Dryopteris filix-mas)*. C: broad buckler-fern *(Dryopteris dilatata)*. D: rigid buckler-fern *(Dryopteris villarsii)*. E: alpine lady-fern *(Athyrium alpestre)*. Each drawing represents one pinna. ⅓ ×.

c. **Buckler-fern,** *Lastrea* Bory

Disconnected buckler-fern, *Lastrea dryopteris* (L.) Bory *(Dryopteris disjuncta* [Rupr.] Morton) (Plate 3.3)

20–40 cm tall; leaves triangular in outline, 2-pinnate, without glands. Forests, tall-herb stands; humid, stony soils poor in calcium; 800–1800 m; not common. Eurosibirian-North American plant. F3, R2, N3, H4, D3, L2, T3, K2. Spores ripe: 6–9.

The closely related species **Robert's buckler-fern,** *Lastrea robertiana* (Hoffm.) Newman differs from the disconnected buckler-fern by minuscule glands on the leaf stalk; they are recognizable only with a magnifying glass. Both species have a similar general distribution and grow in similar sites, but *L. robertiana* occurs on calcium-rich soils.

d. **Lady-fern,** *Athyrium* Roth

Alpine lady-fern, *Athyrium alpestre* (Hoppe) Milde *(A. distentifolium* Tausch) (Fig. 30E)

30–120 cm tall; leaves lanceolate in outline, 2–3-pinnate; pinnae of the 2nd rank pinnatisect, the segment margins touching one another. Green alder thickets, tall-herb stands, woods; humid soils poor in calcium; 1500–2200 m; rather common. Eurosibirian-North American plant. F4, R2, N3, H4, D3, L2, T2, K2. Spores ripe: 7–9.

The **lady-fern,** *Athyrium filix-femina* (L.) Roth has pinnae of the 2nd rank which do not touch one another. It has a similar general distribution and grows on similar sites as the alpine lady-fern but usually at lower altitudes.

e. **Bracken,** *Pteridium* Gleditsch

Bracken, *Pteridium aquilinum* (L.) Kuhn (Fig. 30A)

40–200 cm tall; leaves with long stalks, triangular in outline, 2–3-pinnate; pinnae entire or sinuate. Light woods, pastures; acid soils; often in large stands; 400–1600 m; common. Cosmopolitan plant. F3, R2, N2, H4, D4, L3, T3, K3. Spores ripe: 7–9.

f. **Spleenwort,** *Asplenium* L.
Spores in long stripes on the under surface of the leaf. About 8 species of the genus occur in the Alps.

Green spleenwort, *Asplenium viride* Huds.   (Fig. 31B)
5–15cm tall; leaves narrowly lanceolate in outline, simply pinnate; leaf stalk red below, green in the area of pinnae. Cliffs. stone-walls; calciferous substratum; 600–2800 m; rather common. Eurosibirian-North American plant. F3, R4, N2, H3, D1, L3, T2, K2. Spores ripe: 7–9.

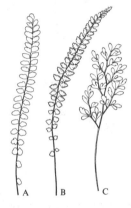

Fig. 31. Ferns.
A: maidenhair spleenwort *(Asplenium trichomanes)*.
B: green spleenwort *(Asplenium viride)*.
C: wall-rue *(Asplenium ruta-muraria)*. $\frac{1}{3}$ ×.

Maidenhair spleenwort, *Asplenium trichomanes* L.   (Fig. 31A)
Differs from green spleenwort by leaf stalks which are deep brown throughout their whole length. Cliffs, stone-walls; 600–1800 m; not common. Cosmopolitan plant (cool regions). F3, R3, N2, H2, D1, L3, T3, K3. Spores ripe: 6–8.

Wall rue, *Asplenium ruta-muraria* L.   (Fig. 31C)
5–15 cm tall; leaves triangular in outline, 2–3-pinnate. Cliffs, stone-walls; calciferous substratum; 200–2600 m; rather common. Eurosibirian-North American plant. F2, R4, N3, H2, D1, L4, T3, K3. Spores ripe: 6–10.

g. **Rock-brake** or **parsley-fern,** *Cryptogramma* R. Br.
Parsley-fern, *Cryptogramma crispa* (L.) R. Br. *(Allosurus crispus* [L.] Röhling)   (Fig. 32)
10–20 cm tall; leaves 2–4-pinnate, the outer ones without sporangia with flat segments, the inner ones with narrow, cylindrically rolled, spore-bearing segments. Coarse scree, rock crevices; substratum poor in calcium; 600–2700 m; not common. European mountain plant. F2, R2, N1, H2, D1, L4, T2, K3. Spores ripe: 8–9.

127

Fig. 32.   Parsley fern *(Cryptogramma crispa)*. ⅓ × (from *6.1.k.*).

7.3. Seed-bearing or phanerogamous plants

Seed-bearing plants are unable to reproduce by spores; the most important rôle in their reproduction is played by seeds, complex multicellular structures which originate from ovules carried in ovaries. The development leading from ovule to seed is usually initiated at the moment of fertilization (pollen grain germinates on the stigma and a fine pollen tube grows from the stigma towards the ovule where the male reproductive cell fertilizes the egg-cell). The fertilized egg-cell gives rise to the embryo which then represents the central part of the seed. In contrast to spore-bearing plants, Phanerogams all have flowers and can be assigned into two main groups viz. the Gymnosperms with ovules not enclosed in ovaries, and the Angiosperms with ovules completely enclosed in ovaries usually crowned by style and stigma. Coniferous plants (pine family, cypress family) belong to the former group whereas all other families discussed here form the latter group. The Angiosperms are further divided into Mono- and Dicotyledones; the monocotyledons mostly have parallel-veined leaves and trimerous flowers; they include genuine grasses, sedges, rushes, lilies, irises, the amaryllis family, and orchids. The dicotyledonous plants usually have net-veined leaves and tetra- or pentamerous flowers; they comprise all further phanerogamous families presented in this book.

128

6th family: **pine family,** *Pinaceae*

Woody plants with needles. Seeds frequently open on scales arranged in cones. The family is represented in the Alps by 7 species.

a. **Fir,** *Abies* Mill.

    Silver fir, *Abies alba* Mill. (Fig. 33A)

    Tree up to 45 (60) m tall; bark smooth, white-grey, frequently with reddish shimmer; needles nearly in one plane, flat, with 2 white stripes underneath; cones upright, with scales falling off separately. Forms woods together with spruce or beech; humid, well-developed soils; 600–1700 m; common (above all in the outer ranges). Mountain plant of Central and Southern Europe. F4w, R3, N3, H4, D5, L1, T3, K2. Flowering time: 5.

b. **Spruce,** *Picea* Dietr.

    Spruce, *Picea excelsa* (Lam.) Link *(P. abies* [L.] Karsten)

(Fig. 33B)

    Tree up to 45 (60) m tall; bark scaly, reddish, needles arranged around branches, 4angular, without white stripes; cones hanging, shed whole. Forms woods alone or together with silver fir, larch, or pine; all substrata; 600–2100 m; common. North European-Alpine plant. F3, Rx, N3, H4, Dx, L1, T2, K3. Flowering time: 5.

c. **Larch,** *Larix* Mill.

    Larch, *Larix decidua* Mill. *(L. europaea* DC.) (Fig. 33C)

    Tree up to 40 m tall; bark brittle, grey; needles bright-green, soft, in bunches, shed in autumn; cones small, rounded, upright. Forms woods alone or together with spruce, or Arolla pine; medium soils; 800–2400 m; common (nearly exclusively inner ranges); often planted. Mountain plant of Central and Southern Europe (eastern). F3, R2, N2, H2, D4, L4, T2, K4. Flowering time: 6.

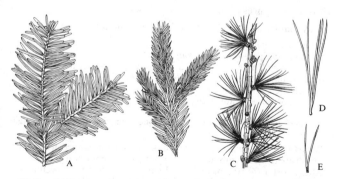

Fig. 33. Coniferous trees. A: branch of silver fir *(Abies alba)*. B: branch of spruce *(Picea excelsa)*. C: branch of larch *(Larix decidua)*. D: needle bunch of Arolla pine *(Pinus cembra)*. E: needle bunch of mountain pine *(Pinus montana)*. ⅓ × .

d. **Pine,** *Pinus* L.
   Arolla pine, *Pinus cembra* L. (Fig. 33D)
   Tree up to 20 m tall; needles in bunches of 5, bluish on the inner surface; cones large, rounded. Forms woods alone or together with larch or spruce; acid humous soils; 1600–2400 m; rather common (nearly exclusively inner ranges). Mountain plant of Central and Southern Europe. F3, R2, N2, H4, D4, L3, T2, K5. Flowering time: 6–8.
   Protected: *Vo*/No.

   Mountain pine, *Pinus montana* Mill. *(P. uncinata* Ramond)
   (Fig. 33E)
   Tree up to 20 m tall; needles in bunches of 2, dark green, shiny; cones small, tapering, sessile. Forms light woods alone or with other coniferous trees; meagre, very dry or wet soils (e.g. dolomite, serpentine, bogs); 1400–2400 m (also lower, esp. in bogs); rather common. Mountain plant of Central and Southern Europe (western). Fx, Rx, N2, Hx, Dx, L4, T2, K4. Flowering time: 6–7.

   Dwarf mountain pine, *Pinus mugo* Turra *(P. pumilio* Haenke)
   Prostrate to ascending bush up to 2 m tall; otherwise as the mountain pine. Forms light stands in meagre, shallow, and often unstable soils as well as in snow-glide paths; rather common (rare in the west); 1000–2400 m. Mountain plant of Central and southern Europe (eastern). F2, R3, N2, Hx, Dx, L4, T2, K4. Flowering time: 6–7.
   Protected: *F.*

   Scots pine *(Pinus silvestris* L.) common at lower altitudes and growing up to 2000 m in the Central Alps has needles bluish on the inner surface and pedicellate cones. It forms light, large forests esp. in the Central Alps on dry soils and represents a Eurosibirian species.

7th family: **cypress family,** *Cupressaceae*

Woody plants, with needles or scales; cones often berry-like.

a. **Juniper,** *Juniperus* L.
   Common juniper, *Juniperus communis* L. (Fig. 34A)
   Bush or small tree up to 6 m tall; leaves needle-like, 8–20 mm long and ca. 1 mm wide, prickly; cones berry-like. Pine forests, dry grassland; meagre dry soils; 400–1800 m; rather common (esp. the Central Alps). Eurosibirian plant. F2w, R3, N2, H4, Dx, L4, T4, K4. Flowering time: 5–6.
   Berries of juniper are used as a spice as well as in some sorts of liquor (gin, genever).

   Dwarf juniper, *Juniperus nana* Willd. *(J. sibirica* Burgsd.)(Fig. 34B)
   Prostrate dwarf shrub up to 50 cm tall; as the common juniper, but needles shorter (4–10 mm long) and wider (ca. 1.5 mm) as well as less prickly. Pastures, dwarf shrubs, light woods; dry soils poor in bases; 1800–2600 m; rather common. Eurosibirian-North American plant. F2, R2, N2, H3, D3, L4, T2, K4. Flowering time: 7–8.

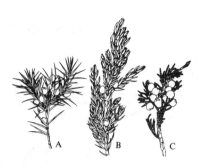

Fig. 34. Coniferous bushes. A: juniper *(Juniperus communis)*. B: dwarf juniper *(Juniperus nana)*. C: savin *(Juniperus sabina)*. ⅓× (from *6.1.k.*).

Savin, *Juniperus sabina* L. (Fig. 34C)
Prostrate dwarf shrub up to 60 cm tall; leaves on young branches needle-like, later scale-like, short; cones berry-like. Light forests, cliff steppes; dry soils; 600–2200 m; not common (nearly exclusively in the Central Alps). Eurasiatic mountain plant. F1, R3, N2, H3, D4, L4, T3, K5. Flowering time: 5.
Protected: *SO*.

8th family, **genuine grasses,** *Gramineae (Poaceae)*

Stems (culms) segmented by nodes; leaves gramineous with sheaths encircling the stem, distichous; flowers inconspicuous, grouped in spikelets which form spikes or panicles. The family is represented in the Alps by far more than 100 species which are partly difficult to determine.

a. **Bent,** *Agrostis* L.
Spikelets very small, on capillary pedicels. There are 7 species of the genus in the Alps.

Rock bent, *Agrostis rupestris* All. (Fig. 37D)
10–20 cm tall, forming tussocks; with short underground stolons; spikelets up to 4 mm long, grouped in a loose, wide panicle; panicle branches without teeth. Grassland, scree, rocky crevices; dry soils poor in calcium; 1500–3000 m; rather common (esp. the Central Alps). Mountain plant of Central and Southern Europe. F2, R2, N2, H3, D3, L5, T1, K4. Flowering time: 7–8.

b. **Woodreed,** *Calamagrostis* Adanson
Shaggy woodreed, *Calamagrostis villosa* (Chaix) J. F. Gmel.
40–100 cm tall; with stolons; leaves 5–10 mm wide, long, limp, with scattered fine hairs above, silky below. Forests, dwarf shrubs; soils poor in calcium; 1200–2400 m; common, frequently in large stands (esp.

inner ranges). Eurosibirian plant. F3, R2, N2, H4, D4, L3, T2, K3.
Flowering time: 7–8.

c. **Oat-grass,** *Trisetum* Pers.
   Yellow oat-grass, *Trisetum flavescens* (L.) Pal.   (Fig. 37A)
   20–80 cm tall; leaves pilose; spikelets 5–8 mm long, with 5–8 mm
long awns, in loose, mostly gold-shining panicles. Fertilized meadows;
nutrient-rich soils; 400–2200 m; common. Eurosibirian plant. F3, R3,
N4, H3, D4, L4, T3, K3. Flowering time: 6–7.

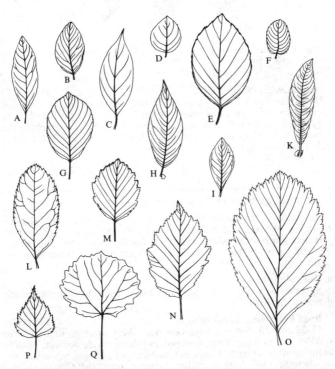

Fig. 35.   Leaves of foliage trees and bushes. A: black-berried honeysuckle *(Lonicera nigra)*.
B: blue-berried honeysuckle *(Lonicera coerulea)*. C: alpine honeysuckle *(Lonicera alpigena)*.
D: common cotoneaster *(Cotoneaster integerrima)*. E: beech *(Fagus silvatica)*. F: snowy
mespilus *(Amelanchier ovalis)*. G: alpine buckthorn *(Rhamnus alpina)*. H: bay willow *(Salix pentandra)*. I: hastate willow *(Salix hastata)*. K: large-leaved willow *(Salix appendiculata)*. L:
false medlar *(Sorbus chamaemespilus)*. M: green alder *(Alnus viridis)*. N: grey alder *(Alnus incana)*. O: whitebeam *(Sorbus aria)*. P: silver birch *(Betula pendula)*. Q: aspen *(Populus tremula)*. ⅓ × .

Distichous oat-grass, *Trisetum distichophyllum* (Vill.) P.B.(Fig. 37B)
10–20 cm tall; underground stolons several m in lenght; leaves bluegreen, distichous. Scree and talus slopes; calcium-rich substrata; 1300–3000 m; not common. Mountain plant of Central and Southern Europe (western). F3, R4, N3, H2, D3↑, L4, T2, K2. Flowering time: 7–8.

d. **oat,** *Helictotrichon* Bess. (Fig. 37E)
Variegated oat, *Helictotrichon versicolor* (Vill.) Pilger *(Avena versicolor* Vill).

15–30 cm tall; spikelets over 1 cm long, violet-, green-, and brown-yellow-speckled, in a loose panicle. Grassland; dry soils poor in calcium; 1800–3000 m; rather common. Mountain plant of Central and Southern Europe. F2, R2, N2, H4, D4, L4, T1, K3. Flowering time: 6–7.

e. **Feathergrass,** *Stipa* L.
Feathergrass, *Stipa pennata* L. s.l. (Plate 4.2)
30–80 cm tall; spikelets with up to 30 cm long, feather-like awns. Dry grassland, cliff steppes; very dry soils; 400–2000 m; rare (nearly exclusively the Central Alps). Eurasiatic plant group. F1, R4, N2, H2, D3, L5, T4, K5. Flowering time: 6.
Protected: *BE, GR, SG/B/Ao.*
This group consists of numerous closely related species which belong to the most beautiful grasses characteristic of steppe areas. The long feathery awn is shed together with the fruit at dispersal; fruits are transported by the wind.

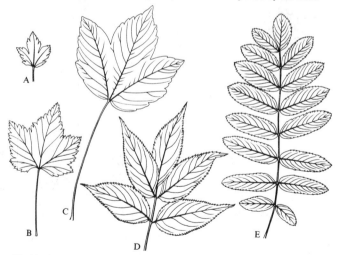

Fig. 36. Leaves of foliage trees and bushes. A: mountain currant *(Ribes alpinum)*. B: rock currant *(Ribes petraeum)*. C: sycamore *(Acer pseudoplatanus)*. D: red-berried elder *(Sambucum racemosa)*. E: rowan *(Sorbus aucuparia)*. ⅓ × .

133

f. **Fescue,** *Festuca* L.

Spikelets many-flowered, mostly longer than 5 mm, often with awns, in panicles. The genus includes more than 25 species in the Alps; they are difficult to distinguish between but frequently represent characteristic components in given vegetation types.

Coloured fescue, *Festuca varia* Haenke   (Plate 4.1)

15–35 cm tall; forms thick tussocks; leaves bristle-like, prickly when young (unpleasant surprise when one sits on it). Grassland, rocky crevices; meagre soils poor in calcium; 300–2800 m; not common (only southern Central Alps and Southern Alps). Mountain plant of Central and Southern Europe. F2, R2, N2, H2, D3, L5, T2, K4. Flowering time: 7–8.

Haller's fescue, *Festuca halleri* All.   (Plate 4.3)

5–15 cm tall; forming tussocks; leaves thin, bristle-like; spikelets in panicle-like inflorescences up to 3 cm long. Grassland; dry soils poor in calcium; 2100–3200 m; not common (mostly the Central Alps). Mountain plant of Central and Southern Europe. F2, R2, N2, H3, D4, L4, T1, K4. Flowering time: 7–8.

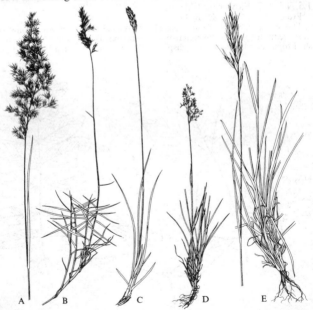

Fig. 37. Grasses. A: yellow oat-grass *(Trisetum flavescens)*. B: distichous oat-grass *(Trisetum distichophyllum)*. C: blue sesleria *(Sesleria coerulea)*. D: rock bent *(Agrostis rupestris)*. E: variegated oat *(Helictotrichon versicolor)*. ⅓ × .

Violet fescue, *Festuca violacea* Gaud. (Plate 4.4)
15–40 cm tall; forming tussocks; leaves very thin, bristle-like, soft, long; awns tinged violet. Pastures, meadows; meagre soils poor in calcium; 1700–2800 m; rather common. Mountain plant of Central and Southern Europe. F3, R2, N3, H3, D4, L4, T2, K4. Flowering time: 7–8.

g. **Meadow-grass,** *Poa* L.
Spikelets few-flowered, mostly shorter than 5 mm, without awns. The genus is represented in the Alps by ca. 15 species, difficult to distinguish between.

Alpine meadow-grass, *Poa alpina* L. (Plate 5.1)
10–50 cm tall; forming tussocks; spikelets brownish, often tinged violet. Meadows, pastures, resting places of animals; nutrient-rich soils; 800–3200 m; common. Eurosibirian-North American plant. F3, R3, N4, H3, D4, L4, T2, K3. Flowering time: 6–9.
Spikelets of alpine meadow-grass may often carry small bulbils instead of flowers; they give rise to new plantlets which either fall of or touch the soil with the culm and then take root.

h. **Sesleria,** *Sesleria* Scop.
Blue sesleria, *Sesleria coerulea* (L.) Ard. *(S. varia* [Jacq.] Wettst.)
(Fig. 37C)
10–50 cm tall; forming tussocks; leaves bluish; spikelets violet to blue, seldom pale, multilaterally grouped in a head-like inflorescence. Grassy slopes, pine forests; calcium-rich soils; 500–2800 m; rather common. Central European plant. F2, R4, N2, H3, D2, L4, T2, K3. Flowering time: 5–8.

Two-lined sesleria, *Sesleria disticha* (Wulfen) Pers. (Plate 5.4)
10–20 cm tall; forming tussocks; spikelets green-, yellowish-, and bluish-speckled, grouped in rows by two in a head-like inflorescence. Pastures, grassy slopes; soils poor in calcium, often exposed to the wind; 2300–3100 m; rather common. Mountain plant of Central and Southern Europe. F2, R1, N1, H3, D4, L5, T1, K4. Flowering time: 7–8.

i. **Timothy,** *Phleum* L.
Spikelets in a compact, spike-like inflorescence.

Alpine timothy, *Phleum alpinum* L. (Plate 5.2)
20–50 cm tall; the uppermost sheath (basal part of the leaf which encircles the stem) expanded. Fertilized meadows, pastures; nutrient-rich soils; 1300–2600 m; common. Mountain plant of Central and Southern Europe. F3, R3, N4, D4, L4, T2, K3. Flowering time: 7–8.

k. **Mat-grass,** *Nardus* L.
Mat-grass, *Nardus stricta* L. (Plate 5.3)
10–25 cm tall; forming dense tussocks; leaves bristle-like, tough; spikelets in a loose unilateral spike. Pastures, meadows; soils poor in calcium; 600–2800 m; common, frequently forming distinct stands. Eurosibirian plant. F3, R2, N2, H3, D4, L4, T2, K3. Flowering time: 6–7.

135

9th family: **sedges,** *Cyperaceae*

Similar to grasses; stem without nodes, often trigonous; leaves arrangement tristichous; flowers inconspicuous, often in spikes or heads. There are ca. 100 species in the Alps; they are difficult to distinguish between.

a. **Cottongrass,** *Eriophorum* L.

Flowers in heads which develop into conspicuous woolly glomerules when old (perianth bristles elongate and become cottony after flowering).

Scheuchzer's cottongrass, *Eriophorum scheuchzeri* Hoppe (Plate 6.1)

10–30 cm tall; with stolons; 1 head per stem, 2–3 cm thick when fully developed. Lakesides, swamps; wet soils poor in calcium; 1900–2600 m; not common (mostly in the Central Alps). Arctic-Alpine plant. F5w, R2, N2, H4, D4, L5, T1, K3. Flowering time: 6–8.
Protected: BE, NW, OW/L.

Sheathed cottongrass, *Eriophorum vaginatum* L.

20–50 cm tall; without stolons; 1 head per stem, 1.5–1.8 cm thick when fully developed; the uppermost cauline leaf reduced and encircling the stem with expanded sheath (feature exclusive for this species!). Swamps; acid, meagre, wet soils; 800–2400 m; not common. Eurosibirian-North American plant. F5w, R1, N1, H5, D5, L4, T2, K3. Flowering time: 5–6.
Protected: AG, *BL*, BE, *GE*, JU, NW, OW, *SH*, TG, ZH/L.

Narrow-leaved cottongrass, *Eriophorum angustifolium* Honck.
(Plate 6.2)

20–50 cm tall; with long stolons; 3–7 heads per stem, hanging on smooth peduncles, when old 1.5–2 cm long. Swamps; wet, meagre, acid, peaty soils; 400–2400 m; not common. Eurosibirian-North American plant. F5w, R2, N2, H5, D5, L5, T2, K3. Flowering time: 5–6.
Protected: AG, *BL*, BE, *GE*, JU, NW, OW, *SH*, TG, ZH/L.

Broad-leaved cottongrass, *Eriophorum latifolium* Hoppe

30–60 cm tall; without stolons; 5–12 heads per stem, hanging on rough peduncles, 1–1.6 cm long when old. Fens; wet, meagre, base-rich, peaty soils; 400–2200 m; not common. European plant. F5w, R4, N2, H5, D5, L4, T3, K3. Flowering time: 5–6.
Protected: AG, *BL*, BE, *GE*, JU, NW, OW, *SH*, TG, ZH/L.

b. **Deergrass,** *Trichophorum* Pers.

Turfy deergrass, *Trichophorum caespitosum* (L.) Hartm. (Fig. 38A)

5–25 cm tall; forms dense lawns; spikelets single, terminal, 3–5 mm long, without woolly hairs. Mires, swamps; wet soils poor in calcium; 1000–2500 m; rather common. Eurosibirian-North American plant. F4w, R2, N2, H5, D5, L4, T2, K3. Flowering time: 7.

Alpine deergrass, *Trichophorum alpinum* (L.) Pers. (Plate 6.3)

10–20 cm tall; shortly creeping with densely standing shoots; spikelets single, terminal, 5–7 mm long, when old with woolly hairs up to 2.5 mm long. Mires; wet soils poor in calcium; 500–2100 m; not common. Eurosibirian-North American plant. F5, R2, N2, H5, D5, L5, T2, K3. Flowering time: 5–6.

c. **Elyna,** *Elyna* Schrad.

Mouse-tail-like elyna, *Elyna myosuroides* (Vill.) Fritsch (Fig. 38B)
5–25 cm tall; forming dense tussocks; brown-yellow shiny sheaths at the base; leaves bristle-like, often longer than flowering stems; spikelets single, terminal, thin, 1–2.5 cm long. Grassland; meagre, base-containing soils, often on wind-exposed sites; 1800–2900 m; rather common. Arctic-Alpine plant. F2, R3, N1, H4, D3, L5, T1, K4. Flowering time: 7–8.

d. **Sedge,** *Carex* L.
Flowers male or female, often in unisexual spikes. The genus is represented in the Alps by ca. 70 species difficult to distinguish from each other.

Evergreen sedge, *Carex sempervirens* Vill. (Plate 6.4; Fig. 38E)
10–30 cm tall; forming tussocks; lower dead sheaths form a dense fibrous dark-red tuft; stem cylindrical; 1 male and 2–4 short-pedicellate female spikes per stem. Grassland; dry soils; 1000–2900 m; common. Mountain plant of Central and Southern Europe. F2, R3, N2, H3, D3, L4, T1, K4. Flowering time: 6–8.

Rust-coloured sedge, *Carex ferruginea* Scop. (Fig. 38D)
30–60 cm tall; with stolons; without fibrous tuft; stem weakly trigonous; female spikes with peduncles longer than those of evergreen sedge, hanging. Grassland, wild hay meadows; humid, base-rich soils; 1000–2500 m; common (esp. outer ranges). Mountain plant of Central and Southern Europe. F4, R4, N3, H3, D4, L4, T2, K2. Flowering time: 7–8.

Alpine sedge, *Carex curvula* All. (Plate 7.1)
5–20 cm tall; forming dense tussocks; leaves 1–2 mm wide, curved back, tips often dead and brownish-yellow; spikes grouped into heads, female ones below, male ones above. Grassland; soils poor in calcium; 2000–3000 m; common (nearly exclusively in the inner ranges). Mountain plant of Central and Southern Europe. F2, R2, N2, H3, D3, L5, T1, K4. Flowering time: 7–8.

Black sedge, *Carex atrata* L. (Plate 7.2)
20–40 cm tall; forms loose tussocks, with short underground stolons; 1 terminal spike with male flowers below and female ones above as well as 3–5 female spikes 1–2 cm long with peduncles up to 3 cm long. Grassland; humid, base-rich soils; 1500–2700 m; not common. North European-Alpine plant. F4w, R3, N3, H4, D3, L4, T1, K2. Flowering time: 6–7.

Cushion sedge, *Carex firma* Host (Plate 7.3)
5–20 cm tall; forming tussocks; leaves short, rigid, up to 4 mm wide (wider than those of evergreen sedge and rust-coloured sedge); 1 male and 1–3 female spikes with peduncles at most up to 1 cm long, upright. Rocky slopes, grassland, hilltops, cliff ledges; soils rich in calcium, often

wind-exposed; 1500–2900 m; rather common. Mountain plant of Central and Southern Europe (eastern). F2, R5, N1, H3, D3, L5, T1, K4. Flowering time: 6–8.
Protected: F.

Small-flowered sedge, *Carex parviflora* Host *(C. nigra* auct.)
(Plate 7.4)
8–20 cm tall; differs from the black sedge as follows: female spikes sessile, 0.5–1 cm long. Snow-patches, open grasslands; stony, humid soils containing calcium: 2300–3000 m; not common. Mountain plant of Central and Southern Europe. F4, R4, N2, H4, D3, L4, T1, K2. Flowering time: 7–8.

Brown sedge, *Carex fusca* All. *(C. nigra* [L.] Reichb.)   (Fig. 38F)
10–50 cm tall; with stolons; 1–2 male spikes and 2–5 female ones below which are brown and 1–3 cm long. Swamps, mires, shores; wet, peaty soils poor in bases; 500–2400 m; rather common. Eurosibirian-North American plant. F4w, R2, N2, H5, D5, L4, T2, K3. Flowering time: 6–7.

Davall's sedge, *Carex davalliana* Sm.   (Fig. 38C)
10–30 cm tall; forming tussocks; leaves bristle-like; 1 terminal spike per stem; dioecious; ripe fruits slightly curved and deflexed. Fens, flushes; wet, base-rich, peaty soils; 500–2400 m; rather common. Central European plant. F5w, R4, N2, H4, D5, L5, T3, K2. Flowering time: 5–7.

Mt. Baldo sedge, *Carex baldensis* L.   (Fig. 38G)
10–40 cm tall; forms loose tussocks; spikes with male and female flowers forming conspicuously white heads. Grassland; stony, calcium-rich, dry soils; 600–2400 m; very rare (in Switzerland only at the Ofen-pass). Southern Alpine plant. F2, R5, N2, H3, D3, L4, T3, K4. Flowering time: 5–7.
Protected: V*, R. CH.

10th family: **rush family,** *Juncaceae*

Gramineous plants; stem without nodes, cylindrical; leaves surrounding the stem; flowers inconspicuous, with 6 perianth segments, grouped in a head-, or panicle-like inflorescence. The family is represented in the Alps by two genera comprising about 30 species.

a. **Rush,** *Juncus* L.
Leaves glabrous, mostly bristle-like.

Fig. 38. Sedge family. A: turfy deer-grass *(Trichophorum caespitosum)*. B: mousetail-like elyna *(Elyna myosuroides)*. C: Davall's sedge *(Carex davalliana)*. D: rust-coloured sedge *(Carex ferruginea)*. E: evergreen sedge *(Carex sempervirens)*. F: brown sedge *(Carex fusca)*. G: Mt. Baldo sedge *(Carex baldensis)*. ⅓ ×.

Jacquin's rush, *Juncus jacquinii* L. (Plate 8.1)
10–25 cm tall; leaves bristle-like; only the uppermost leaf longer than the inflorescence; inflorescence head-like, consisting of 4–12 shiny black-brown flowers. Grassland; humid soils poor in calcium; 1700–3000 m; not common (mostly inner ranges). Mountain plant of Central and Southern Europe (eastern). F4, R2, N2, H4, D4, L4, T1, K3. Flowering time: 7–8.

Three-leaved rush, *Juncus trifidus* L. (Plate 8.2)
8–25 cm tall; leaves filiform; inflorescence much shorter than the uppermost leaf, head-like, consisting of 1–4 brown flowers. Ridges, knolls, rocky crevices; dry, stony soils poor in calcium; 1800–3000 m; rather common (esp. inner ranges). Arctic-Alpine plant. F2, R2, N1, H3, D3, L5, T1, K4. Flowering time: 7–8.

b. **Woodrush,** *Luzula* DC.
Leaves hairy at least on the margin, flat.

Spiked woodrush, *Luzula spicata* (L.) DC. (Fig. 39A)
8–25 cm tall; leaves short; inflorescence a compact spike, mostly slightly nodding. Grassland, scree; stony soils poor in calcium; 1600–3100 m; not common. Arctic-Alpine plant. F2, R2, N1, H3, D3, L5, T1, K3. Flowering time: 7–8.

Yellow woodrush, *Luzula lutea* (All.) DC. (Plate 8.3)
10–20 cm tall; leaves short, up to 6 mm wide; inflorescence including numerous, 6–10-flowered, compact, yellow glomerules. Grassland; dry soils poor in calcium; 1700–3100 m; rather common (above all in the inner ranges). Mountain plant of Central and Southern Europe (western). F2, R2, N2, H4, D4, L5, T1, K3. Flowering time: 6–8.

Ear-like woodrush, *Luzula spadicea* (All.) DC. *(L. alpino-pilosa* [Chaix] Breitstr.) (Fig. 39C)
10–25 cm tall; leaves rather long, up to 4 mm wide; inflorescence including 2–5-flowered, loosely grouped brown heads. Grassland, scree; humid, stony soils poor in calcium, covered by snow for a long time; 1800–3000 m. Mountain plant of Central and Southern Europe. F4, R2, N2, H3, D2, L5, T1, K2. Flowering time: 7–8.

Greater woodrush, *Luzula sieberi* Tausch *(L. silvatica* auct.)
(Fig. 39B)
30–60 cm tall; leaves long, up to 7 mm wide; inflorescence including 2–4-flowered, loosely arranged brown heads. Woods, dwarf shrub stands; humous soils poor in calcium; 800–2400 m; common. Alpine plant. F3, R2, N2, H4, D4, L2, T2, K3. Flowering time: 6–7.
The closely related **greater woodrush** *(L. silvatica)* with wider leaves occurs at lower altitudes.

Snow woodrush, *Luzula nivea* (L.) DC. (Plate 8.4)
30–70 cm tall; leaves long, up to 5 mm wide; inflorescence including 2–8-flowered heads arranged umbel-like. Woods, forest clearings; dry, humous soils poor in calcium; 500–2200 m; rather common (esp. the

140

Fig. 39. Woodrushes. A: spiked woodrush *(Luzula spicata)*. B: greater woodrush *(Luzula sieberi)*. C: ear-like woodrush *(Luzula spadicea)*. ⅓ ×.

Southern Alps). Mountain plant of Central and Southern Europe (western). F2, R2, N2, H4, D4, L3, T3, K3. Flowering time: 6–7.

11th family: **lily family,** *Liliaceae*

Flowers with 6 coloured tepals, 6 stamens, and a superior ovary; often with a bulb. The family is represented in the Alps by about 50 species.

a. **Leek,** *Allium* L.
  Alpine leek, *Allium victorialis* L.   (Plate 9.1)
  Leaves often gramineous; flowers in umbels; 30–50 cm tall, leek-smelling plant with a bulb; flowers yellowish. Grassland; medium soils; 1700–2600 m; rather rare. Eurasiatic plant. F3, R3, N3, H3, D4, L4, T2, K3. Flowering time: 6–8.
  Protected: BE, FR, *GL*, GR, NE, *NW, SO*.

  Chives, *Allium schoenoprasum* L.   (Plate 9.2)
  15–30 cm tall; leaves cylindric, hollow; flowers purple-red. Swamps, grassy slopes; intermittently wet soils; 1300–2600 m; not common. Eurosibirian-North American plant. F5w, R3, N3, H4, D4, L4, T2, K3. Flowering time: 6–8.

141

b. **Tofieldia,** *Tofieldia* Huds.
   Greater tofieldia, *Tofieldia calyculata* (L.) Wahlenb.   (Plate 9.3)
   10–30 cm tall; no bulb; leaves gramineous, pointed, leaf arrangement distichous; flowers small, yellow, in a 2–6 cm long, spicate inflorescence. Flushes, fens, grassland; intermittently humid, base-rich soils; 500–2500 m; not common. Central European plant. F4w, R4, N2, H3, D5, L4, T3, K3. Flowering time: 7–9.
   Tiny tofieldia, *Tofieldia pusilla* (Mixchx.) Pers. *(T. palustris* auct.)
   Differs from the greater tofieldia as follows: 5–15 cm tall; leaves obtuse; flowers whitish, in a 0.5–1 cm long inflorescence. Grassland; humous soils; 1800–2400 m; rare (above all the inner ranges). Arctic-Alpine plant. F3w, R2, N2, H4, D4, L4, T1, K3. Flowering time: 7–8.
   Protected: *F.*

c. **Asphodel,** *Asphodelus* L.
   White asphodel, *Asphodelus albus* Miller   (Plate 9.4)
   50–120 cm tall; with turnip-like thickened roots; leaves gramineous, trigonous; flowers white, star-shaped, in a compact spicate inflorescence. Meadows, pastures; intermittently dry, nutrient-rich soils; 900–2000 m; very rare (in Switzerland near Lens and Naters in the Wallis, and at the Generoso in the Ticino). Mountain plant of Central and Southern Europe (southern). F2w, R3, N4, H3, D5, L4, T3, K4. Flowering time: 6–7.
   Protected: V. CH/Ao, L.

d. **Lily.** *Lilium* L.
   Fire lily, *Lilium bulbiferum* L.   (Plate 10.1)
   20–90 cm tall; with a bulb; leaves narrow, lanceolate, the upper ones alternate, frequently carrying bulbils in their axils; flowers 1–5, funnel-shaped, subterminal/terminal, upright, yellow-orange to orange-red, with brown speckles. Meadows, rocky places; dry, stony soils; 600–2000 m; rather rare. Mountain plant of Central and Southern Europe (southern). F2, R3, N2, H3, D3, L4, T3, K4. Flowering time: 6–7.
   Protected: V., *CH/B/Ti, Vo/Li/Ao, Bz, L, So, Tn.*

   Martagon lily, *Lilium martagon* L.   (Plate 10.2)
   30–80 cm tall; with a bulb; leaves narrowly lanceolate, verticillate; flowers 3–12, subterminal/terminal, nodding, bright purple-red with darker spots; tepals recurved. Woods, bushes, grassy slopes; base-rich soils; 400–2300 m; not common. Eurosibirian plant. F3, R4, N3, H3, D4, L3, T3, K3. Flowering time: 6–7.
   Protected: *CH/B/Ti, Vo/Li/Ao, Bz, L, So, Tn.*

e. **False hellebore,** *Veratrum* L.
   White false hellebore, *Veratrum album* L.   (Plate 10.3)
   Poisonous; 50–150 cm tall; with thick rhizome; leaves lanceolate, in rows of three; flowers measuring 1–1.5 cm in diameter, star-shaped, whitish to greenish, in a terminal panicle consisting of smaller spicate

142

inflorescences. Meadows, pastures, tall-herb vegetation; humid, nutrient-rich soils; 800–2600 m; common. Eurosibirian plant. F4, R3, N4, H4, D5, L4, T2, K3. Flowering time: 7.

False hellebore is sometimes mistaken for the yellow gentian used in some sorts of liquor; this mistake can be fatal. Leaves of the yellow gentian are bluish, completely glabrous, and crosswise-opposite whereas those of the false hellebore are green, densely hairy underneath, and alternate.

f. **St. Bruno's lily,** *Paradisia* Mazz.
   St. Bruno's lily, *Paradisia liliastrum* (L.) Bert.   (Plate 10.4)
   30–50 cm tall; with a short rhizome; leaves gramineous; flowers 1–10, subterminal/terminal, funnel-shaped, nodding, white. Meadows; medium soils; 800–2400 m; not common (very rare in the northern ranges). Mountain plant of Central and Southern Europe (western). F3, R3, N3, H4, D4, L4, T2, K3. Flowering time: 6–7.
   Protected: BE, FR, *GL, NW, OW, SG,* UR/Ao.

g. **Lloydia,** *Lloydia* Salisb.
   Snowdon lily, *Lloydia serotina* (L.) Rchb.   (Plate 11.1)
   5–15 cm tall; with small bulbs; leaves gramineous, narrow; flowers terminal, mostly single, star-shaped, white, with 3–5 reddish stripes per tepal, measuring 1.2–2 cm in diameter. Grassland, rocky crevices; humous soils poor in calcium, with short duration of snow cover; 1600–3000 m; not common. Arctic-Alpine plant. F2, R2, N1, H4, D4, L4, T1, K4. Flowering time: 6–7.
   Protected: AI, *NW, OW.*

h. **Star-of-Bethlehem,** *Gagea* Salisb.
   Yellow star of Bethlehem, *Gagea fistulosa* (Ram.) Ker-Gawl *(G. liottardi* Schultes)   (Plate 11.2)
   5–20 cm tall; with a bulb; leaves cylindrical; flowers 1–5, terminal, upright, star-shaped, yellow. Grassland, resting places of animals; nutrient-rich soils; 1200–2400 m; not common. Mountain plant of Central and Southern Europe. F3, R3, N4, H3, D5, L4, T2, K2. Flowering time: 5–7.

i. **Meadow saffron,** *Colchicum* L.
   5–20 cm tall; with a bulb; leaves narrow, lanceolate, all radical; stem underground; 1–3 upright flowers rising directly from the ground.

   Alpine meadow saffron, *Colchicum alpinum* Lam. a. DC.
                                                          (Plate 11.3)
   Flowers appearing in late summer, star-shaped, measuring 4–6 cm in diameter, pink to lilac. Meadows; soils poor in calcium; 1500–2200 m; rather rare (in Switzerland only SW of the Ticino and the Rhône). Mountain plant of Central and Southern Europe (southern). F3, R2, N3, H4, D4, L4, T2, K4. Flowering time: 7–8.

   The very similar **autumn crocus** *(Colchicum autumnale L.)* occurs at lower altitudes within the whole Alpine area and has its distribution area in Central Europe.

143

Spring meadow saffron, *(Colchicum bulbocodium* Ker-Gawl. *(Bulbocodium vernum* L.) (Plate 11.4)
Flowers appearing in early spring, star-shaped, measuring 7–9 cm in diameter, pink to lilac. Meadows; intermittently dry soils; 600–2200 m; rare (in Switzerland only in the Wallis). Mountain plant of Central and Southern Europe (southern). F2w, R3, N3, H3, D3, L4, T3, K4. Flowering time: 3–5.

k. **Solomon's seal,** *Polygonatum* Miller
Whorled Solomon's seal, *Polygonatum verticillatum* (L.) All.
(Plate 12.1)
30–80 cm tall; with a tuberous rhizome; leaves narrow, lanceolate, 3–7 verticillate; flowers hanging, white with greenish teeth, in 2–5-flowered short clusters in leaf axils. Woods, tall-herb stands; humid, rather nutrient-rich soils; 800–2300 m; rather common. Eurasiatic mountain plant. F4, R3, N3, H4, D4, L2, T2, K2. Flowering time: 6–7.
Protected: OW.

12th family: **amaryllis family,** *Amaryllidaceae*

Plants of this family may be distinguished from the lily family by the inferior ovary. Only a few species occur in the Alps.

a. **Snowflake,** *Leucojum* L.
Spring snowflake, *Leucojum vernum* L. (Plate 12.2)
10–20 cm tall; with a bulb; leaves gramineous, up to 1 cm wide; flowers 1–2, terminal, nodding, bell-shaped, white with green teeth. Meadows, deciduous forests; humid, nutrient-rich soils; 500–1600 m; not common (very rare in the inner ranges). Central European plant. F3w, R3, N4, H3, D5, L3, T3, K2. Flowering time: 3–4.
Protected: AG, AR, *BL,* FR, GL, JU, NW, SG, *SH, SO,* TG, ZH/Li/*Bz,* L.

b. **Daffodil** or **narcissus,** *Narcissus* L.
Narrow-leaved daffodil, *Narcissus radiiflorus* Salisb. *(N. angustifolius* Curt.) (Plate 12.3)
20–40 cm tall; with a bulb; leaves gramineous, up to 1 cm wide; flowers single, terminal, star-shaped, white with short yellow and red-edged corolla appendage. Meadows; nutrient-rich, rather humid soils; 800–2000 m; not common (frequent only in the west, very rare in the inner Alpine ranges). Mountain plant of Central and Southern Europe. F3, R3, N4, H4, D4, L4, T3, K2. Flowering time: 5–6.
Protected: AR, *BL,* GR, LU, *NW, OW/Bz,* L.

Wild daffodil, *Narcissus pseudonarcissus* L.
Differs from the narrow-leaved daffodil in the following features: flowers pale-yellow, with large dark yellow corolla appendage. Meadows; humous soils poor in calcium; 800–1800 m; not common (above all in the outer ranges). Plant of western Europe. F3, R2, N2, H4, D4, L4, T3, K2. Flowering time: 4–5.
Protected: *AG,* AR, *BL,* BS, *FR,* GR, *NW, OW,* SG.

144

13th family: **iris family,** *Iridaceae*

Differs from the lily family as follows: ovary inferior, only 3 stamens present. Only one species occurs at higher altitudes in the Alps.

a. **Crocus,** *Crocus* L.
   White crocus, *Crocus albiflorus* Kit. *(C, vernus* Wulf.) (Plate 12.4)
   8–15 cm tall; with a bulb; leaves gramineous, with white midrib; flowers white to deep violet, or white with violet stripes, rising singly from the ground. Meadows, pastures; nutrient-rich soils; 800–2500 m; common. Mountain plant of Central and Southern Europe. F3, R3, N4, H4, D4, L4, T2, K3. Flowering time: 3–6.
   Protected: AI, SO.

14th family: **orchids,** *Orchidaceae*

Flowers zygomorphic, often bizarre forms, with 3 outer and 2 lateral inner perianth segments as well as a lower lip. The family is represented in the Alps by about 40 species.

a. **Lady's slipper,** *Cypripedium* L.
   Lady's slipper, *Cypripedium calceolus* L.   (Plate 13.1)
   15–50 cm tall; no tubers; leaves 2–4 on the stem, oval; flowers 1–3, with 4 brown-red expanded perianth segements and a slipper-shaped, yellow lower lip. Light woods; intermittently dry, calcium-rich soils; 600–1900 m; rare. Eurosibirian plant. F2w, R4, N2, H3, D4, L3, T3, K3. Flowering time: 6.
   Protected: V*. V. *CH/B/Ti, Vo/Li/Ao, Bz,* L, *So, Tn/F.*

b. **Fly orchid,** *Ophrys* L.
   Fly orchid, *Ophrys insectifera* L. *(O. muscifera* Huds.) (Plate 13.2)
   15–30 cm tall; with globoid tubers; leaves radical; flowers 2–20, with 3 greenish outer tepals, and 2 narrow, brown inner ones as well as a ligulate brown lip. Light woods; intermittently dry, calcium-containing soils; 500–1800 m; rather rare. Central European plant. F2w, R4, N1, H3, D5, L3, T3, K4. Flowering time: 6.
   Protected: *CH/B/Ti/Li/*L.

c. **Helleborine,** *Epipactis* Zinn (Helleborine Miller)
   With horizontal rhizomes; leaves oval to lanceolate, on the stem; distal part of the lower lip expanded.

   Marsh helleborine, *Epipactis palustris* (L.) Crantz   (Plate 13.4)
   20–40 cm tall; outer 3 perianth segments brownish, 2 inner ones white, often pink at the base; lip white with 2 yellow stripes. Mires, flushes; wet, peaty, calciferous soils; 500–1500 m; not common. Eurosibirian plant. F4w, R4, N2, H5, D5, L4, T3, K3. Flowering time: 6–7.
   Protected: *CH/B/A/*Li/L.

Dark-red helleborine, *Epipactis atropurpurea* Rafin   (Plate 14.1)
20–50 cm tall; tepals and lower lip dark purple-red. Light woods; intermittently dry, calciferous soils; 500–2300 m; not common. Eurosibirian plant. F2w, R4, N1, H3, D5, L3, T3, K4. Flowering time: 6–7.
Protected: *CH/A*/Li/L.

Broad-leaved helleborine, *Epipactis latifolia* All.   (Plate 14.1)
20–50 cm tall; tepals greenish, tinged violet, lower lip whitish to red. Woods; calciferous soils; 500–1700 m; not common. Eurosibirian plant. F3w, R4, N2, H4, D5, L3, T3, K3. Flowering time: 8–9.
Protected: *CH/B/A*/Li/L.

d. **Butterfly orchid,** *Platanthera* Rich.
Lesser butterfly orchid, *Platanthera bifolia* (L.) Rich.   (Plate 14.2)
20–50 cm tall; with turnip-shaped tubers; leaves broadly oval, in a bottom pair; flowers whitish, fragrant, with filiform spurs up to 2 cm long. Meadows, light woods; intermittently humid, meagre, calciferous soils; 400–2100 m; not common. Eurosibirian plant. F3w, R4, N2, H4, D5, L3, T3, K3. Flowering time: 6–7.
Protected: *CH/B*/Ti/Li/L.

e. **Orchid,** *Orchis* L.
With globoid or palmate tuber (always one from a given year together with one from the preceding year); flowers with cylindric spurs, in a spicate inflorescence. The genus is represented in the Alps by about 15 species.

Globose orchid, *Orchis globosa* L. *(Traunsteinera globosa* [L.] Rchb.)
(Plate 13.3)
20–50 cm tall; flowers pink, in a nearly globose inflorescence; outer tepals forming a club-shaped tip. Meadows; humid, calciferous soils; 1200–2400 m; not common (above all in outer ranges). Mountain plant of Central and Southern Europe. F4, R4, N3, H4, D4, L4, T2, K3. Flowering time: 6–7.
Protected: *CH/B*/Ti/Li/L.

Burnt or dark-winged orchid, *Orchis ustulata* L.   (Plate 14.3)
10–30 cm tall; flowers purple-red outside, light pink with dark red speckles inside, small, in a short, compact spike. Grassland; intermittently dry, meagre soils; 300–2000 m; not common. Eurosibirian plant. F3w, R3, N2, H4, D4, L4, T3, K4. Flowering time: 6–7.
Protected: *CH/B*/Ti/Li/L.

Early purple orchid or blue butcher, *Orchis mascula* L.   (Plate 14.4)
10–30 cm tall; leaves often with red spots; flowers red, in a loose spike; spur horizontal or ascending. Meadows, light woods; intermittently humid soils; 400–2300 m; not common. European-West Asiatic plant. F3w, R3, N3, H4, D4, L3, T3, K3. Flowering time: 5–7.
Protected: *AG,* BE, FR, *GE, GR, JU,* NW, *OW, SH,* SO, SZ, *TG, TI, ZH/B*/Ti/Li/L.

Elder orchid, *Orchis sambucina* L. (Plate 15.1)
10–30 cm tall; leaves without spots: stem hollow; flowers purple-red or yellow; spurs horizontal or ascending. Meadows, bushy slopes; intermittently dry, acid soils; 800–2100 m; rather rare (above all in the southern ranges). Central European plant. F2w, R2, N3, H4, D4, L4, T3, K4. Flowering time: 5–6.
Protected: *CH/B/*Ti/Li/L.

Broad-leaved orchid, *Orchis latifolia* L. *(O. majalis* Rchb.)
(Plate 15.2)
20–60 cm tall; leaves mostly with red spots; 3–6 times as long as wide; stem thick, hollow; flowers dark-red; spur horizontal or ascending. Fens, swamps; wet peaty soils; 500–2300 m; not common. Central European plant. F5w, R4, N3, H5, D5, L4, T3, K2. Flowering time: 6–7.
Protected: *AG,* BE, FR, *GE, GR,* JU, *NW, OW, SH,* SO, SZ, *TG, TI, ZH/B/*Ti/Li/L.

Traunsteiner's orchid, *Orchis traunsteineri* Sauter (Plate 15.3)
Differs from the broad-leaved orchid as follows: leaves 6–10 times as long as wide; stem thin, hardly hollow. Fens; wet peaty soils; 400–2100 m; not common. Eurosibirian plant. F5w, R3, N2, H5, D5, L4, T3, K3. Flowering time: 6–7.
Protected: *CH/B/Li/L.*

Spotted orchid, *Orchis maculata* L. *Dactylorrhiza maculata* [L.] Verm.) (Plate 15.4)
Differs from the broad-leaved orchid in the following characters: stem thin, hardly hollow; flowers light violet-red. Meadows, light woods; intermittently humid, meagre soils; 400–2000 m; rather common. Eurosibirian plant. F4w, R3, N3, H4, D5, L3, T3, K3. Flowering time: 6–7.
Protected: *AG,* BE, FR, *GE, GR,* JU, NW, *OW, SH,* SO, SZ, *TG, TI, ZH/B/*Ti/Li/L.

f. **Rein orchid,** *Gymnadenia* R. Br.
Differs from the genus *Orchis* in the consistently palmate tubers and the thin spurs.

Fragrant orchid, *Gymnadenia conopea* (L.) R. Br. (Plate 16.1)
10–40 cm tall; flowers red-violet to flesh-coloured, with filiform spur about 1.5–cm long; plant with a sweet fragrance. Meadows; meagre, intermittently humid soils; 400–2400 m; rather common. Eurosibirian plant. F3w, R4, N2, H4, D5, L4, T3, K3. Flowering time: 6–7.
Protected: *AG,* BE, FR, GE, *GR, JU, NW, OW, SH,* SO, SZ, TG, *TI, ZH/B/*Ti/Li/L.

Sweetest orchid, *Gymnadenia odoratissima* (L.) Rich.
It may be distinguished from the fragrant orchid by the spur which is about 0.5–cm long and the vanilla scent. Meadows, light woods; intermittently dry, calcium-rich soils; 600–2400 m; not common. Central European plant. F2w, R5, N2, H4, D4, L4, T3, K4. Flowering time: 6–7.
Protected: *CH/B/*Ti/Li/L.

g. **White orchid,** *Leucorchis* E. Meyer
   Small white orchid, *Leucorchis albida* (L.) E. Meyer *(Gymnadenia albida* [L.] Rich.) (Plate 16.2)
   10–30 cm tall; flowers small, white, with a short spur. Meadows, pastures; meagre soils poor in calcium; 1000–2500 m; rather common. North European-Alpine plant. F3, R2, N1, H4, D4, L4, T2, K3. Flowering time: 6–7.
   Protected: *CH/B/*Li/L.

h. **Vanilla orchid,** *Nigritella* Rich.
   Black vanilla orchid, *Nigritella nigra* (L.) Rchb. *(N. angustifolia* Rich.) (Plate 16.3)
   5–20 cm tall; leaves gramineous; flowers in a nearly globose, or club-shaped inflorescence, small, black-purple-red, with vanilla fragrance. Meadows, pastures; meagre soils; 1300–2700 m; rather common. Scandinavian-Alpine plant. F3, R3, N2, H4, D4, L4, T2, K3. Flowering time: 6–8.
   Protected: *AI,* AR, BE, FR, GL, *GR, JU,* LU, *NE,* NW, *OW,* SG, *SO,* SZ, *TI,* UR, *ZH/B/Ti,* Vo/Li/Ao, L. *So.*

   Red vanilla orchid, *Nigritella rubra* (Wettst.) Rcht., *(N. miniata* [Crantz] Janchen) (Plate 16.4)
   Differs from black vanilla orchid in the following features: flowers in an oblong-obovate inflorescence, pink. Meadows; calciferous, meagre soils; 1600–2300 m; rather rare (only east from the Gotthard, and in the Bernese Oberland). Mountain plant of Central and Southern Europe (eastern). F3, R4, N2, H4, D4, L4, T2, K3. Flowering time: 6–7.
   Protected: R. *CH/B/Ti,* Vo/Li/L, *So.*

i. **Coral-root,** *Corallorrhiza* Haller
   Coral-root, *Corallorrhiza trifida* Chât. *(C. innata* R. Br.) (Plate 17.1)
   10–25 cm tall; with coral-shaped fleshy rhizomes (visible in the photograph); without green leaves, only with yellowish scales on the stem; tepals yellowish green, with brown-red tips; lower lip white with red spots. Coniferous woods; acid, humous soils; 1000–2000 m; rather rare. Eurosibirian-North American plant. F3, R2, N2, H5, D4, L2, T2, K3. Flowering time: 6–7.
   Protected: *CH/B/*Li/L.

k. **Musk-orchid,** *Herminium* R. Br.
   Musk-orchid, *Herminium monorchis* (L.) R. Br. (Plate 17.2)
   10–25 cm tall; with globose tubers, and stolons; leaves at the base of the stem; flowers small, yellow-green. Meadows; intermittently dry, calciferous, meagre soils; 600–1900 m; not common. Eurosibirian plant. F3w, R4, N2, H4, D4, L4, T3, K4. Flowering time: 6–7.
   Protected: *CH/B/*Li/L.

l. **Dwarf orchid,** *Chamorchis* Rich.
   Alpine dwarf orchid, *Chamorchis alpina* (L.) Rich. (Plate 17.3)
   5–10 cm tall; with entire tubers; leaves gramineous; flowers yellow-green, violet-brown outside; lower lip yellowish. Grassland; stony, dry,

meagre, calcium-rich soils; 1900–2700 m; not common. Arctic-Alpine plant (European). F2, R4, N1, H4, D3, L5, T1, K4. Flowering time: 7–8.
Protected: *CH*/*B*/Li/L.

m.**Twayblade,** *Listera* R. Br.
   Lesser twayblade, *Listera cordata* (L.) R. Br.   (Fig. 40)
   4–20 cm tall; no tubers; only 2, heart-shaped, sessile, opposite leaves; flowers small, green to violet-purple. Woods; humous, humid, acid soils; 1000–2000 m; not common. Eurosibirian-North American plant. F4, R1, N1, H5, D5, L2, T2, K2. Flowering time: 6–7.
Protected: *CH*/*B*/Li/L.

Fig. 40.   Lesser twayblade *(Listera cordata)*, ⅓ × (from *6.1.k.*).

n. **Frog orchid,** *Coeloglossum* Hartm.
   Green frog orchid, *Coeloglossum viride* (L.) Hartm.   (Plate 17.4)
   5–25 cm tall; with bipartite tuber; leaves on stem oval; flowers yellowish-green to brown-red, with a long trilobate lip. Pastures, dwarf shrub stands; meagre soils poor in calcium; 1000–2600 m; not common. Eurosibirian-North American plant. F3, R2, N2, H4, D4, L4, T2, K3. Flowering time: 6–7.
Protected: *CH*/*B*/Li/L.

15th family: **willow family,** *Salicaceae*

Trees, bushes or shrubs (sometimes very small!); flowers in catkins; dioecious; seeds with woolly hairs (dispersal by wind). The family is represented in the Alps by about 25 willow species difficult to distinguish between, and also one species of poplar.

a. **Poplar,** *Populus* L.

Aspen, *Populus tremula* L. (Fig. 35Q, p. 132)
Tree up to 20 m tall; leaves long-petiolate, nearly round, crenate-dentate, trembling in the wind. Bushes, forest edges; soils poor in calcium; 300–1900 m; rather common. Eurosibirian plant. F3, R2, N3, H3, D4, L4, T3, K3. Flowering time: 4.

b. **Willow,** *Salix* L.
Leaves entire, oval to lanceolate, frequently with stipules.

Dwarf willow, *Salix herbacea* L. (Plate 18.1)
Carpet-forming shrub, creeping underground; leaves rounded, thin, finely dentate, light green on both sides. Snow-patches, loose grassland; soils poor in calcium, covered by snow for a long time; 1800–3000 m; rather common (esp. in the inner ranges). Arctic-Alpine plant. F4, R2, N2, H4, D4, L5, T1, K2. Flowering time: 7–8.

Blunt-leaved willow, *Salix retusa* L. (Plate 18.2)
Carpet-forming shrub creeping over the ground; smelling like valerian; leaves up to 2.5 cm long, oval, smooth-edged, shiny above, dark-green below; fruits 3–5 mm long. Snow-patches, scree; base-containing soils covered by snow for a long time; 1500–2800 m; rather common. Mountain plant of Central and Southern Europe. F3, R3, N3, H3, D3, L5, T1, K3. Flowering time: 6–7.
Protected: NW.

Thyme-leaved willow, *Salix serpyllifolia* Scop.
Differs from the blunt-leaved willow in the following characters: leaves up to 0.8 cm long; fruits 2–3 mm long. Coarse scree; stony, wind-exposed soils; 1800–3000 m; common. Alpine plant. F2, R4, N2, H3, D3, L5, T1, K4. Flowering time: 6–7.

Net-leaved willow, *Salix reticulata* L. (Plate 18.3)
Carpet-forming shrub creeping over the ground; leaves oval, up to 4.5 cm long, smooth-edged, distinctly net-veined, deep green above, strongly pilose and grey to white underneath. Stabilized scree, snow-patches; humid, calcium-rich soils covered by snow for a long time; 1500–2800 m; rather common. Arctic-Alpine plant. F3, R4, N2, H3, D3, L4, T1, K2. Flowering time: 7–8.
Protected: NW.

Swiss willow, *Salix helvetica* Vill. (Plate 18.4)
Shrub 0.4–1.5 m tall; leaves lanceolate, smooth-edged, whitely pilose underneath. Talus slopes; soils poor in calcium with late-lying snow; 1800–2500 m; not common. Mountain plant of Central and Southern Europe (western). F4, R2, N2, H4, D2, L4, T2, K2. Flowering time: 6–7.

Bay willow, *Salix pentandra* L. (Fig. 35H, p. 132)
Shrub or tree up to 12 m tall; leaves oval, deep green and shiny above, lighter underneath. River-valley woods, banks of streams; sandy or gravelly soils, often flooded; 1500–2000 m; not common (only in valleys

of the Central and Southern Alps). Eurosibirian plant. F4↑w, R3, N3, H4, D3, L4, T2, K4. Flowering time: 6–7.
Protected: BE.

Large-leaved willow, *Salix appendiculata* Vill. *(S. grandifolia* Ser.)
(Fig. 35K, p. 132)
Shrub or tree up to 6 m tall; leaves lanceolate, green and slightly shiny above, very hairy and therefore grey-green underneath. Woods on slopes, green alder thicket, tall-herb stands; humid soils; 800–2100 m; rather common. Alpine plant. F4w, R3, N3, H4, D5, L3, T2, K3. Flowering time: 5–7.
Protected: AG, BE, BL, GE, GL, JU, NW, SG, SO, SZ, TG, *UR,* ZH.

Hastate willow, *Salix hastata* L. (Fig. 35I, p. 132)
Prostrate shrub, up to 1.5 m tall; leaves lanceolate, finely and regularly dentate, often blue-green underneath. Bushes; in flushes or temporarily flooded soils; 1400–2500 m; rather common. Eurosibirian plant. F4w, R3, N3, H3, D3, L3, T2, K3. Flowering time: 6–8.
Protected: BE, GL, SG, SZ, *UR.*

16th family: **birch family,** *Betulaceae*

Trees, bushes, or shrubs; flowers in catkins; male and female flowers on the same plant. In the Alps 8 species occur, amongst them **hazel** *(Coryllus avellana* L.) which is not presented here.

a. **Alder,** *Alnus* Miller
Fruit groups cone-like. Alders form root nodules inhabited by specialized bacteria which fix the atmospheric nitrogen.

Green alder, *Alnus viridis* (Chaix) DC. (Fig. 35M, p. 132)
Bush up to 3 m tall; leaves oval, pointed, double-dentate, green on both sides. Slopes, banks of streams, avalanche paths; humid, nutrient-rich soils poor in calcium; 1000–2300 m; common. Mountain plant of Central and Southern Europe (eastern). F4w, R2, N4, H3, D4, L4, T2, K2. Flowering time: 4–6.

Grey alder, *Alnus incana* (L.) Moench (Fig. 35N, p. 132)
Tree up to 20 m tall; leaves as those of the green alder but grey-green underneath. River-valley woods, forests on slopes; intermittently wet, often temporarily flooded soils; 300–1700 m; rather common. Central European plant. F4w, R4, N4, H3, D4, L3, T3, K3. Flowering time: 4.

b. **Birch,** *Betula* L.
Silver birch, *Betula pendula* Roth *(B. verrucosa* Ehrh.)
(Fig. 35P, p. 132)
Tree up to 25 m tall; leaves nearly triangular, toothed; bark white at the canopy level. Fruits in thin catkins, hanging. Forests, banks of streams or rivers, rocky bushes; meagre soils; 200–2000 m; rather common. Eurosibirian plant. Fx, Rx, N2, Hx, Dx, L4, T3, K3. Flowering time: 5.

17th family: **beech family,** *Fagaceae*

Trees; male flowers in catkins, female flowers surrounded by a «cupule»; fruits large. The beech family includes beech, oak, and chestnut.

Beech, *Fagus* L.
Beech, *Fagus silvatica* L. (Fig. 35E, p. 132)
Tree up to 40 m tall; leaves smooth-edged or sinuate, with long silky hairs on margins. Woods; medium soils; 300–1700 m; common, often forming stands alone or with silver fir (nearly exclusively in the outer ranges). Central European plant. F3, Rx, N3, H3, D4, L1, T3, K2. Flowering time: 5.

18th family: **dock family,** *Polygonaceae*

Herbs; stem segmented by nodes; leaves with membranous sheath encircling the stem; flowers small. The family is represented in the Alps by 4 genera corresponding to about 15 species.

a. **Dock,** *Rumex* L.
Six green or reddish tepals; the three inner ones much larger when in fruit.

Snow dock, *Rumex nivalis* Hegetschw. (Plate 19.1)
7–20 cm tall; leaves small, up to 4 cm long, hastate, the outer leaves rounded-oval. Coarse scree, snow-patches; stony, calcium-rich soils; 2000–2700 m; not common. Eastern Alpine plant. F4, R4, N2, H1, D3, L5, T1, K2. Flowering time: 7–8.

French sorrel or **rubble dock,** *Rumex scutatus* L. (Plate 19.2)
20–50 cm tall; leaves hastate, up to 5 cm long, often bluish. Talus slopes, coarse scree; stony, dry soils; 300–2200 m; rather common. European mountain plant. F2, R3, N2, H1, D2, L4, T2, K3. Flowering time: 5–7.

Mountain sorrel, *Rumex arifolius* All. *(R. alpester* Jacq.)
(Plate 19.3)
30–80 cm tall; leaves hastate but mostly with rounded tips, lower leaves long-petiolate. Tall-herb stands, fertilized meadows, forests; nutrient-rich, humid soils; 1200–2200 m; common. Eurosibirian plant. F4, R3, N4, H4, D4, L3, T2, K3. Flowering time: 7–8.

Monk's rhubarb, *Rumex alpinus* L. (Plate 19.4)
30–100 cm tall; leaves rounded-oval, cordate at the base, sinuate, up to 30 cm long, with long petioles. Resting places of animals, tall-herb stands, about alp-huts; humid, overmanured soils; 1000–2300 m; common. Mountain plant of Central and Southern Europe. F4, R3, N5, H4, D4, L4, T2. K3. Flowering time: 7–8.

b. **Mountain sorrel,** *Oxyria* Hill
   Mountain sorrel, *Oxyria digyna* (L.) Hill   (Plate 20.1)
   5–15 cm tall; leaves small, reniform; differs from the genus *Rumex* in the four perianth segments. Scree, moraines; stony soils poor in calcium; 1600–2900 m; not common. Arctic-Alpine plant. F3, R2, N2, H2, D2, L5, T1, K2. Flowering time: 7–8.

c. **Knotweed** or **knotgrass,** *Polygonum* L.
   Flowers mostly with 5 tepals, white or red, in spicate or paniculate inflorescences.

   Viviparous knotweed or **alpine bistort,** *Polygonum viviparum* L.
                                                                    (Plate 20.2)
   10–25 cm tall; with serpentinous rhizome; leaves narrowly lanceolate, grey-green underneath; flowers white to pink, lower flowers often with deep brown bulbils in axils (bulbils fall off and grow into new plants); inflorescences thin, spicate. Meadows, pastures, stands of carpet-forming shrubs; meagre soils; 1000–3000 m; common. Arctic-Alpine plant. F3, R3, N2, H4, D4, L4, T1, K4. Flowering time: 6–8.

   Common bistort, *Polygonum bistorta* L.   (Plate 20.3)
   30–80 cm tall; with serpentinous rhizome; leaves oval, cordate or truncate at the base, whitish green underneath; flowers pink, rarely white, in cylindric spicate inflorescence. Meadows, swamps, tall-herb stands; humid, nutrient-rich soils; 800–2000 m; common. Eurosibirian plant. F4w, R3, N4, H4, D4, L3, T2, K3. Flowering time: 6–7.

   Alpine knotgrass, *Polygonum alpinum* All.   (Plate 20.4)
   30–50 cm tall; leaves lanceolate; flowers white, in a multifloral, pyramid-shaped paniculate inflorescence. Meadows; nutrient-rich soils poor in bases; 800–1800 m; not common (nearly exclusively in the southern inner ranges). Eurasiatic mountain plant. F3, R2, N4, H4, D4, L4, T3, K2. Flowering time: 6–7.

19th family: **sandalwood family,** *Santalaceae*

Mostly tropical parasites and semi-parasites with small, inconspicuous flowers. Only one genus of the family is represented in the Alps.

a. **Bastard toadflax,** *Thesium* L.
   Alpine bastard toadflax, *Thesium alpinum* L.   (Plate 21.1)
   10–30 cm tall; leaves small, narrowly lanceolate, glabrous, mostly unilaterally arranged on the stem; flowers with 4 white tepals. Pastures, meadows; intermittently dry, meagre soils; 600–2600 m; rather common. North European-Alpine plant. F3w, R3, N2, H4, D4, L4, T2, K3. Flowering time: 6–7.

20th family: goosefoot family, *Chenopodiaceae*

Lower leaves on the stem often opposite, upper ones alternate; flowers small, inconspicuous, mostly greenish. The family includes many weeds, plants growing in resting places of animals as well as halophytes, but only a few grow higher in the Alps.

a. **Goosefoot,** *Chenopodium* L.

All-good, or **good King Henry,** *Chenopodium bonus-henricus* L.

(Plate 21.2)

15–60 cm tall; slightly mealy on the surface; leaves hastate, up to 10 cm long; flowers in a compact, spicate inflorescence. Resting places of animals, about alp-huts, on borders of paths; nutrient-rich soils; 600–2400 m; rather common. Central European plant. F2, R3, N5, H3, D4, L4, T3, K3. Flowering time: 6–8.

21st family: **pink family,** *Caryophyllaceae*

Leaves opposite; flowers mostly with 5 sepals and 5 free petals as well as 1, mostly superior, ovary. The family is represented in the Alps by about 100 species.

a. **Gypsophila,** *Gypsophila* L.

Gypsophila, *Gypsophila repens* L. (Plate 21.4)

5–25 cm tall; leaves narrowly lanceolate, bluish-green; sepals united; petals white to pink, emarginate, without corolla appendage. Scree, loose grassland; stony, calcium-rich soils; 800–2600 m; not common. Mountain plant of Central and Southern Europe. F3w, R5, N2, H1, D3, L5, T2, K3. Flowering time: 6–8.

b. **Campion** or **catchfly,** *Silene* L.

Sepals united; petals emarginate or divided, often with corolla appendage; styles 3 or 5. There are about 12 species in the Alps.

Rock campion, *Silene rupestris* L. (Plate 21.3)

10–25 cm tall; leaves oval-lanceolate, bluish-green; petals white to pink. Rocky slopes, grassland, light woods; dry, stony soils poor in calcium; 800–2600 m; rather common (esp. in the central and southern ranges). North European-Alpine plant. F2, R2, N2, H3, D3, L4, T2, K4. Flowering time: 6–8.

Nottingham catchfly, *Silene nutans* L. (Plate 22.1)

20–60 cm tall; stem sticky in the upper part; petals white outside, often reddish or greenish; flowers unilaterally oriented, nodding. Dry meadows, light woods; dry, meagre soils; 300–2400 m; rather common. Eurosibirian plant. F2, R3, N2, H3, D4, L3, T3, K4. Flowering time: 6–8.

Bladder campion, *Silene vulgaris* (Moench) Garcke *(S. cucubalus* Wib.) (Plate 22.2)
20–50 cm tall; leaves lanceolate, bluish-green; calyx inflated; petals white (seldom slightly pink). Meadows, scree; dry, meagre, often stony soils; 400–2800 m; rather common. Central European plant. F2, R3, N2, H3, D3, L3, T3, K3. Flowering time: 6–9.
On calciferous scree grow taxa with prostrate stems.

Fountain catchfly, *Silene quadridentata* (Murray) Pers. *Heliosperma quadridentatum* [Murray] Sch. a. Th.) (Plate 22.3)
5–20 cm tall; leaves very narrowly lanceolate, green; petals white. Rocky crevices, scree, ravines; humid, stony, calcium-rich soils; 1400–2200 m; rather rare (mostly in the outer ranges). Mountain plant of Central and Southern Europe. F4, R4, N2, H3, D2, L3, T2, K2. Flowering time: 6–8.

Scapeless moss campion, *Silene exscapa* All. (Plate 22.4)
Forms dense flat cushions; leaves 3–6 mm long, tough; calyx gradually tapering at the base, 3.5–6 mm long; petals 5–10 mm long, light purple-red. Ridges, open grassland; stony, often wind-exposed soils poor in calcium; 2300–3300 m; not common (nearly exclusively in the inner ranges). Mountain plant of Central and Southern Europe (western). F2, R2, N1, H2, D3, L5, T1, K4. Flowering time: 7–8.
Protected: *AI, GL, NW, OW,* SG.

Stemless moss campion, *Silene acaulis* (L.) Jacq.
Differs from scapeless moss campion in the following features: leaves up to 12 mm long, soft; calyx 4–8 mm long, suddenly narrowed at the base; petals 6–14 mm long, often deep purple. Open grassland, scree; base-rich soils; 1700–2900 m; rather common. Arctic-Alpine plant. F3, R4, N1, H3, D3, L5, T1, K3. Flowering time: 6–8.
Protected: *AI, GL, NW, OW,* SG.

Red alpine catchfly, *Silene liponeura* Neumayr *(Viscaria alpina* [L.] G. Don) (Plate 23.1)
5–15 cm tall; leaves narrowly lanceolate, glabrous; flowers terminal, grouped head-like; petals about 1 cm long, red. Grassland; dry, often wind-exposed soils; 2300–2700 m; rare. Arctic-Alpine plant. F2, R3, N2, H3, D3, L5, T1, K3. Flowering time: 7–8.
Protected: *Ao.*

Jupiter catchfly, *Silene flos-jovis* (L.) Clairv. *(Lychnis flos-jovis* [L.] Desr.) (Plate 23.2)
20–60 cm tall; whitely tomentose; flowers measuring 2–3.5 cm in diameter, in an umbel-like inflorescence; petals light purple. Bushes, light woods; dry soils poor in calcium; 1100–2000 m; rare (only in the southern ranges). Western Alpine plant. F2, R2, N3, H3, D3, L4, T2, K4. Flowering time: 6–7.
Protected: R. GR, *TI, VS*/Ao.

Red campion, *Silene dioeca* (L.) Clairv. *Melandrium dioecum* [L.] Sim., *M. diurnum* [Sibth.] Fr.) (Plate 23.3)
30–90 cm tall; leaves broadly lanceolate, hairy; petals 5–25 mm long, purple-red; flowers only with stamens or only with ovary, on different plants. Meadows, tall-herb stands; humid, nutrient-rich soils; 400–2200 m; common. Eurosibirian plant. F4, R3, N4, H3, D4, L3, T3, K3. Flowering time: 5–9.
Protected: *OW*.

c. **Soapwort,** *Saponaria* L.
Rock soapwort, *Saponaria ocymoides* L. (Plate 23.4)
10–25 cm tall; creeping over the ground; leaves up to 3 cm long, glabrous, with ciliate margins; calyx with glandular hairs; petals 12–18 mm long, with corolla appendages, red. Light woods, rocky slopes; stony, loose, base-containing soils; 500–2000 m; not common. Mountain plant of Central and Southern Europe (western). F2, R4, N2, H2, D3↑, L4, T3, K4. Flowering time: 6–9.

d. **Pink,** *Dianthus* L.
Leaves narrow; sepals united, surrounded at the base by 2 or 4 scale-shaped leaves; petals dentate or laciniate, without corolla appendages. The family is represented in the Alps by about 10 species.

Superb pink, *Dianthus superbus* L. (Plate 24.1)
30–60 cm tall; flowers large, measuring 3–5 cm in diameter, pink, with greenish spot and red hairs inside, fragrant; petals deeply laciniate. Meadows; stony, meagre soils; 500–2300 m; not common. Eurosibirian plant. F3w, R3, N2, H3, D4, L4, T2, K3. Flowering time: 6–9.
Protected: *AG*, AR, BE, *BL*, *GE*, JU, *NW*, *OW*, SG, *SH*, *TG*, *ZH*/L/F.

Wood pink, *Dianthus silvester* Wulfen (Plate 24.2)
10–30 cm tall; flowers measuring 1.5–2 cm in diameter, pink; petals dentate. Cliffs, rocky slopes; dry, stony soils; 300–2400 m; not common. Mountain plant of Central and Southern Europe. F1, R3, N2, H2, D1, L5, T3, K4. Flowering time: 6–7.
Protected: *AG*, AR, *BE$_n$*, *GE*, *GL*, *JU*, *NW*, *OW*, SG, *SH*, SZ, *UR*, *ZH*/Li/L.

Glacial pink, *Dianthus glacialis* Hänke (Plate 24.3)
2–8 cm tall; flowers measuring 1.5–2 cm in diameter, purple, with darker spots or stripes; petals dentate. Ridges, cliffs; stony, wind-exposed soils containing calcium; 2400–2800 m; rare (only east of the line: Lenzerheide–Avers). Mountain plant of Central and Southern Europe (eastern). F2, R4, N1, H3, D3, L5, T1, K4. Flowering time: 7–8.
Protected: R. *CH*/L, So.

Carthusian pink, *Dianthus carthusianorum* L. (Plate 24.4)
20–40 cm tall; flowers measuring 1–2 cm in diameter, grouped head-like, dark-purple with dark hairs; petals dentate. Dry meadows, light woods, cliffs; dry, loose soils; 300–2100 m; rather rare (very rare in the northern ranges). Central European plant. F2, R3, N2, H3, D3, L4, T3, K4. Flowering time: 6–9.
Protected: AG, AR, BE, *BL*, GE, JU, *NW*, *OW*, *SH*, *TG*, *ZH*/Ti, Li/L.

156

e. **Mouse-ear** or **chickweed,** *Cerastium* L.
Sepals free with membranous margins; petals white, emarginate.
There are about 10 species in the Alps; they are difficult to distinguish
from each other.

Rigid mouse-ear, *Cerastium strictum* Hänke   (Plate 25.1)
5–15 cm tall; leaves very narrowly lanceolate, green; petals twice as
long as sepals, 6–11 mm long. Pastures, meadows, rocky slopes, stone-
walls; dry, stony soils; 1000–2800 m; rather common. Mountain plant
of Central and Southern Europe. F2, R3, N2, H3, D3, L5, T2, K4.
Flowering time: 6–7.

Starwort mouse-ear, *Cerastium trigynum* Vill. *(C. cerastioides* [L.]
Brit.)   (Plate 25.2)
2–10 cm tall; creeping over the ground; leaves very narrowly lanceolate, green; petals 1.5–2 times as long as the sepals, 7–12 mm long.
Snow-patches, resting places of animals, flushes; nitrogen-rich soils
poor in calcium, with late-lying snow; 1700–2800 m; rather common.
Arctic-Alpine plant. F4, R2, N4, H4, D4, L4, T1, K2. Flowering time:
7–8.

Broad-leaved mouse-ear, *Cerastium latifolium* L.   (Plate 25.3)
3–12 cm tall; forms loose mats; leaves oval to lanceolate, widest in the
lower half, blue-green; petals 1.5–2.25 times as long as the sepals,
12–18 mm long. Talus, scree; stony soils rich in calcium; 1800–3000 m;
not common. Plant of the western Alps. F3, R4, N2, H2, D2↑, L5, T1,
K3. Flowering time: 7–8.

One-flowered mouse-ear, *Cerastium uniflorum* Clairv.   (Plate 25.4)
May be distinguished from the former species by the leaves which are
green and widest in the upper half. Talus, scree; stony soils poor in
calcium; 2000–3400 m; not common (nearly exclusively in the inner
ranges). Plant of the eastern Alps. F3, R2, N2, H2, D2, L5, T1, K3.
Flowering time: 7–8.

f. **Sandwort,** *Minuartia* Loefling
Leaves needle-shaped; sepals free, with narrow membranous margins; petals white, smooth-edged (may also be missing). The genus is
represented in the Alps by about 15 species which often are inconspicuous.

Mossy cyphal sandwort, *Minuarita sedoides* (L.) Hiern *Cherleria
sedoides* L.)   (Plate 26.1)
Forms compact, flat cushions; flowers measuring less than 0.5 cm in
diameter, greenish (petals missing). Grassland, ridges, scree; open stony
soils; 2200–3000 m; rather common (esp. in the inner ranges). Mountain plant of Central and Southern Europe. F3, R3, N1, H3, D3, L5,
T1, K4. Flowering time: 7–8.
Protected: *GL.*

Curved sandwort, *Minuartia recurva* (All.) Sch. and Th. (Plate 26.3)
5–10 cm tall; grass-like; leaves sickle-shaped; flowers measuring
0.5–1 cm in diameter, white; sepals with 5 veins. Grassland, hilltops,

coarse scree; stony, wind-exposed soils poor in calcium; 2100–2900 m; not common (only in the inner ranges). Mountain plant of Central and Southern Europe. F2, R2, N2, H2, D3, L5, T1, K4. Flowering time: 7–8.

Spring sandwort, *Minuartia verna* (L.) Hiern (Fig. 41A)
Differs from the curved sandwort as follows: forms loose tufts; leaves straight; sepals with 3 veins. Open grassland, coarse scree; stony soils containing calcium; 1300–3000 m; rather common. European mountain plant. F2, R4, N1, H2, D2, L5, T2, K3. Flowering time: 6–8.

Larch-leaved sandwort, *Minuartia laricifolia* (L.) Sch. and Th.
(Fig. 41B)
8–20 cm tall; forms loose tufts; leaves 1–2 cm long, straight; flowers measuring 1–1.5 cm in diameter, white; sepals with 3–5 veins. Rocky slopes, light woods; stony soils poor in calcium; 600–2000 m; not common (nearly exclusively in the southern ranges). Plant of the western Alps. F2, R2, N2, H3, D3, L4, T3, K4. Flowering time: 7–8.

Fig. 41. A: spring sandwort *(Minuartia verna)*.
B: larch-leaved sandwort *(Minuartia laricifolia)*. ⅓ × .

g. **Sandwort,** *Arenaria* L.
Differs from Minuartia in its oval to lanceolate leaves.
Two-flowered sandwort, *Arenaria biflora* L. (Plate 26.2)
Prostrate plant forming tufts; leaves ciliate at the base, the distal part rounded; flowers measuring 0.7–1 cm in diameter. Snow-patches, open grassland; humid soils poor in calcium, with late-lying snow; 1700–3000 m; not common (nearly exclusively in the inner ranges). Mountain plant of Central and Southern Europe. F4, R2, N2, H4, D4, L4, T1, K2. Flowering time: 7–8.
Protected: *F.*

158

Fringed sandwort, *Arenaria ciliata* L.
May be distinguished from the former species by the sharp-tipped leaves. Open grassland, coarse scree; stony, calcium-containing soils; 1800–3000 m; not common (nearly exclusively in the inner ranges; the outer ranges are inhabited by a closely related taxon). Mountain plant of Central and Southern Europe (eastern). F3, R4, N2, H3, D3, L4, T1, K4. Flowering time: 7–8.

h. **Moehringia,** *Moehringia* L.
   Ciliated moehringia, *Moehringia ciliata* (Scop.) D. T.   (Plate 26.4)
Prostrate plant, creeping over the ground; leaves needle-like, with fringed margins; flowers measuring 0.7–1 cm in diameter, white. Coarse scree, talus; stony, calcium-rich soils; 1600–3000 m; not common. Mountain plant of Central and Southern Europe. F3, R4, N2, H2, D2, L5, T1, K3. Flowering time: 7–8.

22nd family: **buttercup family,** *Ranunculaceae*

Mostly poisonous; leaves sheath-like at the base; several free ovaries per flower. The family is represented in the Alps by more than 80 species.

a. **Peony,** *Paeonia* L.
   Wild peony, *Paeonia officinalis* L.   (Plate 27.1)
30–90 cm tall; leaves large, divided, biternate; flowers measuring 8–15 cm in diameter, purple. Grassy slopes, light woods; stony, calcium-rich soils; 800–1200 m; very rare (in Switzerland only at the Generoso). Mountain plant of Central and Southern Europe (southern). F2, R4, N3, H3, D3, L3, T3, K2. Flowering time: 5–6.
   Protected: E. *CH/Ao, Bz, L/F.*

b. **Hellebore,** *Helleborus* L.
   Christmas rose, *Helleborus niger* L.   (Plate 27.2)
10–20 cm tall; basal leaves leathery, with 9 lanceolate, dentate leaflets; flowers measuring 4–8 cm in diameter, white to pink. Bushy slopes, light woods; stony, dry, calcium-rich soils; 500–1800 m; rare (only in the southern calciferous Alps). Plant of the Southern Alps. F2, R4, N3, H4, D3, L3, T3, K3. Flowering time: 3–5.
   Protected: *TI/Ti/Bg, Bs, Co, So, Va/F.*

c. **Globe flower,** *Trollius* L.
   Globe flower, *Trollius europaeus* L.   (Plate 27.3)
10–60 cm tall; leaves divided, palmate; flowers yellow, measuring 2.5–3.5 cm in diameter, virtually globular, with many petal-like tepals. Meadows, banks of streams; intermittently humid, humous soils; 700–2400 m; rather common. Eurosibirian plant. F4w, R3, N3, H4, D5, L4, T2, K3. Flowering time: 6–7.
   Protected: *AG, BL, SH, SO, TG, ZH.*

d. **Marsh-marigold,** *Caltha* L.
Marsh-marigold, *Caltha palustris* L. (Plate 27.4)
15–30 cm tall; leaves rounded-reniform, dentate; flowers measuring 2–3 cm in diameter, yellow, with 5 petal-like tepals. Swampy meadows, mires, banks of streams and rivers, wet peaty soils; 400–2400 m; common. Eurosibirian-North American plant. F5, R3, N3, H4, D5, L3, T3, K3. Flowering time: 5–7.
Protected: GE, OW.

e. **Larkspur,** *Delphinium* L.
Alpine larkspur, *Delphinium elatum* L. (Plate 28.2)
60–150 cm tall; leaves large, palmately divided; flowers blue-violet with spreading, 1.5–3 cm long spurs, in a loose, racemose inflorescence. Tall-herb stands; humid, nutrient-rich, calciferous soils; 1200–2000 m; rare (only in the central and northern ranges). Eurosibirian plant. F4, R4, N4, H4, D4, L3, T2, K2. Flowering time: 7–8.
Protected: *CH*/Li/*Ao*.

f. **Aconite,** *Aconitum* L.
Leaves large, palmately divided; flowers helmet-shaped, without spurs. The genus comprises numerous species which are partly difficult to distinguish between and thus not classified in detail here.

Paniculate aconite, *Aconitum paniculatum* Lam. (Plate 28.1)
80–150 cm tall; flowers blue or lilac, with helmet higher than broad, in a loose branched raceme. Tall-herb stands; humid, nutrient-rich soils; 1200–2100 m; not common. Mountain plant of Central and Southern Europe (eastern). F4, R3, N4, H4, D4, L3, T2, K2. Flowering time: 7–9.
Protected: GL, NW, *OW*/Ti.

Common monkshood, *Aconitum napellus* L. s.l. (Plate 28.3)
50–150 cm tall; flowers blue or violet, with helmet broader than high, in a compact raceme. Tall-herb stands, resting places of animals, about alp-huts; humid, nutrient-rich soils; 800–2600 m; common. North European-Alpine plant group. F4, R3, N3, H4, D4, L3, T2, K3. Flowering time: 6–8.
Protected: *AG, BL,* GL, NW, *OW, SH,* TG, ZH/Ti/*Ao*.

Wolfbane aconite, *Aconitum lycoctonum* L. s.l. (Plate 28.4)
50–150 cm tall; flowers yellow, with a narrow helmet much higher than broad, in a racemose or paniculate inflorescence. Tall-herb stands, forests; humid, nutrient-rich soils; 500–2300 m; common. Eurosibirian plant group. F4, R3, N4, H4, D4, L3, T2, K3. Flowering time: 6–8.
Protected: *BL, GE,* GL, NW, *OW, SH,* TG, ZH/Ti/Ao.

Poisonous aconite, *Aconitum anthora* L. (Fig. 42)
25–50 cm tall; flowers yellow, with helmet about as long as broad, in a compact racemose inflorescence. Pastures, bushy slopes; dry calciferous soils; 1000–1800 m; rare (only in the southern Jura and the southernmost Alpine ranges). Mountain plant of Central and Southern Europe. F2, R4, N3, H3, D3, L4, T2, K3. Flowering time: 8–9.
Protected: R.

Fig. 42. Poisonous aconite *(Aconitum anthora)*.
⅓ × (from *6.1.k.*).

g. **Columbine,** *Aquilegia* L.

Leaves triternately compound; flowers large, nodding, with 5 petal-like tepals, each with a spur. The Alpine flora includes various, partly rare species of the genus.

Common columbine, *Aquilegia vulgaris* L. s.l.   (Plate 29.1)

30–80 cm tall; flowers deep violet or pink, measuring 3–5 cm in diameter, with a 1–1.5 cm long, backward directed spur. Light woods, humid meadows, bushes; intermittently humid, base-rich soils; 300–2100 m; not common. Eurosibirian plant group. F3w, R4, N3, H3, D3, L3, T3, K3. Flowering time: 6–7.

Protected: AG, *AR,* BE, BL, GE, GL, JU, NW, *OW,* SG, TG, ZH/*B*/Ti/*Ao,* L.

Alpine columbine, *Aquilegia alpina* L.   (Plate 29.2)

10–60 cm tall; flowers blue, measuring 6–9 cm in diameter, with 1.5–2 cm long spurs bent at the tip. Meadows, bushes; humid, calcium-rich soils; 1600–2500 m; rare. Plant of the western Alps. F3, R4, N3, H3, D4, L3, T2, K3. Flowering time: 6–7.

Protected: V*. V. CH/*B*/Vo, Ti/*Li*/*Ao,* L, *So*/*F.*

h. **Clematis** or **virgin's-bower,** *Clematis* L.

Alpine virgin's-bower, *Clematis alpina* (L.) Miller *(Atragene alpina* L.)
          (Plate 29.3)

Dwarf climbing shrub up to 2 m tall; leaves opposite, biternately compound; flowers measuring 4–6 cm in diameter, nodding, with 4 blue, corolla-like outer tepals, and 10–20 small, white inner tepals; fruits with persistent, long, plumose styles. Light woods, bushes;

161

humous soils; 1000–2200 m; rare. Mountain plant of Central and Southern Europe (eastern). F3, R3, N2, H4, D3, L3, T2, K2. Flowering time: 5–7.
Protected: *BE, FR, GR, TI*/Ti/*Ao,* L/*F.*

i. Hepatica, *Hepatica* Miller
Hepatica, *Hepatica triloba* Gilib. *(Anemone hepatica* L.)
(Plate 29.4)
5–15 cm tall; leaves radical, trilobed, rust-brown underneath; flowers blue, with 3 calyx-like, and 5–10 corolla-like tepals. Forests, bushy slopes; calciferous soils; 300–1900 m; not common. Central European plant. F2, R4, N2, H4, D3, L2, T4, K4. Flowering time: 4–6.
Protected: AG, BE, *BL,* BS, JU, *SO,* TG, ZH.

k. Anemone, *Anemone* L.
Leaves 3–5-lobed or divided; some leaves radical; stem leaves 3–4, whorled; flowers with 5 or more corolla-like tepals; no calyx-like tepals; fruits without persistent long styles.

Mt. Baldo Anemone, *Anemone baldensis* Turra (Plate 30.1)
6–20 cm tall; leaves with 3 petiolate, triternate leaflets; flowers single, terminal, measuring 2.5–4 cm in diameter, white, with 6–10 corolla-like tepals. Open grassland; stony, calciferous soils; 1800–3000 m; rare. Mountain plant of Central and Southern Europe. F2, R4, N2, H2, D3, L5, T1, K3. Flowering time: 7–8.
Protected: *Ti*/*L.*

Narcissus-flowered anemone, *Anemone narcissiflora* L. (Plate 30.2)
20–40 cm tall; leaflets palmately divided with long, narrow segments; flowers 3–8, in a terminal umbel-like group, measuring 2–3 cm in diameter, white, with 5–6 corolla-like tepals. Meadows; base-rich soils with medium nutrient content; 1300–2300 m; not common. Eurosibirian-North American plant. F3w, R4, N3, H3, D4, L4, T2, K3. Flowering time: 6–7.
Protected: *NW, OW, TI*/*B*/Ti/Vo/Li/*L.*

l. Pasqueflower, *Pulsatilla* Miller
Differs from the genus *Anemone* as follows: style persistent, elongated and feathery, forming a mop of hair when old; flowers villous outside.

Mountain pasqueflower, *Pulsatilla montana* (Hoppe) Rchb.
(Anemone montana Hoppe) (Plate 30.3)
15–35 cm tall; leaf segments not wider than 2 mm; corolla-like tepals deep violet, 2–3 cm long. Dry meadows; dry, calciferous soils; 500–1800 m; rare (only in the inner Alpine valleys). Mountain plant of Central and Southern Europe (eastern). F1, R4, N2, H3, D3, L4, T4, K5. Flowering time: 4–6.
Protected: *GR*/V/L.

Haller's pasqueflower, *Pulsatilla halleri* (All.) Willd. *(Anemone halleri* All.) (Plate 30.4)
10–30 cm tall; leaf segments mostly 2–5 mm wide; corolla-like tepals light-violet, 2–3 cm long. Open grassland, rocky slopes; dry, calciferous soils; 1300–2400 m; very rare (in Switzerland only the Mattertal). Mountain plant of Central and Southern Europe (eastern). F1, R4, N2, H3, D3, L4, T2, K5. Flowering time: 5–7.
Protected: R. Ao/F.

White alpine pasqueflower, *Pulsatilla alpina* (L.) Schrank *(Anemone alpina* L.) (Plate 31.1)
10–30 cm tall; leaf segments mostly 5–10 mm wide, dentate; corolla-like tepals white, tinged violet at the outside, 2–3 cm long. Pastures, meadows; stony, calciferous soils; 1400–2500 m; not common (above all in the outer ranges). Mountain plant of Central and Southern Europe. F3, R4, N3, H3, D3, L4, T2, K3. Flowering time: 5–7.
Protected: AR, *BE_n*, BE, GL, NW, *OW,* SG, SZ, *TI/B/*Ti, Vo/Li/L.

Yellow alpine pasqueflower, *Pulsatilla sulphurea* (L.) D. T. and Sarnth. *(Anemone sulphurea* L., *A. apiifolia* Scop.) (Plate 31.2)
May be distinguished from the white alpine pasqueflower by its sulphur-yellow flowers. Meadows, pastures, light woods; soils poor in calcium; 1100–2700 m; rather common. Mountain plant of Central and Southern Europe. F3, R2, N3, H4, D4, L3, T2, K3. Flowering time: 5–7.
Protected: BE, GL, *NW, OW,* SG/*B*/Ti, Vo/*Li*/Ao, *Bz,* L, *Tn.*

Spring pasqueflower, *Pulsatilla vernalis* (L.) Miller *(Anemone vernalis* L.) (Plate 31.4)
5–15 cm tall; tips of the leaf segments 3–6 mm wide, dentate; corolla-like tepals white, tinged blue, pink, or violet outside, 1.5–3 cm long. Grassland, dwarf shrub stands; dry soils poor in nutrients and bases; 1400–2600 m; rather common. North European-Alpine plant. F2, R2, N2, H4, D3, L4, T2, K3. Flowering time: 4–7.
Protected: BE, *FR, GL, NW, OW,* UR/*B*/*Ti*/*Li*/Ao, L.

m. **Callianthemum,** *Callianthemum* Meyer
Coriander-leaved callianthemum, *Callianthemum coriandrifolium* Rchb. (Plate 31.3)
5–25 cm tall; leaves 1–2-pinnate, blue-green; 5–6 calyx- like, and 6–12 white, corolla-like tepals. Grassland; humid, calciferous soils with late-lying snow; 1600–2600 m; rare (nearly exclusively in the inner ranges). Mountain plant of Central and Southern Europe. F4, R4, N2, H3, D4, L4, T1, K2. Flowering time: 6–7.

n. **Buttercup** or **crowfoot,** *Ranunculus* L.
Leaves entire or palmately divided; cauline leaves alternate; flowers mostly with 5 calyx-like, and 5 corolla-like tepals; fruits without persistent, elongated style. The genus is represented in the Alps by about 30 species, partly difficult to distinguish between.

163

Pyrenean buttercup, *Ranunculus pyrenaeus* L.   (Plate 32.1)
5–15 cm tall; leaves narrowly lanceolate, smooth-edged; flowers white, often with less than 5 corolla-like tepals. Pastures; humid soils poor in calcium; 1700–2800 m; not common (very rare in the outer ranges). Mountain plant of Central and Southern Europe (western). F3w, R3, N2, H3, D4, L4, T1, K3. Flowering time: 6–7.
Protected: No.

Grass-of-Parnassus-leaved buttercup, *Ranunculus parnassifolius* L.
(Plate 32.2)
5–15 cm tall; leaves broadly lanceolate to cordate, smooth-edged; flowers white. Scree; stony, humid, calciferous soils; 1900–2800 m; rare (only in the inner ranges). Mountain plant of Central and Southern Europe (western). F3, R5, N2, H2, D2↑, L5, T1, K2. Flowering time: 7.
Protected: *FR.*

Alpine buttercup, *Ranunculus alpester* L.   (Plate 32.3)
5–15 cm tall; leaves palmately divided, glabrous, leaf segments crenate; flowers white. Snow-patches, stabilized scree, open grassland; humid, stony, calcium-rich soils; 1700–2800 m; rather common (above all in the outer ranges). Mountain plant of Central and Southern Europe. F4, R4, N2, H3, D2, L4, T1, K2. Flowering time: 6–8.
Protected: *NE.*

Glacial crowfoot, *Ranunculus glacialis* L.   (Plate 32.4)
5–20 cm tall; leaves palmately divided, glabrous or hairy; flowers first white, then pink, with calyx-like tepals red-brown, pilose outside (in all other species at most whitish pilose). Scree, talus, rocky crevices; humid, stony soils poor in calcium; 2300–3200 m; sporadically higher, up to more than 4000 m; not common (mostly in the inner ranges). Arctic-Alpine plant (European). F4, R2, N2, H2, D2, L4, T1, K3. Flowering time: 7–8.
Protected: *Ti.*

Thora buttercup, *Ranunculus thora* L.   (Plate 33.1)
8–30 cm tall; no radical leaves at the time of flowering; the lowest cauline leaf reniform, dentate; flowers yellow. Open grassland, light woods; dry, stony, calciferous soils; 1300–2400 m; rare (only in the northwestern and southern ranges as well as in the Grisons). Mountain plant of Central and Southern Europe. F2, R5, N2, H3, D3, L4, T2, K4. Flowering time: 6–7.
Protected: *TI.*

Mountain buttercup, *Ranunculus montanus* Willd. *(R. geraniifolius* Gouan)   (Plate 33.2)
5–30 cm tall; leaves palmately divided, almost glabrous; cauline leaves 1–2, sessile; flowers 1–4 per stem, yellow. Pastures, meadows, scree; temporarily humid, nutrient-rich, base-containing soils; 1000–2800 m; common. Plant of the eastern Alps. F3w, R4, N4, H3, D4, L3, T2, K3. Flowering time: 5–8.
Numerous closely related species which also occur in the Alps inhabit different sites but are difficult to distinguish morphologically.

Seguier's buttercup, *Ranunculus seguieri* Vill. (Plate 33.3)
5–15 cm tall; leaves palmately divided, shaggy, tips of segments sharp; flowers white. Scree; humid, stony, clayey, calcium-containing soils; 1700–2400 m; very rare (in Switzerland only in the Brienzer Rothorn massif). Alpine plant. F4, R5, N1, H2, D3↑, L5, T1, K3. Flowering time: 5–7.
Protected: E.

Dwarf buttercup, *Ranunculus pygmaeus* Wahlenb. (Plate 33.4)
1–5 cm tall; leaves small, tripartite, glabrous; flowers yellow, measuring 0.5–1 cm in diameter. Snow-patches; humid, humous soils poor in calcium; 2500–2700 m; very rare (in Switzerland only the Lakes Macun in the Lower Engadine). Arctic-Alpine plant. F4, R2, N2, H4, D4, L4, T1, K1. Flowering time: 7–8.
Protected: E.

Aconite-leaved, or **white crowfoot,** *Ranunculus aconitifolius* L.
(Plate 34.1)
20–70 cm tall; leaves palmately divided; stem branched and multi-flowered, with curly peduncles. Meadows, banks of streams, tall-herb stands; wet, nutrient-rich soils; 600–2500 m; common. Mountain plant of Central and Southern Europe. F5w, R3, N4, H4, D5, L3, T2, K2. Flowering time: 6–7.

Large white buttercup, *Ranunculus platanifolius* L.
May be distinguished from the white crowfoot by the glabrous peduncles. Woods, tall-herb stands; humid, nutrient-rich soils; 1200–2000 m; not common. European mountain plant. F3w, R2, N4, H3, D4, L2, T2, K3. Flowering time: 6–7.

Woolly crowfoot, *Ranunculus lanuginosus* L. (Plate 34.2)
30–60 cm tall; leaves palmately divided, densely tomentose; stem branched, multi-flowered, densely tomentose with expanded hairs; flowers yellow. Woods, tall-herb stands; humid, humous soils; 1000–2000 m; rather common (above all in the outer ranges). Central European plant. F4, R3, N4, H4, D4, L2, T2, K2. Flowering time: 6–8.

o. **Meadow-rue,** *Thalictrum* L.
Leaves 1–3-pinnate with round segments; flowers small, inconspicuous, with distinct stamens; fruits often stalked and hanging.

Columbine-leaved meadow-rue, *Thalictrum aquilegiifolium* L.
(Plate 34.3)
40–120 cm tall; stamen filaments lilac. Bushy banks of streams, tall-herb stands, meadows; intermittently humid, nutrient-rich soils; 800–2400 m; rather common. Eurosibirian plant. F4w, R3, N3, H4, D5, L3, T2, K2. Flowering time: 6–7.
Protected: *AG, BL, SH.*

Lesser meadow-rue, *Thalictrum minus* L. (Plate 34.4)
20–80 cm tall; stamen filaments yellowish. Light woods, meadows; stony, dry soils; 600–2600 m; not common. Eurosibirian plant. F2, R3, N2, H3, D3, L4, T2, K4. Flowering time: 6–7.
Protected: *AG, SH.*

165

23rd family: **fumitory family,** *Fumariaceae*

Plants without milky sap; flowers zygomorphic, with 4 petals.

a. **Fumitory** or **corydalis,** *Corydalis* Vent.

Yellow fumitory, *Corydalis lutea* (L.) DC. (Plate 35.1)
10–30 cm tall; rhizomatous; flowers yellow, with small dentate bracts in the axils. Cliffs, talus, stone-walls; calcium-rich substratum; 500–1800 m; rare (only in the southern calciferous Alps, otherwise occasionally escaping). Plant of the Southern Alps. F2, R4, N3, H2, D1, L3, T3, K2. Flowering time: 5–9.
Protected: BS.

Tuberous fumitory, *Corydalis solida* (L.) Swartz (Plate 35.2)
10–20 cm tall; with a globular tuber; flowers purple, in the axils of palmately divided bracts. Light woods, bushes, pastures; nutrient-rich soils poor in calcium; 500–2300 m; not common (only in the western and southern ranges). Central European plant. F3, R2, N4, H3, D4, L2, T3, K3. Flowering time: 5–6.

Intermediate fumitory, *Corydalis intermedia* (L.) Mérat *(C. fabacea* [Retz.] Pers.) (Fig. 43)
May be distinguished from the tuberous fumitory by the entire bracts. Bushes, pastures, resting places of animals; nutrient-rich soils; 1000–2000 m; not common. Northern European-Alpine plant. F3, R3, N4, H3, D4, L3, T2, K2. Flowering time: 5–6.

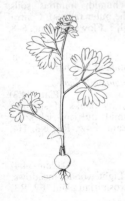

Fig. 43. Tuberous fumitory *Corydalis intermedia)*, ⅓ × (from *6.1.k.*).

166

24th family: **poppy family,** *Papaveraceae*

Plants with milky sap; flowers actinomorphic, with 2 sepals, 4 petals, and numerous stamens; fruit: a capsule.

a. **Poppy,** *Papaver* L.

Alpine poppy, *Papaver alpinum* L. s.l. (Plate 35.3)

5–15 cm tall; leaves 1–2 pinnate; tips of leaf segments 0.5–2 mm wide; flowers white, nodding before flowering. Scree, talus; calciferous substratum; 1900–2600 m; rare (only in the Northern Alps). Alpine plant. F3, R5, N2, H2, D2↑, L5, T1, K3. Flowering time: 7–8.

Protected: R, *CH*.

A western taxon *P. occidentale* (Markgraf) H. and L. reaches to the Brienzer Rothorn, whereas an eastern taxon *P. sendtneri* Kerner has its western limit on the Pilatus.

Orange poppy, *Papaver aurantiacum* Lois *(P. rhaeticum* Ler.)
(Plate 35.4)

May be distinguished from the alpine poppy by the yellow flowers. Coarse scree; base-rich substratum; 1800–2900 m; rare (in Switzerland only in the southeastern Grisons). Mountain plant of Central and Southern Europe. F3, R4, N2, H2, D2↑, L5, T1, K3. Flowering time: 7–8.

Protected: R, *CH*.

Saffron-coloured poppy, *Papaver croceum* Ledeb. *(Papaver nudicaule* auct.)

15–30 cm tall; differs from the alpine poppy as follows: tips of the leaf segments wider than 2 mm; flowers white, yellow, or orange-red. Cliffs, open grassland; stony, nutrient-rich soils; 1500–2500 m; not common (occurs mostly in the inner ranges). Plant of the Altai, in our country grown in gardens; occasionally escaping, partly naturalized. F2, R3, N4, H2, D2, L3, T2, K4. Flowering time: 6–8.

25th family: **mustard family,** *Cruciferae* (Brassicaceae)

Plants without milky sap; flowers actinomorphic, with 4 sepals, 4 petals, and 6 stamens; fruit in form of a silique opening by 2 valves. The family is represented in the Alps by about 100 species which are often inconspicuous and difficult to distinguish from each other.

a. **Pennycress,** *Thlaspi* L.

Leaves entire; fruits flat, less than twice as long as wide, with wing-shaped margin.

Round-leaved pennycress, *Thlaspi rotundifolium* (L.) Gaudin
(Plate 36.1)
5–15 cm tall; leaves rounded, the lower ones suddenly narrowing into the petiole; flowers light lilac; style 1–2 mm long. Scree, talus; calcium-rich substratum; 1500–3000 m; not common (occurs seldom in the inner ranges). Alpine plant. F3, R5, N2, H2, D2↑, L5, T1, K3. Flowering time: 6–7.

Corymbose pennycress, *Thlaspi corymbosum* (Gay) Rchb.
(Plate 36.3)
Differs from the round-leaved pennycress in the following characters: lower leaves gradually narrowing into the petiole; flowers deep lilac, with 2–3.5 mm long style. Scree, talus; calciferous substratum; 2000–3200 m; rare (only in the inner ranges). Plant of the western Alps. F3, R3, N2, H2, D2↑, L5, T1, K3. Flowering time: 7–8.

Mountain pennycress, *Thlaspi montanum* L.   (Plate 36.2)
10–20 cm tall; forms loose tufts; leaves in basal rosette, oval; flowers white. Light woods, cliffs; calcium-rich, stony soils; 600–1500 m; rather rare (in Switzerland only in the Jura). Mountain plant of Central and Southern Europe. F2, R4, N2, H3, D1, L3, T3, K2. Flowering time: 5–6.

b. **Petrocallis,** *Petrocallis* R. Br.
  Pyrenean petrocallis, *Petrocallis pyrenaica* (L.) R. Br.   (Plate 36.4)
Forms loose mats; leaves small, tripartite; flowers lilac. Rock crevices, coarse scree; calcium-rich substratum; 1900–3200 m; rare (nearly exclusively in the outer ranges). Mountain plant of Central and Southern Europe. F2, R5, N1, H3, D1, L5, T1, K4. Flowering time: 6–7.
  Protected: *GL, NW, OW.*

c. **Buckler mustard,** *Biscutella* L.
  Buckler mustard, *Biscutella levigata* L.   (Plate 37.1)
10–30 cm tall; leaves narrowly lanceolate, dentate in the distal part, or smooth-edged; flowers yellow; fruit with the appearance of one-seeded disks placed edge to edge. Pastures, grassland, scree; stony, base-rich soils; 800–2600 m; rather common. Mountain plant of Central and Southern Europe. F2, R4, N2, H3, D3, L4, T2, K3. Flowering time: 6–7.

d. **Erucastrum,** *Erucastrum* Presl
  Erucastrum, *Erucastrum nasturtiifolium* (Poiret) O. E. Schulz
(Plate 37.2)
25–70 cm tall; leaves pinnately divided; petals yellow, 8–12 mm long. Coarse scree, cliffs; humid, base-rich, stony soils; 500–1900 m; rather common. Plant of the southwestern Europe. F3w, R4, N3, H2, D2, L4, T3, K4. Flowering time: 6–8.

168

e. **Kernera,** *Kernera* Medicus
Rock kernera, *Kernera saxatilis* (L.) Rchb. (Plate 37.3)
10–30 cm tall; leaves narrowly oval; petals white, 3–4 mm long; fruits globose. Cliffs, coarse scree; calcium-rich substratum; 800–2700 m; not common. Mountain plant of Central and Southern Europe. F2, R5, N2, H2, D1, L5, T2, K4. Flowering time: 5–7.

f. **Hutchinsia,** *Hutchinsia* R. Br.
Alpine hutchinsia, *Hutchinsia alpina* (L.) R. Br. (Plate 37.4)
5–12 cm tall; leaves in a basal rosette, pinnately divided; flowers in an umbelliferous inflorescence; petals 3.5–5 mm long, white; style 0.2–0.5 mm long. Scree, rock crevices; humid, calcium-rich substratum; 1600–3200 m; not common. Mountain plant of Central and Southern Europe. F4, R4, N2, H3, D2, L5, T1, K2. Flowering time: 6–7.

Short-stemmed hutchinsia, *Hutchinsia brevicaulis* Hoppe
2–5 cm tall; differs from the alpine hutchinsia in the petals (2.5–4 mm long) and the short style (0.1–0.2 mm long). Scree, moraines; humid, base-containing, stony soils; 2200–3000 m; not common (almost exclusively in the inner ranges). Mountain plant of Central and Southern Europe (eastern). F4, R3, N2, H3, D2, L5, T1, K3. Flowering time: 6–7.

g. **Draba,** *Draba* L.
Leaves mostly smooth-edged or dentate; fruits oval, flat. The genus is represented in the Alps by about 12, mostly inconspicuous, species.

Carinthian draba, *Draba carinthiaca* Hoppe (Plate 38.1)
3–12 cm tall; leaves in a basal rosette, small, lanceolate, with stellate hairs on the leaf-blade and single, simple hairs on the margin; peduncles and fruits glabrous; petals 2–3 mm long, white; style 0.1–0.5 mm long. Ridges, loose grassland; stony, wind-exposed soils; 1800–3000 m; not common (mostly in the inner ranges). Mountain plant of Central and Southern Europe. F2, R3, N3, H3, D3, L4, T1, K4. Flowering time: 7–8.

Tomentose draba, *Draba tomentosa* Wahlenb.
Differs from the preceding species as follows: leaves densely tomentose with stellate hairs; peduncles and fruits hairy. Rock crevices, coarse scree; calcium-rich substratum; 2000–3100 m; not common. Mountain plant of Central and Southern Europe (eastern). F2, R5, N2, H2, D1, L5, T1, K4. Flowering time: 7–8.

Evergreen draba, *Draba aizoides* L. (Plate 38.2)
5–10 cm tall; leaves in a basal rosette, without stellate hairs, with long simple hairs on margins; peduncles and fruits glabrous; petals 4–6 mm long, yellow; style 1.5–3 mm long. Coarse scree, ridges, open grassland; stony, calcium-rich soils; 1500–3000 m; rather common. Mountain plant of Central and Southern Europe. F2, R4, N2, H3, D2, L5, T1, K4. Flowering time: 5–7.
Protected: *BL.*

Hoppe's draba, *Draba hoppeana* Rchb.
0.5–3 cm tall; differs from the evergreen draba in the petals (3–4 mm long) and the much shorter style (0.8–1 mm). Scree; stony, base-rich soils with late-lying snow; 2500–3000 m; rare (occurs only in the inner-most ranges). Alpine plant. F3, R4, N2, H2, D2, L5, T1, K2. Flowering time: 7–8.

Ladin draba, *Draba ladina* Br.-Bl.
Differs from the evergreen draba in the following characters: 1–5 cm tall; leaves with single stellate hairs; petals pale yellow; style 0.7–1.2 mm long. Rock crevices, coarse scree; dolomite; 2600–3000 m; very rare (only in the Dolomites of the Lower Engadine). Plant of the Lower Engadine. F2, R5, N2, H2, D1, L5, T1, K4. Flowering time: 7–8.
Protected: R*, R.

Fig. 44. Hoary draba *(Draba incana).* ⅓ × .

Hoary draba, *Draba incana* L. *(D. bernensis* Moritzi)   (Fig. 44)
10–35 cm tall; leaves distributed along the stem, often dentate, with many stellate hairs; peduncles and fruits often almost glabrous; petals 2.5–4.5 mm long, white; style 0.2–0.4 mm long. Coarse scree, resting places of animals, rock crevices; stony, calcium-rich, nutrient-rich soils; 1300–2400 m; rare (only in the northern ranges). Arctic-Alpine plant. F2, R5, N4, H3, D2, L4, T1, K4. Flowering time: 6.

h. **Bittercress,** *Cardamine* L.
Fruits long, rod-shaped, with almost no veins; leaves mostly divided. The Alpine flora includes about 10 species of the genus.

170

Reseda bittercress, *Cardamine resedifolia* L.   (Plate 38.3)
1–15 cm tall; leaves pinnately divided; petals 4.5–6 mm long, white. Coarse scree, rock crevices, open grassland; stony soils poor in calcium; 1500–3200 m; common. Mountain plant of Central and Southern Europe. F3, R2, N2, H2, D2, L4, T1, K3. Flowering time: 6–8.

Alpine bittercress, *Cardamine alpina* L.   (Plate 38.4)
2–10 cm tall; leaves entire, oval; petals 3.5–5 mm long, white. Snow-patches, pastures, flushes; humid soils poor in calcium, with late-lying snow; 2000–2800 m; not common (above all in the inner ranges). Mountain plant of Central and Southern Europe (western). F4, R2, N2, H3, D3, L4, T1, K2. Flowering time: 7–8.

Large bittercress, *Cardamine amara* L.   (Plate 39.1)
10–50 cm tall; leaves pinnate; petals 5–10 cm long, white; anthers purple (the character exclusive to this species!). Flushes, streams, ditches; wet soils; 200–2500 m; rather common. Eurosibirian plant. F5↑, R3, N3, H4, D5, L3, T2, K3. Flowering time: 6–7.

Rivulet bittercress, *Cardamine rivularis* Schur   (Plate 39.2)
10–40 cm tall; leaves pinnately divided, with small, rounded leaflets; petals 7–11 mm long. Fens, swampy pastures, banks of streams; intermittently wet, peaty soils poor in bases; 1200–2200 m; rather rare. Mountain plant of Central and Southern Europe. F4w, R2, N2, H4, D5, L4, T2, K3. Flowering time: 6.
The closely related **cuckoo-flower** *(C. pratensis* L.) has larger leaflets and occurs principally at lower altitudes.

Pinnate bittercress, *Cardamine heptaphylla* (Vill) O. E. Schulz *(Dentaria pinnata* Lam.)   (Plate 39.3)
25–60 cm tall; leaves large, pinnate, with 6–8 lanceolate leaflets; petals 15–22 mm long, white to pale lilac. Beechwoods; humid, humous soils which contain calcium; 400–1600 m; not common (occurs above all in the outer ranges and in the Jura). Mountain plant of Central and Southern Europe (western). F3, R4, N4, H4, D4, L2, T3, K2. Flowering time: 5.

Palmate bittercress, *Cardamine pentaphyllos* (L.) Crantz *(Dentaria digitata* Lam.)
May be distinguished from the pinnate bittercress by the palmate leaves with 5 leaflets and the violet petals. Deciduous forests; rather humid, nutrient-rich, humous soils which contain calcium; 400–1600 m; not common (almost exclusively in the outer ranges and in the Jura). Mountain plant of Central and Southern Europe (western). F4, R4, N4, H4, D4, L2, T3, K2. Flowering time: 5.

i. **Honesty** or **satin-flower,** *Lunaria* L.
Perennial honesty, *Lunaria rediviva* L.   (Plate 39.4)
30–100 cm tall; leaves large, cordate; petals 12–20 mm long, light-violet, lilac, or white; fruits large, flat, lanceolate. Forests in gorges, on slopes; nutrient-rich, stony soils in places where the air is humid; 600–1500 m; rather rare (nearly exclusively in the outer ranges and in

the Jura). Plant of Central Europe. F3, R4, N4, H3, D3, L2, T3, K2.
Flowering time: 5–6.
Protected: *BL*.

k. **Rockcress,** *Arabis* L.
Fruits long, rod-shaped, with a distinct mid-vein on both sides; leaves
entire. There are about 20 species in the Alps.

Bluish rockcress, *Arabis coerulea* L. (Plate 40.1)
2–12 cm tall; stem not branched; leaves oval, dentate, only slightly
hairy; petals 4–5 mm long, light-blue. Scree, moraines; humid, stony,
calcium-rich soils with late-lying snow; 2000–3000 m; not common.
Alpine plant. F4, R4, N2, H2, D2, L5, T1, K2. Flowering time: 7–8.

Dwarf rockcress, *Arabis pumila* Jacq. (Plate 40.2)
5–15 cm tall; stem not branched; leaves rather densely pilose; petals
6–7 mm long, white. Rock crevices, talus; calcium-rich substratum;
1500–3000 m; not common. Mountain plant of Central and Southern
Europe. F3, R5, N2, H2, D1, L5, T1, K4. Flowering time: 6–8.

Alpine rockcress, *Arabis alpina* L. (Plate 40.3)
10–30 cm tall; stem mostly branched; leaves broadly oval, dentate,
with many hairs; petals 6–10 mm long, white. Scree, talus, rock
crevices; stony, base-rich soils; 1200–3000 m; rather common. Arctic-
Alpine plant. F3, R4, N2, H2, D2, L4, T1, K3. Flowering time: 5–8.

Jacquin's rockcress, *Arabis jacquinii* Beck *(A. soyeri* Reut. and Huet)
(Plate 40.4)
10–25 cm tall; stem not branched; leaves oval, glabrous; petals
6–7 mm long, white. Flushes, banks of streams; wet, calcium-containing soils; 1500–2600 m; not common. Mountain plant of Central and
Southern Europe (eastern). F5↑, R4, N2, H4, D4, L4, T2, K3. Flowering time: 6–7.

Tower rockcress, *Arabis turrita* L. (Plate 41.1)
10–70 cm tall; stem occasionally branched in the upper part; leaves
narrowly oval to lanceolate, with hairs (esp. underneath); petals
6–8 mm long, yellowish-white. Light woods, bushes, rocky slopes;
stony, calcium-rich soils; 600–1500 m; not common. Mountain plant of
Central and Southern Europe (southern). F1, R4, N2, H3, D2, L3, T3,
K4. Flowering time: 4–6.

l. **Treacle mustard,** *Erysimum* L.
Swiss treacle-mustard, *Erysimum helveticum* (Jacq.) DC. (Plate 41.2)
10–40 cm tall; leaves narrowly lanceolate, with clinging hairs on both
sides; petals 8–12 mm long, yellow. Rocky slopes, dry grassland; stony
soils poor in calcium; 500–2000 m; not common (above all in the
Central and Southern Alps). Mountain plant of Central and Southern
Europe. F2, R2, N2, H3, D3, L5, T3, K4. Flowering time: 6–7.

m. **Stock,** *Matthiola* R. Br.
Alpine stock, *Matthiola vallesiaca* (J. Gay) Boissier (Plate 41.3)
5–30 cm tall; leaves narrowly lanceolate, densely covered with clinging hairs; petals 15–25 cm long, brown-violet, reddish, or brown-green.
Rock crevices, coarse scree, alluvial areas; stony, calciferous soils;
500–2000 m; very rare (in Switzerland only in the Wallis). Mountain
plant of Central and Southern Europe. F2, R4, N2, H2, D2, L5, T3,
K5. Flowering time: 5–7.
Protected: R. *Ao.*

n. **Rocket,** *Hugueninia* Rchb.
Tansy-leaved rocket, *Hugueninia tanacetifolia* (L.) Rchb. *(Sisym-
brium tanacetifolium* L.) (Plate 41.4)
20–80 cm tall; leaves large, pinnately divided, with scattered hairs;
petals 3.5–4.5 mm long, yellow. Tall-herb stands, scree; humid,
nutrient-rich soils; 1400–2300 m; rather rare (in Switzerland only in the
SW Wallis). Plant of the western Alps. F4, R3, N4, H3, D4, L3, T2, K2.
Flowering time: 7.
Protected: R.

26th family: **stonecrop family,** *Crassulaceae*

Leaves fleshy; flowers actinomorphic, with 4–20 sepals and petals,
stamens twice as many as petals, ovaries as many.

a. **Stonecrop,** *Sedum* L.
Petals 4–6, no compact spheroid rosettes; inflorescence umbel-like.
The genus is represented in the Alps by about 10 species.

Rose-root, *Sedum rosea* (L.) Scop. (Plate 42.1)
10–40 cm tall; perennial; with turnip-like rhizome; leaves flat, the
largest ones 4–6 cm long; petals 4, 1.5–4 mm long, yellow. Rock
crevices, open grassland; substratum poor in calcium; 1600–2800 m;
rare (nearly exclusively in the inner ranges). Arctic-Alpine plant. F3,
R2, N2, H3, D2, L3, T1, K3. Flowering time: 6–8.

Hairy stonecrop, *Sedum villosum* L. (Plate 42.2)
5–15 cm tall; mostly biennial; without sterile rosettes; leaves oblong,
fleshy, up to 1.5 cm long; petals mostly 6, 4–6 mm long, pink. Scree,
flushes, fens; temporarily wet soils poor in calcium; 500–2400 m; North
European-Alpine plant. F4w, R2, N1, H3, D3, L4, T2, K2. Flowering
time: 6–7.
Protected: R.

Blackish stonecrop, *Sedum atratum* L. (Plate 42.3)
3–8 cm tall; no sterile rosettes; leaves oblong, fleshy, up to 0.5 cm
long, mostly tinged dark-red; petals mostly 5, 2–4 mm long, white to
yellow-green. Scree, open grassland; stony, calciferous soils;
1500–2800 m; not common. Mountain plant of Central and Southern
Europe. F3, R4, N2, H2, D2, L5, T1, K3. Flowering time: 7–8.

173

Annual stonecrop, *Sedum annuum* L. (Plate 42.4)
5–12 cm tall; biennial; no sterile rosettes; leaves oblong, fleshy, with spurs directed backwards (the feature exclusive to this species), up to 0.7 mm long, mostly green; petals usually 5, 3–5 mm long, yellow. Scree, open grassland; dry soils poor in calcium; 1000–2000 m; not common. North European-Alpine plant. F2, R2, N1, H3, D3, L5, T2, K3. Flowering time: 7–8.

Alpine stonecrop, *Sedum alpestre* Vill.
3–8 cm tall; perennial; with sterile rosettes; leaves oblong, fleshy, up to 0.7 mm long; petals mostly 5, 3–6 mm long, yellow. Scree, snow-patches; stony soils poor in calcium; 1800–3000 m; not common (above all in the inner ranges). Mountain plant of Central and Southern Europe. F3, R2, N2, H3, D3, L5, T1, K3. Flowering time: 7–8.

b. **Houseleek,** *Sempervivum* L.
Plants with compact spheroid rosettes; petals 6–18; inflorescence umbel- to head-like. The flora of the Swiss Alps includes about 10 species.

Mountain houseleek, *Sempervivum montanum* L. (Plate 43.1)
5–25 cm tall; rosette leaves lanceolate, thickly covered with glands; petals mostly 12, 8–12 mm long, violet. Open grassland, cliffs; stony soils poor in calcium; 1000–3000 m; not common. Mountain plant of Central and Southern Europe. F2, R2, N1, H3, D3, L4, T2, K2. Flowering time: 7–8.
Protected: *NW, OW*/Li/L.

Cobwebby houseleek, *Sempervivum arachnoideum* L. (Plate 43.2)
5–15 cm tall; rosette leaves lanceolate, with glands on margins; leaf tips covered by cobwebby hairs; petals 6–12, 4–8 mm long, carmine-red. Boulders, stone-walls; dry substrata poor in calcium; 1000–2600 m; rather common (mostly in the inner ranges). Mountain plant of Central and Southern Europe. F2, R2, N1, H2, D1, L5, T2, K4. Flowering time: 6–8.
Protected: *NW, OW*/Li/L.

Alpine houseleek, *Sempervivum alpinum* Griseb. and Schenk
(Plate 43.3)
10–40 cm tall; rosette leaves lanceolate, with ciliate margins, otherwise glabrous; petals mostly 12, 8–12 m long, violet. Open grassland; dry, stony soils; 800–2600 m; not common. Mountain plant of Central and Southern Europe. F1, R3, N2, H2, D3, L5, T2, K4. Flowering time: 7–8.
Protected: *BE$_n$, JU, NW, OW*/Li/L.

Wulfen's houseleek, *Sempervivum wulfenii* Hoppe (Plate 43.4)
10–30 cm tall; rosette leaves lanceolate, with ciliate margins (glandular hairs) but otherwise glabrous; petals 15, 8–12 mm long, yellow. Coarse scree, open grassland; stony, dry soils poor in calcium; 1900–2600 m; rather rare (in Switzerland only in the SE Grisons). Plant of the eastern Alps. F2, R2, N2, H3, D3, L5, T1, K4. Flowering time: 7–8.
Protected: R. *CH*/Li/L, *So*.

27th family: **saxifrage family,** *Saxifragaceae*

Flowers mostly with 5 petals and twice as many stamens, and one ovary with 2 styles.

a. **Saxifrage,** *Saxifraga* L.

Flowers mostly in paniculate or racemose inflorescences; stamens 10, seldom 8. The genus is represented in the Alps by about 80 typical mountain species; many of them have limited areas of distribution.

Purple saxifrage, *Saxifraga oppositifolia* L. (Plate 44.1)
Forms flat, mat-like tufts; leaves up to 5 mm long, opposite; flowers single, terminal, red. Coarse scree; humid, stony soils; 800–3200 m; rather common. Arctic-Alpine plant. F4, R4, N2, H2, D2, L5, T1, K3. Flowering time: 5–7.
Protected: *GL, NW, OW,* SZ/Ti/Li.

Two-flowered saxifrage, *Saxifraga biflora* All. (Plate 44.2)
Differs from the purple saxifrage in the flowers terminally grouped by 2–9, red to purple. Scree; humid, calciferous, stony soils; 2200–3000 m; rare. Alpine plant. F4, R4, N2, H2, D2, L5, T1, K3. Flowering time: 7–8.
Protected: *GL, NW, OW*/Ti.

Yellow mountain saxifrage, *Saxifraga aizoides* L. (Plate 44.3)
5–20 cm tall; forms loose tufts; leaves fleshy, narrowly lanceolate, up to 2 cm long, with ciliate margins; flowers terminal, in groups of 5–10, yellow to orange. Scree, flushes; stony, intermittently humid soils; 800–2800 m; rather common. Arctic-Alpine plant. F4↑w, R4, N2, H2, D3, L4, T1, K4. Flowering time: 6–8.
Protected: *BEₙ, OW,* SZ, *TG, ZH*/Ti/L.

Musky saxifrage, *Saxifraga moschata* Wulfen (Plate 44.4)
2–10 cm tall; forms cushions; leaves narrowly lanceolate, smooth-edged, or with 1–2 teeth in the distal part, up to 1 cm long; flowers terminal, grouped by 1–5, yellow-orange or reddish. Scree; calciferous substratum; 1600–3000 m; not common. Mountain plant of Central and Southern Europe. F3, R4, N2, H2, D2, L5, T1, K3. Flowering time: 5–7.

Protected: *GL, NW, OW,* SZ/Ti/L.

The Alpine flora also includes several quite similar taxa e.g. **brittle saxifrage** *(Saxifraga exarata* Vill.) which grows upon siliceous cliffs.

Androsace-like saxifrage, *Saxifraga androsacea* L. (Plate 45.1)
2–8 cm tall; forms loose tufts; leaves lanceolate to spathulate (paddle-shaped), smooth-edged or with 1–3 teeth, up to 2 cm long; flowers terminal, 1–3, white. Snow-patches, scree; stony, humid, calciferous soils with late-lying snow; 1800–3000 m; not common. Eurasiatic mountain plant. F4, R4, N2, H4, D2, L4, T1, K2. Flowering time: 7–8.
Protected: *OW,* SZ/Ti/L.

175

Seguier's saxifrage, *Saxifraga seguieri* Spreng.   (Plate 45.2)
Differs from the preceding species in the following characters: leaves smooth-edged; flowers 1–2, yellow. Scree, snow-patches; humid, stony soils poor in calcium, with late-lying snow; 2000–3000 m; not common (above all in the inner ranges). Alpine plant. F4, R2, N2, H4, D2, L4, T1, K2. Flowering time: 7–8.
Protected: *OW*/*Ti*/L.

Saxifrage with naked stems, *Saxifraga aphylla* Sternb.   (Plate 45.3)
3–8 cm tall; forms loose tufts; leaves spathulate to lanceolate, mostly with 3 large teeth at the tip, up to 1 cm long; flowers single, terminal, yellowish. Scree; calciferous, stony soils with late-lying snow; 1800–3100 m; rather rare (only in the eastern Alps). Plant of the eastern Alps. F3, R5, N2, H2, D2, L4, T1, K2. Flowering time: 7–8.
Protected: *Ti*/L.

Bluish saxifrage, *Saxifraga caesia* L.   (Plate 45.4)
2–10 cm tall; forms cushions; leaves blue-green, rigid, up to 0.6 cm long; flowers terminal, in a group of 2–6, white. Scree, open grassland, cliffs; stony, calcium-rich, often wind-exposed soils; 1500–3000 m; not common. Mountain plant of Central and Southern Europe. F2, R5, N1, H2, D2, L5, T1, K4. Flowering time: 7–8.
Protected: *GL, NW, OW,* SZ/*Ti*/L.

Pyramidal saxifrage, *Saxifraga cotyledon* L.   (Plate 46.1)
20–50 cm tall; with large leaf rosettes; leaves ligulate, up to 6 cm long; flowers terminal, in a group of 10–100, white. Rock crevices; substratum poor in calcium; 900–2500 m; not common (almost exclusively in the southern ranges). North European-Alpine plant. F3, R2, N2, H2, D1, L4, T3, K3. Flowering time: 6–7.
Protected: L.

Drooping saxifrage, *Saxifraga cernua* L.   (Plate 46.2)
10–30 cm tall; forms bulbils in the leaf axils; leaves reniform in outline, 3-, 5-, or 7-partite; flowers single, terminal, white. Rocky ledges, resting places of animals; stony, calciferous, nutrient-rich soils with late-lying snow; 2100–2900 m; very rare (in Switzerland only a few localities in the Wallis, the Bernese Oberland, the Lower Engadine). Arctic-Alpine plant. F4, R4, N4, H3, D2, L3, T1, K2. Flowering time: 7.
Protected: R. L.

Orange-red saxifrage, *Saxifrage mutata* L.   (Plate 46.3)
10–40 cm tall; with large leaf rosettes; leaves ligulate, up to 6 cm long; flowers 5–50 in the upper part of the stem, yellow. Cliffs; humid, calciferous substratum; 600–1900 m; rare (nearly exclusively in the Midlands and in the outer Alpine ranges). Alpine plant. F4w, R4, N2, H1, D1, L3, T3, K3. Flowering time: 7.
Protected: *AG, BE*n, *OW,* SZ, *TG, ZH*/L/F.

White mountain saxifrage, *Saxifraga aizoon* Jacq. *(S. paniculata* Miller) (Plate 46.4)
10–40 cm tall; with compact, tough rosettes; leaves ligulate, up to 4 cm long; flowers 5–40, terminal white, frequently with red dots. Cliffs, open grassland; base-containing substratum; 600–3200 m; rather common. European-North American plant. F2, R3, N2, H2, D1, L5, T2, K3. Flowering time: 6–7.
Protected: *AG, BEn,* BL, *OW,* SZ, *TG/Ti/*L.

Moss saxifrage, *Saxifraga bryoides* L. (Plate 47.1)
2–6 cm tall; with small compact rosettes; forms cushions; flowers mostly 1, terminal, white outside, yellow with orange-red dots inside. Boulders, stabilized scree; substratum poor in calcium; 2000–3300 m; not common (above all in the inner ranges). Mountain plant of Central and Southern Europe. F3, R2, N1, H2, D2, L5, T1, K3. Flowering time: 7–8.
Protected: OW/*Ti/*L.

Stiff-haired saxifrage, *Saxifraga aspera* L. (Plate 47.2)
8–20 cm tall; no compact rosettes; forms loose tufts; flowers 1–10, terminal, white outside, yellow inside. Cliffs, coarse scree; substratum poor in calcium; 1400–2300 m; not common (above all in the inner ranges). Mountain plant of Central and Southern Europe (western). F2, R2, N2, H2, D1, L4, T2, K4. Flowering time: 7.
Protected: *OW/Ti/*L.

Stellate saxifrage, *Saxifraga stellaris* L. (Plate 47.3)
5–20 cm tall; with rosettes; forms loose tufts; flowers 3–16, terminal, white, with 10 yellow dots at the base. Flushes, streams; wet soils; 1400–2800 m; rather common. Arctic-Alpine plant. F5↑, R3, N2, H4, D4, L5, T1, K2. Flowering time: 7–8.
Protected: *OW,* SZ/*Ti/*L.

Round-leaved saxifrage, *Saxifraga rotundifolia* L. (Plate 47.4)
10–50 cm tall; basal leaves with long petioles, reniform; flowers 10–100, in a loose terminal panicle, white with yellow dots at the base. Tall-herb stands, green alder thickets, banks of streams; humid, nutrient-rich soils; 1000–2300 m; rather common. Mountain plant of Central and Southern Europe. F4, R3, N4, H3, D4, L2, T2, K2. Flowering time: 6–9.
Protected: *BEn, OW,* SZ, *ZH/*L.

Saxifrage with wedge-shaped leaves, *Saxifraga cuneifolia* L.
10–20 cm tall; with leaf rosettes; forms loose tufts; basal leaves oval, cuneately narrowing into petiole, 0.5–1.5 cm long; flowers 5–30, terminal, white with red dots at the base. Coniferous woods; stony soils poor in calcium; 800–1900 m; not common (almost exclusively in the inner ranges). Mountain plant of Central and Southern Europe. F3, R2, N2, H3, D2, L2, T2, K3. Flowering time: 6–7.
Protected: *OW/Ti/*L.

177

b. **Grass of Parnassus,** *Parnassia* L.
   Grass of Parnassus, *Parnassia palustris* L. (Plate 48.1)
   5–30 cm tall; basal leaves oval-cordate, petiolate, 0.5–1.5 cm long; flowers single, terminal, white, with 5 glandularly fringed staminodes between the stamens. Swampy meadows, scree; intermittently humid, base-rich soils; 500–2700 m; not common. Eurosibirian-North American plant. F4w, R4, N2, H3, D5, L4, T2, K3. Flowering time: 7–9.
   Protected: *GE.*

c. **Currant,** *Ribes* L.
   Bushes; leaves palmate, 3–5-partite; flowers small, in racemes; petals shorter than the sepals.

   Mountain currant, *Ribes alpinum* L. (Fig. 36A, p. 133)
   Up to 1.5 m tall; leaves up to 3 cm in diameter, with red-headed glandular hairs; flowers in an upright, 5–20-flowered raceme; petals yellowish; berries red, insipid. Bushes, forests on slopes, coarse scree; stony, calciferous soils; 800–2000 m; not common. North European-Alpine plant. F3, R4, N3, H3, D2, L3, T2, K3. Flowering time: 5–6.

   Rock currant, *Ribes petraeum* L. (Fig. 36B, p. 133)
   Up to 1.5 m tall; leaves up to 10 cm in diameter, without glandular hairs; flowers in an overhanging, 10–30-flowered raceme; petals reddish; berries red, acid-aromatic. Woods, bushes, coarse scree; stony soils poor in calcium; 1200–2200 m; not common. Eurasiatic mountain plant. F3, R2, N4, H3, D2, L3, T2, K2. Flowering time: 5–6.

28th family: **rose family,** *Rosaceae*

Leaves mostly with stipules; flowers actinomorphic, mostly with 5, less frequently with 4 or 8 free petals; fruit forms diverse. The family includes our most important fruit trees and berries (apple, pear, peach, plum, cherry, apricot; strawberry, raspberry, dewberry). The family is represented in the Alps by 50–500 species, depending on the species concept of a given author.

a. **Dryas,** *Dryas* L.
   Mountain avens, *Dryas octopetala* L. (Plate 48.1)
   2–10 cm tall; with woody shoots creeping over the ground; flowers terminal, single, measuring 2–4 cm in diameter, with 7–9 white petals; fruits with 2–3 cm long feathery styles forming a mop of hairs. Scree, open grassland; stony, base-rich soils; 1200–2700 m; not common. Arctic-Alpine plant. F2, R4, N2, H1, D2, L5, T1, K4. Flowering time: 6–7.
   Protected: *BL, SO,* VD$_j$/L.

b. **Service tree,** *Sorbus* L.
   Trees or bushes; flowers numerous in an umbelliferous panicle; petals 5; ovary inferior; fruit berry-like. There are 3 species in the Alps.

Rowan, *Sorbus aucuparia* L. (Plate 48.3, Fig. 36E, p. 133)
Tree up to 10 m tall; leaves pinnately divided, with dentate leaflets; flowers white; «berries» red. Light woods, bushes; soils poor in calcium; 600–2400 m; rather common. Eurosibirian plant. F3, R2, N2, H4, D4, L3, T2, K3. Flowering time: 6.

Whitebeam, *Sorbus aria* L. (Fig. 35O, p. 132)
Tree up to 10 m and more; leaves entire, oval 2-dentate, white underneath; flowers white; «berries» orange to red. Light woods, steep slopes; dry, stony soils; 500–2000 m; rather common. Central European plant. F2, R3, N2, H3, D3, L3, T3, K4. Flowering time: 6.

False medlar, *Sorbus chamaemespilus* (L.) Crantz (Fig. 35L, p. 132)
Bush up to 2 m tall; leaves entire, oblong-oval, mostly simply dentate, deep green and glabrous above, green underneath; flowers pink; «berries» red or brown-red. Light woods, dwarf shrub stands; dry, humous, base-containing soils; 1200–2400 m; not common. Mountain plant of Central and Southern Europe. F2, R4, N2, H4, D4, L3, T2, K2. Flowering time: 6–7.
Protected: *SO*.

c. **Cotoneaster,** *Cotoneaster* Medikus
Common cotoneaster, *Cotoneaster integerrima* Medikus
(Fig. 35D, p. 132)
Bush up to 1.5 m tall; leaves oval, 1.5–4 cm long, whitely tomentose underneath; flowers small, 1–5, in the leaf axils, with 5 pinkish-red petals; «berries» red. Light forests on slopes, bushes, steep slopes; dry, stony soils; 800–2600 m; not common. Central European plant. F1, R4, N2, H2, D2, L4, T3, K4. Flowering time: 5–6.

d. **June-berry,** *Amelanchier* Medikus
Snowy mespilus, *Amelanchier ovalis* Medikus (Fig. 35F, p. 132)
Bush up to 3 m tall; leaves oval, 2–4 cm long, floccose beneath when young, later glabrous; flowers up to 4 cm in diameter, with 5, narrow, oval, white petals; «berries» black or bluish-black. Rocky slopes, bushes, light woods; dry, stony, calciferous soils; 600–2000 m; not common. Mountain plant of Central and Southern Europe. F2, R4, N2, H2, D2, L4, T3, K4. Flowering time: 5.
Protected: *GE, NW, OW*.

e. **Rose,** *Rosa* L.
Alpine rose, *Rosa pendulina* L. *(R. alpina* L.) (Plate 48.4)
Bush up to 3 m tall; with numerous prickles, all of the same kind; leaves pinnately divided, with 7–9 oval, dentate leaflets; flowers single in the leaf axils, measuring about 4 cm in diameter, with 5 pink to purple petals; «fruit» bottle-shaped (hip), orange to red. Light woods, bushes, rocky slopes, tall-herb stands; stony soils; 600–2400 m; not common. Mountain plant of Central and Southern Europe. F3, R3, N3, H3, D3, L3, T2, K3. Flowering time: 6–7.
Protected: *SH*.

f. **Lady's mantle,** *Alchemilla* L.
Herbs; with petiolate, palmately divided basal leaves; flowers in terminal bunches, with 4 inner, and 4 outer green sepals, without petals. The genus includes very many microspecies, difficult to determine; they are mostly asexual.

Five-fingered lady's mantle, *Alchemilla pentaphyllea* L.   (Plate 49.1)
Prostrate; hardly 5 cm tall; leaves 5-partite, divided to the base, green on both sides. Snow-patches; humid soils poor in calcium, with late-lying snow; 2100–2900 m; not common (mostly in the inner ranges). Plant of the western Alps. F4 , R2, N3, D4, H3, L4, T1, K2. Flowering time: 7–8.

Common lady's mantle, *Alchemilla vulgaris* L. s.l.   (Plate 49.2)
5–40 cm tall; leaves divided to less than ½, 7–11-partite, with round to triangular, dentate segments, green on both sides. Meadows, pastures, coarse scree; mostly in humid, nutrient-rich soils; 500–2800 m; common. Eurosibirian-North American plant group. Flowering time: 6–7.
The Alpine flora includes more than 60 microspecies of this group; each taxon has particular indicative values.

Alpine lady's mantle, *Alchemilla alpina* L. s.l.   (Plate 49.3)
5–30 cm tall; leaves 5–9-partite, divided nearly to the base; leaf segments narrowly oval, dentate in the distal part, silvery underneath. Meadows, pastures, rocky ledges; stony, dry soils; 1200–2700 m; rather common. Arctic-Alpine plant group. Flowering time: 6–7.
The Alpine flora includes about 30 microspecies of this group; each taxon has particular indicative values.

g. **Sibbaldia,** *Sibbaldia* L.
Sibbaldia, *Sibbaldia procumbens* L.   (Plate 49.4)
2–5 cm tall; leaves consisting of 3 leaflets; leaflets with 3 teeth in the distal part; flowers 5–10, measuring 4–6 mm in diameter, with 5 yellow-green petals which are shorter than the sepals. Snow-patches, grassland; humid soils poor in calcium, with late-lying snow; 1700–3000 m; not common. Arctic-Alpine plant. F4, R2, N3, H4, D4, L4, T1, K2. Flowering time: 6–7.

h. **Cinquefoil,** *Potentilla* L.
Herbs; leaves pinnate or digitate; flowers yellow, white, or pink; calyx with 5 inner sepals, and an epicalyx consisting of 5 sepals. The genus is represented in the Alps by about 30 species.

Tormentil, *Potentilla erecta* (L.) Räuschel *(P. tormentilla* Necker)
(Plate 50.1)
10–30 cm tall; with a thick rhizome, often reddish when broken or crushed; leaves 3–5-partite, the basal ones mostly absent at the time of flowering; petals 4, about 4 mm long, yellow. Pastures, straw meadows, mires; intermittently humid, humous soils; 400–2500 m; rather common. Eurosibirian plant. F3w, Rx, N2, H4, D5, L4, T2, K3. Flowering time: 6–9.

180

Large-flowered cinquefoil, *Potentilla grandiflora* L.   (Plate 50.2)
10–30 cm tall; leaves 3-partite; basal leaves with long petioles, present at the time of flowering; petals 5, 1–1.5 cm long, yellow. Grassland, rocky slopes; dry, stony soils; 1600–2600 m; not common. Mountain plant of Central and Southern Europe (western). F2, R2, N3, H3, D3, L4, T2, K4. Flowering time: 7–8.

Frigid cinquefoil, *Potentilla frigida* Vill.   (Plate 50.3; Fig. 45C)
2–10 cm tall; leaves 3-partite, shaggy on both sides; petals 5, 4–5 mm long, yellow. Grassland; stony, wind-exposed soils poor in calcium; 2400–3200 m; not common. Mountain plant of Central and Southern Europe (western). F2, R2, N2, H4, D3, L5, T1, K4. Flowering time: 7–8.

Golden cinquefoil, *Potentilla aurea* L.   (Plate 50.4; Fig. 45A)
5–20 cm tall; leaves 5-partite, silky pilose on margins and underneath; petals 5, 7–10 mm long, yellow. Pastures, meadows; meagre soils poor in calcium; 1200–2800 m; common. Mountain plant of Central and Southern Europe. F3, R2, N2, H3, D4, L4, T2, K3. Flowering time: 6–8.

Alpine cinquefoil, *Potentilla Crantzii* (Crantz) Beck   (Fig. 45B)
May be distinguished from the golden cinquefoil by the pilose leaves with spreading hairs. Pastures, grassland; dry, base-containing, often wind-exposed soils; 1300–3000 m; rather common. Eurosibirian-North American plant. F2, R4, N2, H3, D3, L4, T2, K4. Flowering time: 6–8.

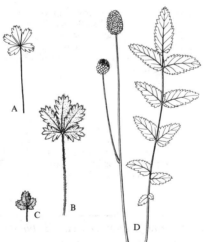

Fig. 45. A: golden cinquefoil *(Potentilla aurea)*. B: alpine cinquefoil *(Potentilla crantzii)*. C: frigid cinquefoil *(Potentilla frigida)*. D: great burnet *(Sanguisorba officinalis)*. ⅓ ×.

181

Caulescent cinquefoil, *Potentilla caulescens* L. (Plate 51.1)
10–25 cm tall; leaves 5-partite, pilose (esp. underneath); petals 5, 7–12 mm long, white. Cliffs; calcium-rich substratum; 800–2400 m; not common. Mountain plant of Central and Southern Europe. F2, R5, N2, H2, D1, L4, T2, K3. Flowering time: 7–8.
Protected: *GE.*

Glossy cinquefoil, *Potentilla nitida* L. (Plate 51.2)
2–10 cm tall; leaves 3-partite, silvery-pilose; petals 5, 10–15 mm long, pink, or rarely white. Cliffs, boulders; calcium-rich substratum; 1700–3100 m; very rare (only in the southern ranges outside Switzerland). Plant of the Southern Alps. F2, R5, N2, H2, D1, L4, T2, K4. Flowering time: 7–8.

i. **Avens,** *Geum* L.
Alpine avens, *Geum montanum* L. *(Sieversia montana* (L.) R. Br.)
(Plate 51.3)
5–25 cm tall; without stolons; leaves pinnately divided, with large terminal leaflet; flowers with 5 outer, and 5 inner sepals; petals mostly 5, 1–2 cm long, yellow; style up to 3 cm long, persistent and feathery on the fruit. Pastures, meadows, dwarf shrub stands; soils poor in calcium; 1200–3000 m; rather common. Mountain plant of Central and Southern Europe. F3, R2, N2, H3, D4, L4, T2, K3. Flowering time: 5–8.

Creeping avens, *Geum reptans* L. *Sieversia reptans* [L.] R. Br.)
(Plate 51.4)
Differs from the alpine avens as follows: up to 15 cm tall; with stolons creeping over the ground; terminal leaflet hardly larger than the lateral ones; petals 2–2.5 cm long. Scree; stony soils poor in calcium; 2200–3200 m; rather rare (above all in the inner ranges). Mountain plant of Central and Southern Europe (eastern). F3, R2, N2, H2, D2, L5, T1, K2. Flowering time: 7–8.
Protected: *GL.*

k. **Burnet,** *Sanguisorba* L.
Great burnet, *Sanguisorba officinalis* L. (Fig. 45D)
30–90 cm tall; leaves pinnately divided with leaflets oval, cordate at the base; flowers in a spherical to ovoid spike, dark-red (the colour indentical to that of the black vanilla orchid), with 4 sepals and no petals. Meadows, fens; intermittently humid, humous soils; 400–2400 m; not common. Eurosibirian plant. F3w, R3, N3, H4, D5, L4, T3, K3. Flowering time: 7–9.

29th family: **pea family,** *Papilionaceae (Fabaceae)*

Leaves compound, with stipules at the base; flowers zygomorphic; corolla consisting of the standard (the uppermost petal), two wings (the lateral petals), and the keel (the two lowermost petals, united); fruit usually in form of a dehiscent pod. This family includes many vegetables (e.g. beans, peas, lentils). There are about 100 species in the Alps.

Many plants of the pea family have root nodules with bacteria fixing the atmospheric nitrogen.

a. Greenweed, *Genista* L.

German greenweed, *Genista germanica* L. (Plate 52.1)
Dwarf shrub 15–50 cm tall, with thin thorns; leaves small, lanceolate, hairy; flowers yellow, in short upright racemes. Light woods, heaths; dry soils poor in calcium; 200–2000 m; not common (almost exclusively in the southern ranges). Plant of Central Europe. F2, R1, N2, H4, D4, L3, T3, K4. Flowering time: 6–7.
Protected: TG.

b. Goatroot or restharrow, *Ononis* L.

Yellow goatroot, *Ononis natrix* L. (Plate 52.2)
20–40 cm tall; leaves consisting of 3 oval, dentate leaflets, with glandular hairs; flowers yellow, in an upright raceme. Alluvial areas, slopes; dry, stony, calciferous soils; 500–1800 m; not common (in Switzerland only in the valley of the Rhône, and in the southern Ticino). Mountain plant of Central and Southern Europe (southern). F2, R4, N2, H2, D3, L3, T4, K4. Flowering time: 6–7.

c. Kidney-vetch, *Anthyllis* L.

Leaves pinnately divided, mostly with a larger terminal leaflet; flowers in a head enveloped in digitate bracts. The Alpine flora includes about 5 species, amongst them the **ladies' fingers** *(Anthyllis vulneraria* L.) which occurs at lower altitudes.

Alpine kidney-vetch, *Anthyllis alpestris* (Kit.) Rchb. (Plate 52.3)
5–25 cm tall; leaves with large terminal leaflet and few lateral leaflets; flowers measuring 2–3 cm in diameter; calyx mostly pale; corolla golden-yellow. Pastures, open grassland; stony, calciferous soils; 1500–2800 m; rather common. Mountain plant of Central and Southern Europe. F2, R4, N2, H3, D3, L5, T1, K4. Flowering time: 6–7.

Cherler's kidney-vetch, *Anthyllis cherleri* Brügger (Plate 52.4)
Differs from the alpine kidney vetch as follows: calyx often with red tips; corolla pale yellow, pink, or purple, with dark-red keel tip. Pastures, grassland, scree; stony soils poor in calcium; 1300–2600 m; not common (almost exclusively in the inner ranges). Mountain plant of Central and Southern Europe (western). F2, R3, N2, H3, D4, L4, T2, K3. Flowering time: 6–7.

d. Clover or trefoil, *Trifolium* L.

Leaves consisting of 3 leaflets; flowers sessile or with short peduncles, in heads or spikes which are mostly not enveloped in bracts. The genus is represented in the Alps by about 30 species.

Alpine clover, *Trifolium alpinum* L.   (Plate 53.1)
5–15 cm tall; leaflets narrowly lanceolate; heads 3–12-flowered, measuring 3–5 cm in diameter, flesh-red to purple. Pastures, dwarf shrub stands; dry soils poor in calcium; 1400–2800 m; rather common (esp. in the inner ranges). Mountain plant of Central and Southern Europe (western). F2, R2, N2, H3, D4, L4, T2, K3. Flowering time: 6–8.

Mountain clover, *Trifolium montanum* L.   (Plate 53.2)
15–40 cm tall; leaflets lanceolate, acute; heads multi-flowered, measuring 1–1.5 cm in diameter, white (often slightly yellowish or reddish). Meadows, light woods; dry, meagre, base-containing soils; 400–2400 m; rather common. Eurosibirian plant. F2w, R4, N2, H3, D4, L4, T3, K3. Flowering time: 6–7.

Snow clover, *Trifolium nivale* Sieber   (Plate 53.3)
5–15 cm tall; leaflets oval; heads multi-flowered, measuring 2.5–3.5 cm in diameter, white, yellowish-white, or reddish. Meadows, pastures; medium soils; 1600–2800 m; rather common. Mountain plant of Central and Southern Europe. F3, R3, N3, H3, D4, L4, T1, K3. Flowering time: 6–9.
The species is closely related to the **red clover** *(Trifolium pratense* L.) which occurs at lower altitudes; the two species hybridize and form intermediary types.

Thal's clover, *Trifolium thalii* Vill.   (Plate 53.4)
5–15 cm tall; leaflets rounded-oval; heads multi-flowered, measuring 1–2 cm in diameter, at first white, later reddish. Pastures, meadows, open grassland; stony, calciferous soils; 1400–2800 m; rather common. Mountain plant of Central and Southern Europe (western). F3, R4, N3, H3, D4, L4, T2, K3. Flowering time: 7–8.
The closely related **white clover** *(Trifolium repens* L.), which occurs mostly at lower altitudes, has creeping aboveground stolons.

Hill clover, *Trifolium alpestre* L.   (Plate 54.1)
15–35 cm tall; leaflets narrowly lanceolate, strongly pilose; flower heads multi-flowered, spherical, measuring 2–3 cm in diameter, red. Light woods, bushy slopes; dry, sandy soils; 400–1900 m; rather rare (almost exclusively in the central and southern ranges). Central European plant. F2w, R3, N2, H3, D3, L3, T4, K4. Flowering time: 6–7.

Purple clover, *Trifolium rubens* L.   (Plate 54.2)
20–60 cm tall; leaflets narrowly lanceolate, glabrous; flower spikes multi-flowered, obovate to cylindrical, 3–7 cm long, purple. Light woods, bushy slopes; dry, sandy soils; 500–2000 m; rather rare (occurs above all in the central and southern ranges). Central European plant. F2, R3, N2, H3, D3, L3, T4, K4. Flowering time: 6–7.

Brown clover, *Trifolium badium* Schreber   (Plate 54.3)
8–25 cm tall; leaflets oval; heads multi-flowered, spherical to obovate, 1.3–2 cm long, golden-yellow, turning brown when old. Meadows, pastures; calciferous soils; 800–2700 m; rather common. Mountain plant of Central and Southern Europe. F3, R4, N3, H3, D4, L4, T2, K3. Flowering time: 7–8.

184

e. **Birdsfoot-trefoil,** *Lotus* L.

Alpine birdsfoot-trefoil, *Lotus alpinus* (DC.) Schleicher (Plate 54.4)
3–50 cm tall; leaves with 5 leaflets (two of them at the leaf base); flowers 1–3, terminal, yellow, often tinged red, frequently turning orange when old; keel tips red. Scree, pastures, grassland; stony soils; 1800–2800 m; rather common. Mountain plant of Central and Southern Europe. F3, R3, N3, H3, D3, L5, T1, K3. Flowering time: 6–8.

The **common birdsfoot-trefoil,** also called **bacon and eggs** *(Lotus corniculatus* L.) which occurs at lower altitudes, is up to 40 cm tall and has 3–8-flowered inflorescences; keel tips are mostly pale.

f. **Milk-vetch,** *Astragalus* L.
Leaves pinnate, with terminal leaflet; flowers in a head or a compact spike; keels obtuse; fruits often inflated, surpassing the calyx. The genus is represented in the Alps by about 20 species.

Alpine milk-vetch, *Astragalus alpinus* L. (Plate 55.1)
8–20 cm tall; stem upright, leaves with 15–23 leaflets; flowers white to bluish, with the keel tips violet in the distal part; wings short, rounded in the distal part; fruits hanging, pilose. Meadows, pastures; stony, calcium-rich soils; 1500–2700 m; not common. Arctic-Alpine plant. F2, R4, N2, H3, D3, L4, T1, K4. Flowering time: 7–8.

Droopy-flowered milk-vetch, *Astragalus penduliflorus* Lam. *(Phaca alpina* L.) (Plate 55.2)
15–40 cm tall; stem upright; leaves with 15–23 leaflets; flowers yellow; fruits hanging, inflated. Meadows, light woods; stony, meagre soils; 1300–2600 m; not common (occurs above all in the inner ranges). Mountain plant of Central and Southern Europe. F3, R3, N2, H3, D3, L4, T2, K3. Flowering time: 7–8.

Southern milk-vetch, *Astragalus australis* (L.) Lam. (Plate 55.3)
Differs from the alpine milk-vetch as follows: leaflets 9–15; wings longer, emarginate; fruits glabrous. Open grassland, scree; dry, stony, calciferous soils; 1200–2800 m; not common. Eurosibirian plant. F2, R4, N2, H3, D3, L4, T2, K4. Flowering time: 7–8.

Glacial milk-vetch, *Astragalus frigidus* (L.) A. Gray *(Phaca frigida* L.) (Plate 55.4)
10–30 cm tall; stem upright; leaves with 7–15 leaflets; flowers white to yellowish; fruits hanging, inflated. Meadows, steep slopes; calciferous soils; 1500–2700 m; not common. Arctic-Alpine plant (Eurasiatic). F3, R4, N3, H3, D4, L4, T1, K3. Flowering time: 7–8.

g. **Oxytropis,** *Oxytropis* DC.
Differs from the milk-vetch in the keel tipped by a sharp appendage or point. The Alpine flora includes about 10 species of the genus.

Jacquin's oxytropis, *Oxytropis jacquinii* Bunge *(O. montana* auct.) (Plate 56.1)
5–15 cm tall; mostly prostrate; leaves with 27–41 leaflets; flowers purple-violet (blue when dried out); calyx teeth ¼–⅓ as long as the calyx tube; fruits upright. Open grassland, ridges; stony, calcium-rich

soils; 1700–2800 m; rather common. Mountain plant of Central and Southern Europe (eastern). F2, R5, N2, H2, D3, L5, T1, K3. Flowering time: 7–8.

Laplandish oxytropis, *Oxytropis lapponica* (Wahlenb.) J. Gray
Differs from the Jacquin's oxytropis as follows: flowers lighter in colour; calyx teeth ⅔–⅘ as long as the calyx tube; fruits hanging. Grassland, ridges; stony, calciferous soils; 1500–2600 m; rather rare (above all in the inner ranges). Arctic-Alpine plant (Eurasiatic). F2, R4, N2, H3, D3, L5, T1, K4. Flowering time: 7–8.

Yellow oxytropis, *Oxytropis campestris* (L.) DC.   (Plate 56.2)
5–15 cm tall; leaves with 21–31 leaflets, sparsely hairy to virtually glabrous; flowers yellowish to white, rarely tinged violet, often with 2 violet spots on the both sides of the keel; fruits upright. Meadows, pastures; dry, calciferous soils; 1200–2900 m; rather common. Arctic-Alpine plant. F2, R4, N2, H3, D3, L4, T1, K3. Flowering time: 7–8.

Downy-beaked oxytropis, *Oxytropis pilosa* (L.) DC.   (Plate 56.3)
15–30 cm tall; leaves with 19–27 leaflets, densely tomentose with spreading hairs; flowers light-yellow; fruits upright. Pine forests, dry grassland; dry, base-rich soils; 600–1700 m; rather rare (only in the Central Alps). East European-Central Asiatic plant. F1, R4, N2, H3, D3, L3, T4, K4. Flowering time: 6–7.

Haller's oxytropis, *Oxytropis halleri* Bunge *(O. sericea* (Lam.) Simonk.)   (Plate 56.4)
5–20 cm tall; leaves with 17–33 leaflets, silky-pilose; flowers violet to lilac; fruits upright. Open grassland, ridges; dry, wind-exposed soils; 1500–2700 m; rather rare. Mountain plant of Central and Southern Europe. F1, R3, N2, H3, D3, L5, T1, K4. Flowering time: 5–7.

h. **Horseshoe-vetch,** *Hippocrepis* L.
Horseshoe-vetch, *Hippocrepis comosa* L.   (Plate 57.1)
5–25 cm tall; leaves pinnate, with 11–17 leaflets and small stipules; flowers 5–12, in a crown-like terminal group, yellow; fruits with horseshoe-shaped segments. Grassland, light woods, rocky slopes; dry, stony, calciferous soils; 300–2700 m; rather common. Central European plant. F2, R4, N2, H3, D3, L4, T3, K4. Flowering time: 6–7.

i. **Crown vetch,** *Coronilla* L.
Alpine crown vetch, *Coronilla vaginalis* Lam.   (Plate 57.2)
10–25 cm tall; leaves pinnate, with 5–13 leaflets, blue-green, with large stipules; flowers 3–10, terminal, yellow; fruits breaking up into narrowly oval, 1-seeded joints. Pine forests, steep slopes; dry, stony, calciferous soils; 1000–2200 m; rather rare (very rare in the inner ranges). Mountain plant of Central and Southern Europe (eastern). F2, R5, N2, H3, D3, L4, T2, K3. Flowering time: 5–7.

186

k. **Sainfoin,** *Onobrychis* Miller
   Mountain sainfoin, *Onobrychis montana* DC.   (Plate 57.3)
   10–25 cm tall; leaves pinnate, with 11–15 leaflets; flowers in a spicate inflorescence, purple; wings nearly as long as the calyx. Meadows, pastures; dry, calciferous soils; 1300–2200 m; not common. Mountain plant of Central and Southern Europe. F2, R4, N3, H3, D4, L4, T2, K3. Flowering time: 7.
   The closely related **common sainfoin** *(Onobrychis viciifolia* Scop.) grows at lower altitudes and differs from the preceding in the wings distinctly shorter than the calyx.

l. **French honeysuckle,** *Hedysarum* L.
   Alpine French honeysuckle, *Hedysarum obscurum* L. *(H. hedysaroides* [L.] Sch. and Th.)   (Plate 57.4)
   5–25 cm tall; leaves pinnate, with 9–19 leaflets; flowers hanging, 10–35, in a terminal raceme, purple; fruit flat, segmented (loment). Meadows, pastures; calciferous soils; 1600–2800 m; not common. Mountain plant of Central and Southern Europe. F3, R4, N3, H3, D4, L4, T2, K3. Flowering time: 7–8.

m. **Vetchling,** *Lathyrus* L.
   Stem angled or winged; leaves pinnate, without the terminal leaflet, with tendril or tip; flowers in one- to multi-flowered racemes; staminal tube transversely truncate. The genus is represented in the Alps by about 10 species.

   Meadow vetchling, *Lathyrus pratensis* L. s.l.   (Plate 58.1)
   20–80 cm tall; leaves with 2 leaflets and awn-like tip or tendril; flowers 3–13, yellow. Meadows, tall-herb stands, roadsides; medium soils; 300–2200 m; rather common. Eurosibirian plant group. F3, R3, N3, H3, D4, L3, T3, K3. Flowering time: 6–7.

   Yellow everlasting vetchling, *Lathyrus occidentalis* (Fisch. and Mey.) Fritsch *(L. laevigatus* auct.)   (Plate 58.2)
   20–60 cm tall; leaves with 8–10 leaflets and awn-like tip; flowers 3–12, light-yellow. Meadows, tall-herb stands; calciferous soils; 1100–2000 m; rather rare (esp. in the Northern Alps). Mountain plant of Central and Southern Europe (western). F3, R4, N3, H3, D4, L3, T2, K2. Flowering time: 6–7.

n. **Vetch.** *Vicia* L.
   Differs from the vetchling in the never winged stem, and the staminal tubes which are obliquely truncate. The Alpine flora includes only a few species.

   Tufted vetch, *Vicia cracca* L.   (Plate 58.3)
   20–80 cm tall; stem upright or climbing; leaves with 12–20 leaflets and a branched tendril; flowers blue-violet, in unilateral, 15–40-flowered racemes. Meadows, bushes, arable fields; medium soils; 300–2300 m; rather common. Eurosibirian plant. F3, R3, N3, H3, D4, L4, T3, K4. Flowering time: 6–8.

Wood vetch, *Vicia silvatica* L. (Plate 58.4)
50–150 cm tall; stem prostrate or climbing; leaves with 12–18 leaflets; leaf tendril usually branched; flowers white with violet tinged standard and violet keel tip, in 10–20-flowered racemes. Light woods, clearings, bushes; medium soils; 600–2100 m; not common. Eurosibirian plant. F3, R3, N3, H3, D4, L3, T3, K2. Flowering time: 6–8.

30th family: **cranesbill family,** *Geraniaceae*

a. **Cranesbill,** *Geranium* L.
Leaves palmately divided; flowers actinomorphic, with 5 free petals, and a long-beaked ovary. The genus is represented in the Alps by about 10 species.

Wood cranesbill, *Geranium silvaticum* L. (Plate 59.1)
30–70 cm tall; flowers measuring 1.5–2.5 cm in diameter, red-violet. Meadows, light woods, bushes; nutrient-rich soils; 700–2300 m; common. Eurosibirian plant. F3, R3, N4, H3, D4, L3, T2. K3. Flowering time: 6–7.

Dusky cranesbill, *Geranium lividum* L. Hérit *(G. phaeum* L. p.p.)
(Plate 59.2)
30–60 cm tall; flowers measuring 2–2.5 cm in diameter, with flat petals (flowers in other species are slightly bowl-shaped), light-violet to pink. Meadows, tall-herb stands; humid, nutrient-rich soils; 1000–2000 m; rather rare (mostly in the inner ranges). Alpine plant. F4, R3, N4, H3, D4, L3, T2, K3. Flowering time: 6–7.

Rivulet cranesbill, *Geranium rivulare* Vill. (Plate 59.3)
20–50 cm tall; flowers measuring 1–1.8 cm in diameter, white with red veins. Light woods, bushes, banks of streams; soils poor in calcium; 1600–2300 m; rather rare (grows only in the inner ranges). Plant of the western Alps. F3, R2, N3, H4, D4, L3, T2, K3. Flowering time: 7–8.

Bloody cranesbill, *Geranium sanguineum* L. (Plate 59.4)
20–60 cm tall; flowers measuring 2.5–4 cm in diameter, purple. Light woods, bushes, rocky slopes; dry soils; 400–1700 m; not common. Central European plant. F2, R3, N2, H3, D3, L3, T4, K4. Flowering time: 6–7.
Protected: *BL,* ZH.

31st family: **flax family,** *Linaceae*

a. **Flax,** *Linum* L.
Alpine flax, *Linum alpinum* Jacq. (Plate 60.1)
10–30 cm tall; leaves narrowly lanceolate, densely distributed on the stem; flowers with 5 free petals, measuring 2–3 cm in diameter, blue. Meadows, rocky slopes; dry, stony, calcium-rich soils; 1400–2200 m;

rather rare (occurs above all in the outer ranges). Mountain plant of Central and Southern Europe. F2, R5, N2, H3, D3, L4. T2, K3. Flowering time: 6–7.

32nd family: **spurge family,** *Euphorbiaceae*

a. **Spurge,** *Euphorbia* L.
Plants poisonous, with milky sap. Female and male flowers grouped in false flowers; calyx and corolla missing. There are only a few species in the Alps.

Cypress spurge, *Euphorbia cyparissias* L.   (Plate 60.2)
15–45 cm tall; leaves narrowly lanceolate, densely distributed on the stem; flowers enveloped in yellow, oval leaves. Meadows, grassland, scree, forest edges; dry, meagre soils; 300–2600 m; rather common. Central European plant. F2, R3, N2, H3, D4, L4, T3, K3. Flowering time: 6–7.

33rd family: **milkwort family,** *Polygalaceae*

a. **Milkwort,** *Polygala* L.
Leaves entire, smooth-edged; flowers zygomorphic; both lateral sepals (wings) corolla-like; petals united. The family is represented in the Alps by about 10 species.

Shrubby milkwort, *Polygala chamaebuxus* L.   (Plate 60.3)
5–20 cm tall; woody at the base; leaves lanceolate, leathery; flowers 1–1.5 cm long; wings white, less frequently purple; corolla yellow. Light woods, bushes, dwarf shrub stands; intermittently dry, base-rich soils; 600–2400 m; rather common. Mountain plant of Central and Southern Europe. F2w, R4, N2, H3, D3, L3, T2, K3. Flowering time: 4–7.
Protected: *BL.*

Subalpine milkwort, *Polygala alpestris* Rchb.   (Plate 60.4)
5–15 cm tall; not woody; leaves not leathery, oval to lanceolate; the lower leaves shorter than the upper ones; flowers 4–6 mm long, blue-violet. Grassland, pastures; dry, base-rich soils; 1200–2500 m; rather common. Mountain plant of Central and Southern Europe. F2, R4, N2, H3, D3, L4, T2, K3. Flowering time: 6–7.

34th family: **buckthorn family,** *Rhamnaceae*

a. **Buckthorn,** *Rhamnus* L.
Shrubs; leaves entire, with small stipules; flowers small, unisexual, tetra- or pentameric; fruit: a berry. The family is represented in the Alps by only a few species.

Dwarf buckthorn, *Rhamnus pumila* Turra (Plate 61.1)
Carpet-forming shrub, mostly clinging to the ground; leaves round-ed-oval, with fine teeth; flowers small, yellow-green; fruits blue-black. Rock crevices; calcium-rich substratum; 1000–2500 m; not common. Mountain plant of Central and Southern Europe (southern). F1, R4, N2, H2, D1, L4, T2, K4. Flowering time: 6–7.

Alpine buckthorn, *Rhamnus alpina* L. (Fig. 35G, p. 132)
Shrub up to more than 2 m tall; leaves oval, with fine teeth; flowers greenish; fruits blue-black. Cliffs, boulders, bushes; dry, calciferous soils; 600–2100 m; rather rare (nearly exclusively in the western part). Mountain plant of Central and Southern Europe (western). F2, R4, N2, H3, D2, L3, T3, K4. Flowering time: 5–6.

35th family: **maple family,** *Aceraceae*

a. **Maple,** *Acer* L.
Sycamore, *Acer pseudoplatanus* L. (Fig. 36C, p. 133)
Tree up to 30 m tall; leaves divided to about half-way, palmate, 5-lobed; lobes more or less ovate, acute, coarsely and irregularly crenate-serrate; flowers inconspicuous, yellowish-green, in pendulous racemose inflorescences; fruits: schizocarps splitting into 2 samaras, wings of fruits spreading at an acute to obtuse angle. Foliage woods, pastures; intermittently humid, nutrient-rich soils; 400–1700 m; rather common (above all in the outer ranges). Central European plant. F3w, R3, N4, H3, D4, L2, T3, K2. Flowering time: 5.

36th family: **St. John's-wort family,** *Hypericaceae*

a. **St. John's-wort,** *Hypericum* L.
Leaves mostly opposite; flowers with mostly 5 free petals and numerous stamens. The genus is represented in the Alps by about 10 species.

Spotted St. John's-wort, *Hypericum maculatum* Crantz *(H. quadran-gulum* auct.) (Plate 61.2)
20–50 cm tall; stem quadrangular; leaves oval, with translucent dots; flowers measuring 1.5–2 cm in diameter, yellow (turning blood-red when crushed); stamens in 3 bunches; ovary with 3 styles. Meadows, pastures, bushes; intermittently humid, nutrient-rich soils; 1200–2500 m; rather common. Eurosibirian plant. F4w, R3, N4, H4, D5, L3, T2, K3. Flowering time: 6–8.

37th family: **rockrose family,** *Cistaceae*

a. **Rockrose,** *Helianthemum* Miller
Leaves entire, the lower ones opposite; flowers with 5 free petals and numerous stamens; ovary with 1 style and a trifid stigma. Like the whole family, the rockrose mostly grows in the Mediterranean area; the Alpine flora includes about 6 species.

Large-flowered rockrose, *Helianthemum grandiflorum* (Scop.) Lam.
(Plate 61.3)
10–20 cm tall; woody at the base; leaves lanceolate, pilose, with small, very narrowly lanceolate stipules; flowers measuring 2–3 cm in diameter, yellow. Grassland, dwarf shrub stands; dry soils; 1500–2700 m; rather common. Mountain plant of Central and Southern Europe. F2, R3, N2, H3, D4, L4, T2, K3. Flowering time: 6–8.

Alpine rockrose, *Helianthemum alpestre* (Jacq.) DC.   (Plate 61.4)
5–10 cm tall; woody at the base; leaves lanceolate, virtually glabrous, without stipules; flowers measuring 1–1.5 cm in diameter, yellow. Open grassland, rocky slopes; stony, calcium-rich, wind-exposed soils; 1000–2900 m; not common. Mountain plant of Central and Southern Europe. F2, R5, N2, H3, D2, L5, T1, K4. Flowering time: 6–7.

38th family: **violet family,** *Violaceae*

a. **Violet** or **pansy,** *Viola* L.
Leaves with stipules; flowers zygomorphic; petals 5, free; the lowest petal with a spur; ovary one, superior. The genus is represented in the Alps by about 20 species.

Alpine pansy, *Viola calcarata* L.   (Plate 62.1)
3–12 cm tall; leaves obtusely dentate, oval to lanceolate; stipules ¼–½ as long as the leaves, with 0–2 lobes on either side; flowers measuring 2.5–3.5 cm in diameter, violet, less frequently yellow or white, with dark streaks and a yellow spot at the base. Spur 1–1.5 cm long. Pastures, scree; medium soils; 1600–2800 m; rather common. Plant of the western Alps. F3, R3, N2, H3, D3, L5, T1, K3. Flowering time: 6–8.
Protected: *FR, NW, OW*/L.

Two-flowered violet, *Viola biflora* L.   (Plate 62.2)
5–15 cm tall; leaves reniform, obtusely dentate; stipules small, oval; flowers measuring 1–1.5 cm in diameter, yellow, with brown streaks at the base; spur 1–3 mm long. Tall-herb stands, alder thicket, under boulders; intermittently humid, nutrient-rich soils; 900–2500 m; rather common. Eurosibirian-North European plant. F4w, R3, N4, H4, D5, L2, T2, K2. Flowering time: 5–8.
Protected: OW.

Mountain pansy, *Viola lutea* Huds. (Plate 62.3)

Differs from the alpine pansy as follows: up to 20 cm tall; stipules pinnate below; flowers always yellow; spur 0.5–1.2 cm long. Rocky slopes, open grassland; dry, meagre, stony, calciferous soils (but it grows upon granite in the Vosges); 1400–2100 m; rare (only in the NW Alps). Mountain plant of Central and Southern Europe. F2, R4, N2, H4, D3, L4, T2, K2. Flowering time: 6–8.
Protected: *OW*.

Mt. Cenis violet, *Viola cenisia* L.

Differs from the alpine pansy as follows: long creeping stolons; leaves smooth-edged; stipules smooth-edged; flowers light-violet, measuring 2–2.5 cm in diameter, without dark streaks; spur 1–1.2 cm long. Calcareous scree, or boulder fields; 1900–2600 m; rare (above all in the northern and western ranges). Plant of the western Alps. F3, R5, N1, H2, D2↑, L5, T1, K2. Flowering time: 7–8.
Protected: *FR, NW, OW*.

Wild pansy, *Viola tricolor* L. (Plate 62.4)

15–30 cm tall; leaves obtusely dentate; the lower leaves rounded-oval, the upper ones lanceolate; stipules ½ to almost as long as the leaves, pinnate, with 2–5 lobes on either side; flowers measuring 1.5–2.5 cm in diameter, violet-blue or yellow; sometimes the upper petals violet-blue or white and the lower ones yellow with dark streaks and a yellow spot at the base; spur 0.4–0.8 mm long. Meadows, roadsides, arable fields; medium soils; 300–2100 m; rather common. Eurosibirian plant. F3, R3, N3, H3, D4, L3, T2, K3. Flowering time: 5–7.

Pinnate violet, *Viola pinnata* L. (Fig. 46)

5–15 cm tall; leaves palmately divided, 3–5-partite, with narrowly oval segments; stipules small, lanceolate; flowers measuring 1–1.5 cm in diameter, light-violet. Scree, talus, light woods, open grassland; dry, stony, calcium-rich soils; 1200–2300 m; rare (almost exclusively in the inner ranges). Alpine plant. F1, R5, N2, H2, D2, L4, T3, K4. Flowering time: 6.
Protected: *TI/Ao/F*.

Fig. 46. Pinnate violet
(Viola pinnata). ⅓× (from *6.1.k.*).

Sand violet, *Viola rupestris* F. W. Schmidt *(V. arenaria* DC.)
(Plate 63.1)
3–8 cm tall; leaves rounded-cordate, obtusely dentate; stipules small, narrowly oval; flowers measuring 0.8–1.4 cm in diameter, light blue-violet; spur 3–5 mm long. Light pine woods, open grassland, rocky slopes; dry, stony soils; 600–2500 m; not common (occurs above all in the inner ranges). Eurosibirian plant. F1, R3, N1, H3, D3, L3, T3, K4. Flowering time: 5–6.

39th family: **spurge-laurel family,** *Thymelaeaceae*

a. **Mezereon,** *Daphne* L.
Poisonous small shrubs; leaves entire, smooth-edged; flowers with 4 sepals united at the base, without petals; ovary single, superior; fruit fleshy, one-seeded. There are about 5 species in the Alps.

Common mezereon, *Daphne mezereum* L. (Plate 63.2)
25–100 cm tall; leaves lanceolate, up to 10 cm long; flowers appearing before leaves, terminally arranged in a spicate group, pink, silky out-side; fruits scarlet, spherical. Woods, tall-herb stands, coarse scree; calciferous soils; 400–2400 m; not common. Eurosibirian plant. F3, R4, N3, H3, Dx, L2, T3, K3. Flowering time: 4–7.
Protected: *AG, AI, AR, BE*ₙ, *BL,* GE, *GL, GR, JU, NW, OW, SG, SH, SO, SZ, TG,* UR, *ZH/B/Ti,* Vo/Li/*Bz, Tn,* L, *Ao.*

Alpine mezereon, *Daphne alpina* L. (Plate 63.3)
20–60 cm tall; leaves oval to lanceolate, up to 5 cm long; flowers appearing after leaves, 2–10, in an umbel-like terminal group, white, silky outside; fruits red, obovate. Rocky slopes, boulders; dry, stony, calcium-rich soils; 600–2000 m; rare. Mountain plant of Central and Southern Europe (southern). F1, R4, N2, H3, D1, L4, T3, K4. Flowering time: 5–6.
Protected: R. *CH*/Bz, Tn, L.

Striated mezereon, *Daphne striata* Tratt. (Plate 63.4)
5–15 cm tall; leaves narrowly oval, up to 2.5 cm long; flowers termi-nal, in 5–15-flowered, head-like group, fragrant, glabrous outside; fruits brown-orange, obovate. Pine forests, pastures, dwarf shrub stands; stony, meagre soils; 1700–2700 m; rather common (only east of Obwalden–Binntal). Plant of the eastern Alps. F2, R4, N2, H4, D3, L3, T2, K3. Flowering time: 6–7.
Protected: *AR, GL, NW, OW, SG,* SZ, *UR/B/*Ti, Vo/*Bz, Tn,* L/F.

40th family: **willowherb family,** *Oenotheraceae (Onagraceae)*

a. **Willowherb,** *Epilobium* L.
Leaves entire; petals 4; ovary inferior; fruits rod-shaped; seeds with a mop of hair. The genus is represented in the Alps by about 20 species.

Fireweed or **narrow-leaved willowherb,** *Epilobium angustifolium* L.
(Plate 64.1)
50–150 cm tall; leaves narrowly lanceolate, smooth-edged, 5–20 cm long, alternate; flowers purple, measuring 1.5–2.5 cm in diameter, in a terminal, multi-flowered, upright raceme. Forest clearings, bushes, gravel pits, scree; stony, nutrient-rich soils poor in calcium; 400–2500 m; rather common. Eurosibirian-North American plant. F3, R2, N4, H3, D3, L3, T3, K4. Flowering time: 6–8.

Alpine willowherb, *Epilobium alpestre* (Jacq.) Krocker (Plate 64.2)
30–80 cm tall; leaves broadly lanceolate, dentate, 3–10 cm long, in groups of 3 (rarely of 4), verticillate; flowers 3–10, terminal, red. measuring 1–1.8 cm in diameter. Tall-herb stands, green alder thicket; humid, nutrient-rich soils; 1300–2200 m; rather common (above all in the outer ranges). Mountain plant of Central and Southern Europe. F4, R4, N4, H4, D4, L3, T2, K2. Flowering time: 6–8.

Chickweed willowherb, *Epilobium alsinifolium* Vill. (Plate 64.3)
5–25 cm tall; with long underground stolons; leaves broadly lanceolate, 3–6 cm long, dentate, opposite; flowers 1–6, pink, measuring 1–1.5 cm in diameter, in a nodding terminal inflorescence; peduncles and fruits virtually glabrous. Flushes; wet soils; 1200–2600 m; rather common. North European-Alpine plant. F5, R3, N3, H3, D4, L4, T2, K2. Flowering time: 7–8.

Pimpernel-leaved willowherb, *Epilobium alpinum* L. *(E. anagallidifolium* Lam.)
Differs from the chickweed willowherb as follows: short aboveground stolons (no underground stolons); leaves up to 2 cm long, without distinct teeth; flowers measuring 0.5–1 cm in diameter; peduncles and fruits virtually glabrous. Scree, snow-patches, flushes; humid, calcium-rich soils; 1500–2800 m; rather common (esp. in the inner ranges). Mountain plant of Central and Southern Europe (western). F4, R2, N2, H2, D2, L4, T1, K2. Flowering time: 7–8.

Nodding willowherb, *Epilobium nutans* Schmidt
Differs from the preceding as follows: flowers light-violet; peduncles and fruits densely tomentose with clinging hairs. Flushes, banks of streams; wet soils poor in calcium; 1600–2400 m; not common. Mountain plant of Central and Southern Europe. F5, R2, N2, H4, D4, L4, T2, K2. Flowering time: 7–8.

Fleischer's willowherb, *Epilobium fleischeri* Hochst. (Plate 64.4)
10–30 cm tall; creeping; leaves alternate, narrowly lanceolate, 1–4 cm long and at most 0.3 cm wide, smooth-edged; flowers red, measuring 1.5–2.5 cm in diameter, terminal, in a short upright raceme. Alluvial areas, talus; stony, base-rich soils; 1000–2400 m; not common. Alpine plant. F3w, R4, N3, H2, D2, L5, T2, K3. Flowering time: 7–8.

194

41st family: **carrot family,** *Umbelliferae (Apiaceae)*

Often aromatic; leaves mostly with a broad, sheath-like base encircling the stem segmented by nodes; flowers in mostly compound umbels or in heads, small; petals 5, free; ovary inferior, with 2 styles. The family is represented in the Alps by far more than 50 species, partly very difficult to determine.

a. **Masterwort,** *Astrantia* L.

Leaves palmately divided; flowers in simple umbels, enveloped in white or red, lanceolate bracts. There are 3 species in the Alps.

Small masterwort, *Astrantia minor* L.　　　　　(Plate 65.1)
    10–40 cm tall; leaves divided to the base; umbels measuring 1–1.5 cm in diameter, enveloped in white bracts. Grassland, bushes, rock crevices; soils poor in calcium and nutrients; 1200–2500 m; not common (occurs above all in the Central and Southern Alps). Mountain plant of Central and Southern Europe (western). F3, R2, N2, H4, D4, L3, T2, K3. Flowering time: 7–8.
    Protected: AR, SG.

Big masterwort, *Astrantia major* L.　　　　　(Plate 65.2)
    30–100 cm tall; leaves divided not quite to the base; umbels measuring 2–3 cm in diameter, enveloped in reddish or white bracts. Meadows, tall-herb stands; base-rich soils; 700–2000 m; rather common. Mountain plant of Central and Southern Europe. F3, R4, N3, H3, D4, L3, T2, K3. Flowering time: 6–8.
    Protected: *AI,* AR, NW, OW, SG, *SH,* ZH.

b. **Hare's-ear,** *Bupleurum* L.

Leaves entire, smooth-edged; umbels enveloped in green, conspicuous bracts, forming a compound umbel; flowers yellow-green. The Alpine flora includes about 10 species.

Stellar hare's-ear, *Bupleurum stellatum* L.　　　　(Plate 65.3)
    10–30 cm tall; leaves narrowly lanceolate, net-veined; bracts of the umbels united up to more than the middle, and forming a cupular envelope. Grassland, rock crevices; dry soils poor in calcium and nutrients; 1700–2700 m; not common (almost exclusively in the inner ranges). Plant of the western Alps. F2, R2, N2, H3, D3, L4, T1, K4. Flowering time: 7–8.

Crowfoot-leaved hare's-ear, *Bupleurum ranunculoides* L. (Plate 65.4)
    10–40 cm tall; leaves narrowly lanceolate, with 9–20 linear veins; bracts of the umbels free or virtually free. Grassy, steep slopes; dry, calcium-rich soils poor in nutrients; 1200–2400 m; not common (almost exclusively in the outer ranges). Mountain plant of Central and Southern Europe. F2, R5, N2, H3, D3, L4, T2, K4. Flowering time: 7–8.

c. **Laser**, *Laserpitium* L.

Leaves repeatedly divided; umbels without, or with exceedingly small bracts, forming a compound umbel; fruit with 4 wingy ridges on either side. The genus is represented in the Alps by about 6 species.

Haller's laser, *Laserpitium halleri* Crantz (Plate 66.1)

15–50 cm tall; leaves 2–3-pinnate, with at least 1 mm wide, up to 4 mm long segments; bracts with membranous margins; flowers white. Meadows, grassland; dry, meagre soils poor in calcium; 1400–2700 m; not common (almost exclusively in the inner ranges). Plant of the middle part of the Alps. F2, R2, N2, H3, D4, L4, T2, K4. Flowering time: 6–8.

Broad-leaved laser, *Laserpitium latifolium* L. (Plate 66.2, Fig. 47D)

30–150 cm tall; leaves 1–2-pinnate, with ultimate segments oval, cordate at the base, 3–15 cm long; bracts with membranous margins; flowers white. Meadows, bushes, light woods; intermittently dry, base-rich soils; 600–2400 m; not common. Central European plant. F2w, R4, N3, H2, D5, L3, T3, K4. Flowering time: 7–8.

Gaudin's laser, *Laserpitium gaudinii* Moretti (Fig. 47E)

Differs from the broad-leaved laser as follows: the ultimate segments deeply 3-partite; bracts mostly missing; flowers yellowish-green. Pine forests, grassland, talus; dry soils poor in nutrients; 1000–2400 m; not common (almost exclusively in the central and southern ranges). Plant of the middle part of the Alps. F2, R3, N2, H2, D3, L3, T2, K4. Flowering time: 7–8.

Mountain laser, *Laserpitium siler* L. (*Siler montanum* Crantz) (Fig. 47C)

30–150 cm tall; leaves 3–4-pinnate, with ultimate segments lanceolate and smooth-edged; bracts with membranous margins; flowers white. Scree, rock crevices; dry, calcium-rich substratum; 600–2000 m; not common. Mountain plant of Central and Southern Europe. F2, R5, N2, H2, D2, L4, T3, K4. Flowering time: 6–7.

d. **Cow parsnip** or **hogweed**, *Heracleum* L.

Common hogweed, *Heracleum sphondylium* L. s.l. (Plate 66.3)

30–150 cm tall; leaves simply pinnate, leaflets broadly oval, pinnatisect, serrate; flowers white, rarely pink. Meadows, tall-herb stands; nutrient-rich soils; 200–2400 m; common. Eurosibirian plant group. F3, R3, N4, H4, D4, L3, T3, K3. Flowering time: 6–9.

The Alpine flora includes various microspecies of the group. **Mantegazzi's hogweed** (*Heracleum mantegazzianum* Somm. and Levier) introduced from the Caucasus is up to 3.5 m tall and has enormous leaves; it occurs occasionally as an escapee in tall-herb stands, on roadsides, and banks of streams.

e. **Masterwort**, *Peucedanum* L.

Masterwort, *Peucedanum ostruthium* (L.) Koch (Plate 66.4)

30–100 cm tall; leaves 3-ternate with petioled leaflets, segments oval, dentate; flowers white. Tall-herb stands, alder thicket, rock piles; nutrient-rich soils; 1400–2700 m; rather common. Alpine plant. F3, R3, N4, H4, D4, L3, T2, K3. Flowering time: 6–8.

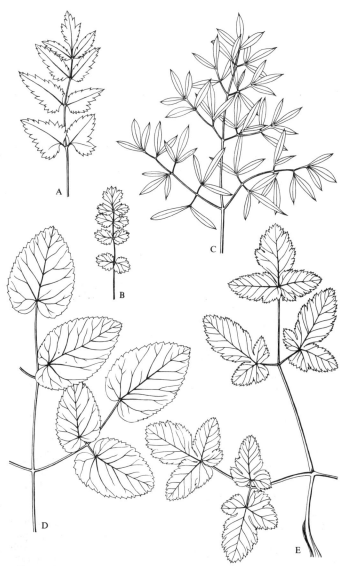

Fig. 47. Plants of the carrot family. A: greater burnet-saxifrage *(Pimpinella major)*. B: burnet-saxifrage *(Pimpinella saxifraga)*. C: mountain laser *(Laserpitium siler)*. D: broad-leaved laser *(Laserpitium latifolium)*. E: Gaudin's laser *(Laserpitium gaudinii)*. ⅓ ×.

f. **Burnet-saxifrage,** *Pimpinella* L.

Greater burnet-saxifrage, *Pimpinella major* (L.) Huds. (Fig. 47A)
30–80 cm tall; leaves simply pinnate; leaflets 3–9, oval, rounded, or cordate at the base, acute, dentate; no bracts; flowers white, or reddish. Meadows, tall-herb stands; soils rather rich in nutrients; 600–2000 m; rather common. Central European plant. F3, R3, N4, H3, D4, L3, T3, K3. Flowering time: 6–9.

Lesser burnet-saxifrage, *Pimpinella saxifraga* L. (Fig. 47B)
Differs from the preceding as follows: 20–50 cm tall; leaves with 7–11 rounded leaflets. Meadows, light woods; dry soils; 400–2000 m; not common. Eurosibirian plant. F2, R3, N2, H3, D4, L4, T3, K4. Flowering time: 7–10.

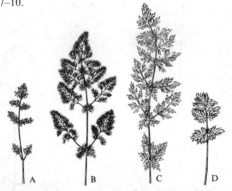

Fig. 48. Plants of the carrot family. A: athamantha *(Athamanta cretensis)*. B: spignel *(Meum anthamanticum)*. C: caraway *(Carum carvi)*. D: alpine lovage *(Ligusticum mutellina)*. ⅓ ×.

g. **Athamantha,** *Athamanta* L.

Athamantha, *Athamanta cretensis* L. (Plate 67.1; Fig. 48A)
10–30 cm tall; leaves repeatedly divided, with pinnate segments; segments 0.2–1 mm wide and 2–10 mm long; umbels enveloped in small, membranous bracts; flowers white, pilose outside (petals). Scree, rock crevices; calcium-rich substratum; 900–2500 m; not common. Mountain plant of Central and Southern Europe. F2, R5, N2, H2, D2, L5, T2, K4. Flowering time: 5–7.

h. **Caraway,** *Carum* L.

Caraway, *Carum carvi* L. (Fig. 48C)
30–70 cm tall; squarrosely branched; leaves 2–3-pinnate, with pinnatisect segments which are 0.5–1 mm wide and 5–15 mm long; umbels enveloped in small bracts; flowers white or reddish, glabrous outside; fruits used as a spice (the caraway). Meadows, pastures, roadsides; medium soils; 400–2200 m; common. Eurosibirian plant. F3, R3, N3, H3, D4, L4, T3, K3. Flowering time: 6–9.

i. **Spignel,** *Meum* Miller
Spignel, *Meum athamanticum* Jacq. (Fig. 48B)
    20–50 cm tall; leaves 3-pinnate; leaf segments capillary, 2–6 mm long, acute; umbels not enveloped in bracts; flowers white, glabrous. Pastures, heaths; acid soils poor in nutrients; 800–2500 m; rare. European mountain plant. F3, R2, N2, H4, D4, L4, T2, K2. Flowering time: 6–8.

k. **Lovage,** *Ligusticum* L.
Alpine lovage, *Ligusticum mutellina* (L.) Crantz
(Plate 67.2; Fig. 48D)
    10–30 cm tall; leaves 2-pinnate; leaf segments about 1 mm wide and 3–10 mm long; umbels enveloped in narrowly lanceolate, smooth-edged bracts; petals white to red, glabrous. Meadows, pastures, alder thicket; medium soils; 1500–2700 m; common. Mountain plant of Central and Southern Europe. F3, R3, N3, H3, D4, L4, T2, K2. Flowering time: 6–8.

Dwarf alpine lovage, *Ligusticum mutellinoides* (Crantz) Vill. *(L. simplex* [L.] All.)
    Differs from the preceding as follows: 3–15 cm tall; tips of the bracts often 3-partite. Open grassland, hilltops; stony, wind-exposed soils; 2000–3000 m; not common (occurs mostly in the northern ranges). Mountain plant of Central and Southern Europe (eastern). F3, R3, N2, H4, D3, L5, T1, K4. Flowering time: 7–8.

l. **Chervil,** *Chaerophyllum* L.
    Leaves repeatedly divided, pinnate; umbels enveloped in small bracts, forming a compound umbel; fruit narrowly cylindrical, with 2-partite beak. There are about 8 species in the Alps.

Mountain chervil, *Chaerophyllum cicutaria* Vill. *(Ch. hirsutum* auct.)
(Plate 67.3)
    20–100 cm tall; the lowest leaflet of the first rank nearly as large as the remainder of the leaf-blade; leaves and stem virtually glabrous, or with only a few bristly hairs; flowers white or reddish. Meadows, tall-herb stands, banks of streams; humid, nutrient-rich soils; 600–2200 m; common. Central European plant. F4, R3, N4, H3, D4, L3, T3, K2. Flowering time: 6–7.

Villar's chervil, *Chaerophyllum villarsii* Koch
    Differs from the mountain chervil as follows: the lowest leaflets of the first rank much smaller than the remainder of the leaf-blade; the lower leaf surface and the stem with spreading, bristly hairs; flowers white. Meadows, light woods, tall-herb stands; intermittently dry soils; 1200–2400 m; rather common. Mountain plant of Central and Southern Europe. F3w, R3, N3, H3, D4, L3, T2, K3. Flowering time: 6–8.

m. **Eryngo,** *Eryngium* L.
Alpine eryngo, *Eryngium alpinum* L. (Plate 67.4)
    30–60 cm tall; leaves triangular-oval, cordate at the base, sharply dentate; flowers in a blue spadix enveloped in blue, pinnatisect, long-awned bracts. Tall-herb stands, meadows; humid, nutrient-rich, cal-

ciferous soils; 1500–2300 m; rare (above all in the west). Mountain plant of Central and Southern Europe (eastern). F3, R4, N4, H3, D4, L4, T2, K2. Flowering time: 7–8.
Protected: *CH/Vo/Li/F.*

42nd family: **wintergreen family,** *Pyrolaceae*

a. **Wintergreen,** *Pyrola* L.
Leaves winter-green, leathery, entire; petals 5, free; ovary single, superior. The genus is represented in the Alps by 6 species.

One-flowered wintergreen, *Pyrola uniflora* L. *(Moneses uniflora* [L.] Gray) (Plate 68.1)
5–15 cm tall; leaves rounded; flowers single, terminal, measuring 1.5–2.5 cm in diameter, wheel-shaped, nodding, white. Coniferous forests; acid, humous soils poor in nutrients; 1000–2000 m; not common. Eurosibirian-North American plant. F3, R2, N2, H5, D4, L2, T2, K3. Flowering time: 6–8.
Protected: *BL, SH.*

Serrated wintergreen, *Pyrola secunda* L. *(Orthilia secunda* [L.] House) (Plate 68.2)
10–20 cm tall; leaves broadly lanceolate, acute; flowers up to 30, in a narrow, unilateral raceme, 3–4 mm long, narrow bell-shaped, yellow-green. Woods; humous soils; 600–2200 m; not common. Eurosibirian-North American plant. F3, R3, N2, H5, D4, L2, T3, K3. Flowering time: 6–7.
Protected: *SH.*

Round-leaved wintergreen, *Pyrola rotundifolia* L. (Plate 68.3)
10–30 cm tall; leaves rounded; flowers 8–30, in a multilateral, narrow raceme, measuring 8–15 mm in diameter, broad bell-shaped, white or rarely pink. Forests, bushes; stony, humous soils; 600–2400 m; rather common. Eurosibirian-North American plant. F3, R3, N2, H5, D3, L2, T2, K3. Flowering time: 7–9.
Protected: *GE, SH/F.*

43rd family: **crowberry family,** *Empetraceae*

a. **Crowberry,** *Empetrum* L.
Crowberry, *Empetrum hermaphroditum* (Lange) Hagerup *(E. nigrum* auct.) (Plate 68.4)
Dwarf shrub 10–20 cm tall; leaves almost needle-like, 4–5 mm long and 1–1.5 mm wide; flowers singly in the leaf axils, red, each with 3 free sepals and petals, 3 stamens and a superior ovary; fruit spherical, berry-like, dark-blue. Dwarf shrub stands; humous soils poor in calcium and nutrients; 1700–2600 m; rather common (above all in the inner ranges). Eurosibirian-North American plant. F3, R2, N2, H5, D4, L4, T2, K3. Flowering time: 5–6.

44th family: **heath family,** *Ericaceae*

Plants woody; leaves entire, often leathery. Petals 4–7, mostly united; ovary superior, or inferior, with 1 style. The family is represented in the Alps by about 15 species.

a. **Ling heather,** *Calluna* Salisb.
  Ling heather, *Calluna vulgaris* (L.) Hull   (Plate 69.1)
  Dwarf shrub 10–50 cm tall; leaves scale-like, 1–3 mm long and 0.3–0.6 mm wide; flowers in compact,, upright, unilateral racemes, nodding, pink, with 4 petals, narrow bell-shaped; fruit in form of a capsule. Dwarf shrub stands, heaths, pastures, mires; meagre, humous soils poor in calcium; 400–2600 m; rather common. Eurosibirian plant. F3, R2, N1, H5, D4, L3, T2, K3. Flowering time: 7–10.
    Protected: GE.

b. **Heath,** *Erica* L.
  Common heath, *Erica carnea* L. *(E. herbacea* L.)   (Plate 69.2)
  Dwarf shrub 10–30 cm tall; leaves needle-shaped, 6–10 mm long and 0.8–1.2 mm wide; flowers in compact, upright, unilateral racemes, nodding, red, with 4 petals, globular to subcylindrical but strongly contracted at the mouth; fruit: a capsule. Pine forests, grassland; dry, humous, calciferous soils; 500–2500 m; rather common. Mountain plant of Central and Southern Europe (eastern). F2, R4, N2, H4, D3, L3, T2, K4. Flowering time: 3–6.
    Protected: GE, *ZH*.

c. **Alpenrose,** *Rhododendron* L.
  Poisonous shrub; sepals and petals 5; fruit: a capsule. The Alpine flora includes 2 species.

  Hairy alpenrose, *Rhododendron hirsutum* L.   (Plate 69.3)
  Dwarf shrub 30–80 cm tall; leaves oval, green underneath, with flat, ciliate margins; corolla about 1.5 cm long, narrow bell-shaped, pink. Pine forests, dwarf shrub stands; humous, calciferous soils with late-lying snow; 800–2500 m; not common (occurs above all in the outer ranges). Plant of the eastern Alps. F3, R4, N2, H5, D4, L3, T2, K2. Flowering time: 6–7.
    Protected: AR, *BE$_n$,* LU, NW, OW, SG, *TI, ZH/B*/Li/L/F.

  Rust-leaved alpenrose, *Rhododendron ferrugineum* L.   (Plate 69.4)
  Differs from the hairy alpenrose as follows: leaves narrowly oval, leathery, rust-brown underneath, with glabrous revolute margins; corolla red. Forests, dwarf shrub stands; humous soils poor in calcium, with late-lying snow; 1000–2500 m; rather common. Mountain plant of Central and Southern Europe. F3, R2, N2, H5, D4, L3, T2, K2. Flowering time: 6–7.
    Protected: *AG,* AR, *BE$_n$,* LU, NW, OW, SG, VD$_j$, *ZH/B*/Li/L.

d. **Whortleberry,** *Vaccinium* L.
  Leaves rounded, oval, or broadly lanceolate; ovary inferior; fruit spherical, berry-like. There are 4 species in the Alps.

Blueberry, *Vaccinium myrtillus* L.   (Plates 70.1 and 70.2)
Dwarf shrub 10–50 cm tall; leaves summer-green, green on both sides, finely dentate; flowers green, often tinged purple; berries blue-black, with dark juice. Forests, dwarf shrub stands; acid, humous soils; 300–2600 m; common. Eurosibirian plant. F3, R1, N2, H5, D4, L2, T3, K3. Flowering time: 5–6.

Alpine bilberry, *Vaccinium gaultherioides* Bigelow *(V. uliginosum* auct.)   (Plate 70.2)
Dwarf shrub 10–20 cm tall; leaves summer-green, blue-green above, grey-green below, smooth-edged; flowers white to pink; berries blue, with light juice. Forests, dwarf shrub stands; acid, humous soils; 1500–2700 m; rather common (esp. in the inner ranges). Eurosibirian-North American plant. F3, R1, N2, H5, D4, L3, T2, K3. Flowering time: 6–7.
The closely related, slightly larger **bog bilberry** *(Vaccinium uliginosum* L.) occurs in bogs (also at lower altitudes).

Cowberry, *Vaccinium vitis-idaea* L.   (Plate 70.3)
Dwarf shrub 5–25 cm tall; leaves evergreen, leathery, smooth-edged, deep green above, lighter-coloured below, margins slightly revolute; flowers white; berries red. Forests, dwarf shrub stands, pastures; humous soils poor in bases; 600–2700 m; rather common. Eurosibirian-North American plant. F3, R2, N2, H5, D4, L3, T2, K3. Flowering time: 6–7.

d. **Alpine azalea,** *Loiseleuria* Desv.
Trailing azalea, *Loiseleuria procumbens* (L.) Desv.   (Plate 70.4)
Shrub forming flat carpets; leaves oval, 4–7 mm long and 1.5–2 mm wide, leathery, evergreen; flowers small, with 5 free red sepals and 5-partite, united, broadly bell-shaped, light-pink corolla; fruit: a capsule. Ridges, hilltops, dwarf shrub stands; dry, humous soils poor in bases and nutrients; 1800–2800 m; rather common. Arctic-Alpine plant. F2, R2, N1, H4, D3, L5, T1, K4. Flowering time: 6–7.

e. **Bearberry,** *Arctostaphylos* Adans.
Flowers nodding, globular to subcylindrical but strongly contracted at the mouth; fruit berry-like. The Alpine flora includes 2 species.

Common bearberry, *Arctostaphylos uva-ursi* (L.) Sprengel
          (Plate 71.1)
Dwarf shrub 5–10 cm tall; leaves evergreen, leathery, green on both sides, not dotted underneath, with flat, entire, glabrous margins; flowers white or pink; fruit red. Light woods, dwarf shrub stands, pastures; dry, meagre soils; 600–2600 m; rather common. Eurosibirian-North American plant. F2, R3, N2, H3, D3, L3, T2, K4. Flowering time: 5–7.

Alpine bearberry, *Arctostaphylos alpina* (L.) Sprengel   (Plate 71.2)
Dwarf shrub 5–20 cm tall; leaves summer-green, green on both sides (red in autumn); with finely dentate margins and ciliate at the base; flowers pink or greenish; fruit red when young, virtually black when

ripe. Light pine woods, dwarf shrub stands; humous, base-containing soils with late-lying snow; 1800–2600 m; not common. Eurosibirian-North American plant. F3, R3, N2, H5, D3, L3, T2, K2. Flowering time: 5–6.

45th family: **primrose family,** *Primulaceae*

Herbs; leaves entire; flowers each with 5 united sepals and petals; stamens 5, inserted in the corolla tube; ovary superior; fruit: a capsule. The family is represented in the Alps by far more than 30 species, amongst them many typical mountain plants.

a. **Snowbell,** *Soldanella* L.
Leaves leathery, circular to reniform, entire, smooth-edged; corolla bell-shaped to funnel-shaped, with 5, fringe-like, laciniate segments. The Alpine flora includes 6 species.

Dwarf, or **delicate snowbell,** *Soldanella pusilla* Baumg. (Plate 71.3)
4–8 cm tall; stem one-flowered; corolla narrowly bell-shaped, incised at most to one/third, light-violet. Snow-patches, grassland; humid soils poor in bases with late-lying snow; 1800–2800 m; rather common (esp. in the inner eastern ranges, reaches west to the Kandertal–Simplon). Mountain plant of Central and Southern Europe (eastern). F3, R2, N2, H4, D4, L5, T1, K2. Flowering time: 6–8.
Protected: AR.

Alpine snowbell, *Soldanella alpina* L. (Plate 71.4)
5–15 cm tall; stem mostly 2–3-flowered; corolla funnel-shaped, incised far deeper than the uppermost ⅓, blue-violet. Meadows, pastures, snow-patches; humid, base-rich soils; 1100–2700 m; rather common. Mountain plant of Central and Southern Europe. F4, R3, N3, H4, D4, L4, T2, K2. Flowering time: 5–7.
Protected: AR.

b. **Primrose,** *Primula* L.
Leaves in a basal rosette; flowers in an umbel; corolla wheel-shaped, with a long tube. The genus is represented in the Alps by about 15 species.

Oxlip, *Primula elatior* L. (Plate 72.1)
5–25 cm tall; leaves oval, mostly contracted at the base, irregularly dentate; corolla light-yellow, with 5–10 mm long, shallowly notched lobes. Woods, meadows; nutrient-rich soils; 300–2600 m; rather common. Central European plant. F3, R3, N4, H4, D4, L2, T3, K3. Flowering time: 4–7.

Cowslip, *Primula veris* L. (Plate 72.2)
5–20 cm tall; leaves oval, mostly contracted to cordate at the base, irregularly dentate; corolla deep yellow with orange spots, with 2.5–6 mm long, shallowly notched lobes. Meadows; intermittently

humid, meagre, base-rich soils; 400–2100 m; not common. Central European plant. F3w, R4, N2, H4, D5, L4, T3, K3. Flowering time: 5–7.

Haller's primrose, *Primula halleri* J. F. Gmel. *(P. longiflora* All.)
(Plate 72.3)
8–25 cm tall; leaves lanceolate, contracted into petiole, almost smooth-edged, whitish with meal underneath; calyx much shorter than the corolla tube; corolla red-violet, with 7–10 mm long, deeply emarginate lobes. Grassland; calcium-rich soils; 1800–2500 m; rare (occurs only in the inner ranges). Mountain plant of Central and Southern Europe (eastern). F2, R5, N2, H4, D3, L4, T2, K4. Flowering time: 6–7.
Protected: R. *Ti.*

Bird's-eye primrose, *Primula farinosa* L.   (Plate 72.4)
5–20 cm tall; leaves oval, contracted into petiole, finely dentate to smooth-edged, with whitish meal underneath; calyx only a little shorter than the corolla tube; corolla red-lilac, with 4–7 mm long, deeply emarginate lobes. Fens, flushes, grassland; intermittently humid, base-rich, meagre soils; 500–2800 m; not common. Eurosibirian-North American plant. F4w, R4, N2, H4, D5, L4, T2, K3. Flowering time: 6–7.
Protected: *AG, BE$_n$, JU, NE, SH, TG, ZH/B/*Ti.

Glutinous primrose, *Primula glutinosa* Wulfen   (Plate 73.1)
3–8 cm tall; leaves oval, gradually narrowing into petiole, sticky, dentate in the distal part; calyx about as long as the corolla tube; corolla deep blue, later violet, with a dark ring by the entrance to the throat; corolla lobes 4–7 mm long, deeply emarginate. Grassland, stabilized scree; humous soils poor in calcium; 2500–2800 m; rare (may be found from Arosa eastwards). Plant of the eastern Alps. F2, R2, N2, H4, D3, L5, T1, K2. Flowering time: 7–8.
Protected: R. *B/*Ti.

Auricula, *Primula auricula* L.   (Plate 73.2)
5–20 cm tall; leaves broadly lanceolate, gradually narrowing into petiole, grey-green, with meal on the margins, smooth-edged or with single teeth; calyx ⅓–½ as long as the corolla tube; corolla golden-yellow, with meal by the entrance to the throat, lobes 6–10 mm long, emarginate. Rock crevices, open grassland; calciferous substratum; 600–2500 m; not common. Mountain plant of Central and Southern Europe (eastern). F3w, R5, N2, H3, D2, L4, T2, K3. Flowering time: 5–7.
Protected: *AG, AR, BL, BS, BE, FR, GL, GR, JU, LU, NW, OW, SG, SO, SZ, TI, UR, ZH/B/*Ti, Vo/Li/*Bz, Tn, L/F.*

Entire-leaved primrose, *Primula integrifolia* L.   (Plate 73.3)
2–5 cm tall; leaves lanceolate, small, gradually narrowing towards the base (almost no petiole), virtually glabrous, smooth-edged; calyx ½–¾ as long as the corolla tube; corolla red-violet, white by the entrance to the throat, without meal, lobes 6–10 mm long, deeply emarginate. Hollows, snow-patches, open grassland; humid soils poor

in calcium, with late-lying snow; 1800–2900 m; rather common (above all in the inner ranges). Mountain plant of Central and Southern Europe (western). F4, R2, N2, H4, D4, L4, T1, K2. Flowering time: 6–7.
Protected: SG, *TI/B/Ti.*

Stinking primrose, *Primula hirsuta* All. (Plate 73.4)
3–10 cm tall; leaves oval, gradually narrowing into a short petiole, slightly sticky, dentate; calyx ⅓–½ as long as the corolla tube; corolla violet-pink, white by the entrance to the throat, without meal, lobes 6–10 mm long, deeply emarginate. Grassland, stabilized scree, rock crevices; stony soils poor in calcium; 1500–2800 m; rather common (esp. in the inner ranges). Mountain plant of Central and Southern Europe (western). F3, R2, N2, H3, D2, L4, T2, K3. Flowering time: 5–7.
Protected: *OW,* SG/*B*/Ti/*F.*

Broad-leaved primrose, *Primula latifolia* Lapeyer. *(P. viscosa* All.)
5–15 cm tall; leaves oval, gradually narrowing into petiole, slightly sticky, dentate; calyx ⅓–½ as long as the corolla tube; corolla violet, blue-violet when old, the entrance to the throat of the same colour but with meal, lobes 4–7 mm long, emarginate. Boulders, coarse scree; substratum poor in calcium; 2000–3000 m; rare (occurs only in the inner ranges). Mountain plant of Central and Southern Europe (western). F3, R1, N2, H3, D2, L4, T1, K3. Flowering time: 6–7.
Protected: SG/*B*/*F.*

c. **Rock-jasmine,** *Androsace* L.
Leaves in a basal rosette, or arranged like tiles on a roof; flowers single, or in an umbel-like inflorescence; corolla wheel-shaped, with a short tube; 5 yellow (often reddish when old) scales by the entrance to the throat. The Alpine flora includes more than 15 species of the genus.

Ciliate rock-jasmine, *Androsace chamaejasme* Wulfen (Plate 74.1)
3–12 cm tall; leaves in a basal rosette, lanceolate, smooth-edged, with 0.5–1 mm long, simple hairs on margins; stem with 0.5–2 mm long, simple hairs; flowers 2–8; corolla with 3–5 mm long, mostly emarginate lobes, white, often reddish when old. Grassland, ridges; stony, calciferous, meagre soils; 1500–2800 m; rather common. Arctic-Alpine plant. F2, R4, N2, H4, D3, L4, T1, K3. Flowering time: 6–7.
Protected: *CH.*

Rock-jasmine with obtuse leaves, *Androsace obtusifolia* All.
(Plate 74.2)
5–10 cm tall; leaves in a basal rosette, narrowly lanceolate, smoothedged; leaves and stem with single, 1–3-radial hairs; flowers 2–8; corolla with 2–3 mm long, mostly emarginate lobes, white or reddish. Grassland, pastures; meagre, humous soils poor in calcium; 1800–2800 m; rather common (esp. in the inner ranges). Mountain plant of Central and Southern Europe (eastern). F3, R2, N2, H4, D4, L4, T1, K3. Flowering time: 7–8.
Protected: *CH*/No.

Milk-white rock-jasmine, *Androsace lactea* L.   (Plate 74.3)
5–20 cm tall; leaves in a basal rosette, narrowly lanceolate, smooth-edged, with short, 1–3-radial hairs, otherwise the leaves and stem glabrous; flowers 1–6; corolla with 4–4.5 mm long, distinctly emarginate lobes, white. Rock crevices, open grassland; calcium-rich substrata; 800–2200 m; rather rare (in Switzerland only in the Jura and NW Alpine ranges). Mountain plant of Central and Southern Europe (eastern). F2, R5, N2, H3, D1, L4, T2, K3. Flowering time: 6–7.
Protected: *CH*.

Flesh-coloured rock-jasmine, *Androsace carnea* L.   (Plate 74.4)
3–8 cm tall; leaves in a basal rosette, narrowly lanceolate, smooth-edged; leaf margins, leaf-blade as well as the stem with 1–8-radial hairs; flowers 1–8; corolla with 2–3.5 mm long, mostly emarginate lobes, pink. Open grassland; humous soils poor in calcium; 2000–3000 m; not common (only in the inner ranges west of the Simplon). Mountain plant of Central and Southern Europe (western). F3, R2, N2, H4, D4, L4, T1, K3. Flowering time: 5–7.
Protected: *CH*.

Vandelli's rock-jasmine, *Androsace vandellii* (Turra) Chiov. *(A. imbricata* Lam.)   (Plate 75.1)
Forms half-dome-shaped cushions up to 3 cm high, with leaves arranged like tiles on a roof; leaves narrowly oval, small, whitish tomentose (hairs multi-radial); flowers single; flower stalks as long as the leaves; corolla with 2–3 mm long, emarginate lobes, white or reddish. Rock crevices; substratum poor in calcium; 1600–3200 m; rare (occurs only in the inner ranges). Mountain plant of Central and Southern Europe (western). F2, R1, N1, H2, D1, L5, T1, K4. Flowering time: 7.
Protected: *CH*.

Alpine rock-jasmine, *Androsace alpina* (L.) Lam. *A. glacialis* Hoppe)
(Plate 75.2)
Forms flat carpets; leaves in basal rosettes, small, with 2–8-radial hairs; flowers single; flower stalks up to twice as long as the leaves; corolla with 2–3 mm long, mostly emarginate lobes, pink. Stabilized scree; stony, humid soils poor in calcium, with late-lying snow; 2400–3000 m (sporadically grows higher than 4000 m); not common (occurs only in the inner ranges). Alpine plant. F4, R2, N2, H2, D2, L5, T1, K2. Flowering time: 7–8.
Protected: *CH/Ti/Ao*.

Swiss rock-jasmine, *Androsace helvetica* (L.) All.   (Plate 75.3)
Differs from the Vandelli's rock-jasmine as follows: leaves with simple hairs, grey-green; flower stalks much shorter than the leaves. Rock crevices; calcium-rich substratum; 2000–3000 m; not common (absent in the southernmost ranges). Mountain plant of Central and Southern Europe (western). F2, R4, N1, H2, D1, L5, T1, K4. Flowering time: 5–7.
Protected: *CH/Ti*.

Woolly rock-jasmine, *Androsace villosa* L. (Plate 75.4)
Differs from the ciliate rock-jasmine as follows: 2–5 cm tall; rosettes form dense carpets; hairs on the leaf margin and those on the lower leaf surface 1–2 mm long. Open grassland; stony, calcium-rich soils, often free of snow in winter; 1500–2500 m; very rare (in Switzerland only in the southern Jura). Mountain plant of Central and Southern Europe (southern). F2, R4, N2, H3, D3, L5, T2, K4. Flowering time: 6–7.
Protected: R. *CH.*

Charpentier's rock-jasmine, *Androsace brevis* (Hegetschw.) Cesati *(A. charpentieri* Heer) (Plate 76.1)
Differs from the alpine rock-jasmine as follows: hairs 2–3-radial; single peduncles 2–3 times as long as leaves; corolla lobes mostly emarginate. Stabilized scree, ridges; stony, wind-exposed soils poor in calcium; 2000–2700 m; very rare (in Switzerland only east of Bellinzona). Rhaetic-Bergamo plant. F2, R2, N2, H3, D2, L5, T1, K4. Flowering time: 6–7.
Protected: R*. R. *CH.*

Yellow rock-jasmine, *Androsace vitaliana* (L.) Lap. *(Douglasia vitaliana* [L.] Benth. and Hook.) (Plate 76.2)
Forms loose carpets; up to 2 cm tall; leaves in basal rosettes, narrowly lanceolate, with 2–6-radial hairs on the margins; flower stalks shorter than leaves; flowers single; corolla with 4–9 mm long, emarginate lobes, yellow; 1800–2800 m; rare (only in the inner southern ranges). Mountain plant of Central and Southern Europe (western). F3, R2, N2, H3, D2, L5, T1, K3. Flowering time: 6–7.
Protected: *CH//Ti.*

Downy rock-jasmine, *Androsace pubescens* DC.
Differs from the alpine rock-jasmine as follows: hairs on leaves 1–2-radial; corolla white. Coarse scree, rock crevices; stony, calciferous soils; 2000–3400 m; rare. Mountain plant of Central and Southern europe (western). F3, R4, N1, H3, D1, L5, T1, K3. Flowering time: 6–7.
Protected: R. *CH.*

d. **Starflower,** *Trientalis* L.
Chickweed wintergreen, *Trientalis europaea* L. (Plate 76.3)
6–25 cm tall; leaves in the terminal part of the stem verticillate, lanceolate; flowers singly in axils of the upper leaves; corolla starshaped, measuring 1–1.5 cm in diameter, white. Light coniferous woods; humid, acid, humous soils; 800–2000 m; exceedingly rare (only a few localities in Switzerland). Eurosibirian-North American plant. F4, R2, N2, H5, D4, L3, T2, K2. Flowering time: 6–7.
Protected: R. *GR, SZ/F.*

e. **Cyclamen,** *Cyclamen* L.
European cyclamen, *Cyclamen europaeum* L. *(C. purpurascens* Miller) (Plate 76.4)
5–15 cm tall; plant with a tuber; leaves reniform to cordate, deep green above, reddish below; flowers single; corolla with a short tube,

207

and 5 reflected lobes, carmine-red, fragrant. Foliage woods; stony, calciferous soils; 400–1300 m; rather rare (occurs exclusively in the southern Alpine ranges as well as at the southern foot of the Jura). Mountain plant of Central and Southern Europe. F3, R4, N3, H3, D3, L2, T4, K2. Flowering time: 6–9.

Protected: *AG, BE, FR,* GE, GL, *GR, JU, NW, OW,* SG, SO, SZ, *TI,* UR/*B*/Ti, Vo/L/*Ao.*

f. **Cortusa,** *Cortusa* L.
   Cortusa, *Cortusa matthioli* L. (Plate 77.1)
20–50 cm tall; leaves rounded-cordate, measuring up to 10 cm in diameter, lobate and dentate; flowers 5 – 10, in an umbel; corolla purple, 7–12 mm long. Bushes, tall-herb stands, flushes; intermittently humid, base-rich soils; 1200–1900 m; rather rare (in Switzerland only the Lower Engadine and the valley of Münster). Mountain plant of Central and Southern Europe (eastern). F4w, R4, N3, H3, D5, L3, T2, K3. Flowering time: 6–7.

Protected: R. *Ao/F.*

46th family: **sea-lavender family,** *Plumbaginaceae*

a. **Thrift,** *Armeria* Willd.
   Alpine thrift, *Armeria alpina* (DC.) Willd. *(Statice montana* Mill.)
(Plate 77.2)
5–20 cm tall; leaves gramineous, in a basal rosette; flowers in a head-like, 2–3 cm thick inflorescence enveloped in membranous bracts; petals 5, united, pink; ovary single, superior. Grassland; stony soils poor in calcium; 1700–2900 m; rather rare (occurs only in the central and southern ranges). Mountain plant of Central and Southern Europe. F2, R2, N2, H3, D3, L4, T1, K4. Flowering time: 7–8.

Protected: *CH*/L, *So.*

47th family: **gentian family,** *Gentianaceae*

Leaves opposite, entire, and smooth-edged, glabrous, mostly with parallel principal veins; sepals and petals 4–5, united; ovary superior; fruit: a capsule. The family is represented in the Alps by about 50 species, amongst them many typical mountain plants.

a. **Felwort,** *Lomatogonium* A. Br.
   Carinthian felwort, *Lomatogonium carinthiacum* (Wulfen) Rchb.
(Plate 77.3)
2–12 cm tall; annual; leaves oval to lanceolate; flowers single, terminal, star-shaped, measuring 1–2 cm in diameter; corolla light-blue, rarely white. Alluvial areas; intermittently wet, meagre soils; 1400–2500 m; exceedingly rare (only a few localities in the inner ranges). Eurasiatic mountain plant. F4w , R3, N2, H2, D3, L4, T2, K4. Flowering time: 8.

b. **Felwort,** *Swertia* L.

Marsh felwort, *Swertia perennis* L. (Plate 77.4)
15–40 cm tall; leaves oval to lanceolate, stem quadrangular; flowers in terminal panicles, star-shaped, measuring 2–3 cm in diameter; corolla deep violet, dark-mottled. Fens, flushes; wet, calciferous, humous soils; 700–1800 m; rather rare (esp. the northern ranges). Central European plant. F5, R4, N2, H5, D5, L4, T2, K2. Flowering time: 7–8.
Protected: BE, *GL,* JU, *NE,* SG, *ZH.*

c. **Gentian,** *Gentiana* L.
Corolla bell-, or funnel-shaped; fruit spindle-like. The genus is varied and presents great difficulties to the taxonomist. It is represented in the Alps by about 50 species. Rhizomes of larger species (esp. those of the yellow gentian) are used in some sorts of bitter liquor.

Yellow gentian, *Gentiana lutea* L. (Plate 78.1)
50–100 cm tall; leaves broadly lanceolate, blue-green; flowers distinctly pedicellate, in groups of 3–10 in axils of the upper leaves; corolla broadly bell-shaped, 5–6-partite nearly to the base, yellow. Pastures, meadows, tall-herb stands; base-rich soils; 1000–2400 m; rather common (above all in the northern ranges). Mountain plant of Central and Southern europe. F3, R4, N3, H3, D4, L4, T2, K2. Flowering time: 6–7.
Protected: BE, BL, GL, JU, LU, NW, *OW, SH,* SZ/*B*/Ti, Vo/L, *So.*

Dotted gentian, *Gentiana punctata* L. (Plate 78.2)
20–60 cm tall; leaves lanceolate, green, shiny; flowers sessile, 1–3 in axils of the upper leaves; corolla narrowly bell-shaped, only in the distal part 5–8-partite, light-yellow with reddish dots. Pastures, grassland, dwarf shrub stands; meagre soils poor in calcium; 1400–2600 m; rather common (esp. in the inner ranges). Mountain plant of Central and Southern Europe (eastern). F3, R2, N2, H3, D4, L4, T2, K3. Flowering time: 7–8.
Protected: BE, GL, *NW, OW,* SZ/*B*/Ti, Vo.

Purple gentian, *Gentiana purpurea* L. (Plate 78.4)
Differs from the preceding as follows: calyx incised to the base on one side; corolla purple, dark-mottled, yellow inside. Pastures, tall-herb stands; bushes; soils poor in bases; 1600–2300 m; not common. Scandinavian-Alpine plant. F3, R2, N2, H4, D4, L4, T2, K2. Flowering time: 7–8.
Protected: BE, GL, LU, NW, *OW, SG,* SZ, UR/L, *So.*

Pannonic gentian, *Gentiana pannonica* Scop.
Differs from the dotted gentian in the following characters: calyx with 5 recurved lobes; corolla nearly to the middle 5–8-partite, red-violet, dark-mottled, yellowish inside. Pastures, tall-herb stands; nutrient-rich, base-rich soils; 1500–2200 m; rare (in Switzerland only in the Churfirsten). Plant of the eastern Alps. F3, R3, N4, H3, D4, L4, T2, K2. Flowering time: 7–8.
Protected: *SG*/*B*/Ti, Vo.

Willow gentian, *Gentiana asclepiadea* L. (Plate 78.3)
30–80 cm tall; leaves lanceolate, green; flowers sessile, 1–3 in axils of the upper leaves; corolla narrowly bell-shaped, with 5 lobes, dark-blue, with violet dots inside. Straw meadows, forests on slopes, pastures; intermittently humid, calciferous soils; 600–2200 m; rather common. Mountain plant of Central and Southern Europe. F4w, R4, N3, H3, D5, L3, T3, K3. Flowering time: 8–9.
Protected: *AG,* BE, *BL,* BS, *GE,* GL, JU, OW, *SH, TG,* ZH/*B*/Ti, Vo, Ao, L.

Koch's gentian, *Gentiana kochiana* Perr. and Song *(G. acaulis* auct.)
(Plate 79.1; Fig. 49B)
4–8 cm tall; leaves lanceolate, soft; flowers single; calyx lobes 1.5–2 times as long as wide, connected by white membranous stripes which are ¼ to nearly as long as the calyx lobes; corolla narrowly bell-shaped, dark-blue, with olive-green vertical stripes inside. Pastures, grassland; meagre soils poor in calcium; 1200–2800 m; rather common. Mountain plant of Central and Southern Europe. F3, R2, N2, H3, D4, L4, T2, K3. Flowering time: 5–7.
Protected: AR, *BE*ₙ, BE, GL, NW, OW, SG, SZ, UR, *ZH*/*B*/Vo/Li/Ao, L.

Clusius's gentian, *Gentiana clusii* Perr. and Song. (Fig. 49A)
Differs from the preceding as follows: leaves tough; calyx lobes 2.5–3.5 times as long as wide; the connecting membranous stripes at most ⅙ as long as the calyx lobes; corolla without the olive-green, vertical stripes. Grassland, rocky ledges; 1000–2800 m; rather common. Mountain plant of Central and Southern Europe (eastern). F2, R5, N2, H3, D3, L5, T2, K4. Flowering time: 5–7.
Protected: *AG,* AR, *BE*ₙ, BE, *BL,* GL, *JU,* NW, OW, SG, SO, SZ, UR, ZH/*B*/Vo/Li/Ao, L.

Spring gentian, *Gentiana verna* L. (Plate 79.4)
Basal leaves in a rosette, acute, much larger than the cauline leaves; calyx cylindrical, ⅗–¾ as long as the corolla tube, angles narrowly winged; corolla cylindrical with 5 spreading lobes (separated by 2-par-

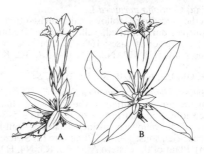

Fig. 49. A: Clusius's gentian *(Gentiana clusii)*. B: Koch's gentian *(Gentiana kochiana)*.
⅓ × .

tite, upright, white teeth), deep blue. Pastures, meadows, grassland; intermittently humid, base-rich, meagre soils; 600–2900 m; rather common (formerly occurred also in the Swiss Midlands). Mountain plant of Central and Southern Europe. F3w, R4, N2, H3, D4, L4, T2, K3. Flowering time: 4–7.

Protected: *AG*, BE, *BL, GE,* JU, NW, OW, *SH, SO, TG, ZH/B.*

Short-leaved gentian, *Gentiana brachyphylla* Vill. (Plate 79.2)
Differs from the preceding as follows: basal leaves not longer than 1 cm, only slightly larger than the cauline leaves; calyx not winged on the angles, ⅖–⅗ as long as the conspicuously thin corolla tube. Open grassland, coarse scree; stony soils poor in calcium; 2000–3000 m (occasionally grows higher than 4000 m); not common (nearly exclusive to the inner ranges). Mountain plant of Central and Southern Europe (western). F3, R2, N2, H3, D3, L5, T1, K4. Flowering time: 7–8.

Protected: BE, GL, NW, OW/*B*/Ao, L.

Bavarian gentian, *Gentiana bavarica* L. (Plate 79.3)
Differs from the spring gentian as follows: lower cauline leaves gathered in a group but not in rosette, broadly rounded in the distal part, up to about 1 cm long; calyx very narrowly winged on the angles, ½–⅔ as long as the corolla tube. Flushes, snow-patches, coarse scree; humid soils with late-lying snow; 1600–3000 m; not common. Alpine plant. F4w, R3, N2, Hx, Dx, L4, T1, K2. Flowering time: 7–8.

Protected: BE, GL, NW, OW, SZ/*B*/Ao, L.

Field gentian, *Gentiana campestris* L. *(Gentianella campestris* [L.] Börner) (Plate 80.1)
Mostly biennial; 3–20 cm tall; stem branched, tetragonous; flowers in axils of the upper leaves; calyx quadripartite almost to the base, with 2 broadly lanceolate, and 2 narrowly lanceolate lobes; corolla with 1–3 cm long tube and 4 spreading, 6–10 mm long lobes; throat barbed, violet. Pastures; intermittently dry, meagre soils; 1000–2500 m; rather common. North European-Alpine plant. F3w, R3, N2, H3, D4, L4, T2, K3. Flowering time: 7–9.

Protected: *AG*, BE, GL, JU, OW, ZH/*B*/L.

Scabrous gentian, *Gentiana aspera* Hegetschw. *(G. germanica* auct.)
Differs from the preceding as follows: calyx lobes 5, unequal, united in the lowest third; corolla lobes 5, 9–15 mm long, and 5–10 mm wide, blue-violet. Pastures, scree; stony, meagre, calciferous soils; 1400–2200 m; not common. Plant of the eastern Alps. F2, R4, N2, H3, D4, L4, T2, K3. Flowering time: 7–9.

Protected: BE, GL, OW, SZ/*B*/Ti/L.

German gentian *(Gentiana germanica* L.) occurring at lower altitudes differs from the scabrous gentian in the narrower corolla lobes.

Branched gentian, *Gentiana ramosa* Hegetschw. (Plate 80.2)
May be distinguished from the field gentian by the following characters: calyx lobes 5, more or equal, united in the lower half; corolla lobes 5, with 6–9 mm long segments, lilac. Pastures; meagre soils poor in calcium; 1700–2800 m; not common (occurs only in the inner ranges).

211

Plant of the middle part of the Alps. F2, R2, N2, H3, D4, L4, T1, K3. Flowering time: 7–9.
Protected: BE, Ti/Li.

Tender gentian, *Gentiana tenella* Rottb. (Plate 80.4)
May be distinguished from the field gentian by the following characters: up to 10 cm tall; flowers much smaller; calyx lobes only slightly unequal; corolla tube 0.3–1 cm long; corolla lobes 3–6 mm long, violet or lilac. Open grassland, resting places of animals; nitrogen-rich, humous soils; 1600–2900 m; rather rare (occurs above all in the inner ranges). Arctic-Alpine plant. F3, R3, N4, H4, D4, L4, T1, K3. Flowering time: 7–9.
Protected: BE, GL, OW/*B*/L.

Fringed gentian, *Gentiana ciliata* L. (Plate 80.3)
10–20 cm tall; mostly biennial; stem simple or branched, tetragonous; flowers single; calyx 4-partite in the upper third, with 4 narrowly lanceolate lobes; corolla narrowly funnel-shaped, with 4 spreading, fringed lobes, blue. Grassy slopes, scree; stony, intermittently dry, calciferous soils; 600–2500 m; not common. Central European plant. F3w, R4, N2, H2, Dx, L3, T3, K3. Flowering time: 8–10.
Protected: *AG,* BE, *BL,* GL, JU, NW, OW, *SH,* SZ, TG, *ZH*/*B*/*Ti*/L.

Snow gentian, *Gentiana nivalis* L. (Plate 81.1)
2–15 cm tall; annual; stem thin, branched, multi-flowered; basal leaves in a rosette; calyx clinging to the corolla, not winged, with 5 narrowly lanceolate lobes; corolla cylindrical, with 1.2–1.7 cm long tube and 5 spreading lobes (between lobes occur 2-partite, upright, white teeth), deep blue. Grassland; meagre soils; 1500–2800 m; not common. Arctic-Alpine plant. F3, R3, N2, H3, D3, L4, T1, K3. Flowering time: 7–8.
Protected: BE, GL, OW, SZ/*B*.

Inflated gentian, *Gentiana utriculosa* L. (Plate 81.2)
Differs from the preceding as follows: calyx conspicuously inflated, with 2–3 mm broad wings on the angles; corolla tube 1.5–2.5 cm long. Fens, grassland; intermittently humid, base-rich soils; 600–2300 m; rather rare. Mountain plant of Central and Southern Europe (eastern). F4w, R4, N2, H3, D5, L4, T2, K3. Flowering time: 6–8.
Protected: *AG,* BE, GL, OW, *SH, SZ, TG, ZH*/*B*/L/*F*.

48th family: **milkweed family,** *Asclepiadaceae*

a. **Vincetoxicum,** *Vincetoxicum* Wolf
Common vincetoxicum, *Vincetoxicum officinale* Moench *(Cynanchum vincetoxicum* [L.] Pers.) (Plate 81.3)
30–90 cm tall; leaves opposite, lanceolate, shortly petiolate; flowers small, measuring 4–7 mm in diameter; corolla funnel-shaped, united at the base, with short corolla appendage, white to yellow-green; fruits

spindle-like; seeds with a mop of hair. Light woods, scree; stony, intermittently dry, calciferous soils; 600–1800 m; not common. Eurosibirian plant. F2, R4, N2, H2, Dx, L3, T3, K3. Flowering time: 6–8.

49th family: **bindweed family**, *Convolvulaceae*

a. **Dodder**, *Cuscuta* L.
   Common dodder, *Cuscuta epithymum* (L.) Murray   (Plate 81.4)
   Leafless, twining, parasite (on thyme, legumes, rockrose, etc.); stem very slender, filiform, greenish-white to reddish, attached to the host by small suckers; flowers in dense heads along the stem; corolla small, bell-shaped, 5-lobed, red or white; fruit in form of a spherical capsule. Grassland, pastures; dry, meagre soils; 600–2200 m; not common. Eurosibirian plant. F2, R3, N2, H3, D4, L4, T3, K3. Flowering time: 7–9.

50th family: **phlox family**, *Polemoniaceae*

a. **Jacob's ladder**, *Polemonium* L.
   Blue Jacob's ladder, *Polemonium coeruleum* L.   (Plate 82.1)
   30–70 cm tall; leaves pinnate; flowers in an upright panicle; corolla broadly funnel-shapped, 5-lobed, blue; ovary superior; fruit in form of a capsule. Bushes, tall-herb stands, resting places of animals; nutrient-rich soils; 1000–2300 m; rather rare (occurs only in the inner ranges east of the Hinterrhein valley). Eurosibirian plant. F3, R3, N4, H3, D4, L3, T2, K4. Flowering time: 6–8.
   Protected: L, So/F.

51st family: **borage family**, *Boraginaceae*

Leaves alternate, entire, very often with coarse and stiff hairs; flowers with 5 united sepals and petals, in characteristic scorpioidal cymes; corolla with scales in the throat; stamens inserted on the corolla; ovary superior, 4-lobed, with 1 style. The family is represented in the Alps by more than 20 species.

a. **Viper's bugloss**, *Echium* L.
   Viper's bugloss, *Echium vulgare* L.   (Plate 82.2)
   20–90 cm tall; with dense, coarse and stiff hairs; leaves lanceolate, slightly sinuate; corolla funnel-shaped, slightly zygomorphic,

14–22 mm long, first pink then blue. Grassland, roadsides; dry, stony, nutrient-rich soils; 200–2200 m; not common (occurs mainly in the Central and Southern Alps). Plant of the Mediterranean region. F1, R3, N4, H2, D3, L4, T5, K4. Flowering time: 6–9.

b. **Lungwort,** *Pulmonaria* L.
Narrow-leaved lungwort, *Pulmonaria angustifolia* L. s.l. (Plate 82.3)
10–25 cm tall; basal leaves large, lanceolate, softly hairy; corolla cylindrical in the lower part, funnel-shaped in the upper part, about 1.5 cm long, first red then blue-violet. Light woods, grassland; base-rich, humous soils; 1200–2600 m; rather rare (occurs in the central and southern ranges). Mountain plant of Central and Southern Europe. F3, R4, N3, H4, D4, L4, T2, K4. Flowering time: 6–7.

c. **Cerinthe,** *Cerinthe* L.
Glabrous cerinthe, *Cerinthe glabra* Miller *(C. alpina* Kit.)
(Plate 82.4)
30–45 cm tall; glabrous; leaves large, oval, encircling stem with obtuse lobes; corolla cylindrical, with 5 short lobes which are bent backward in the terminal part; lower part yellow, upper part tinged blue outside, with 5 red spots inside. Tall-herb stands, bushes; base- and nutrient-rich soils; 1200–2300 m; rather rare (occurs above all in the northern ranges). Mountain plant of Central and Southern Europe. F3, R4, N4, H3, D4, L3, T2, K2. Flowering time: 6–8.

d. **Forget-me-not,** *Myosotis* L.
Alpine forget-me-not, *Myosotis alpestris* W. F. Schmidt (Plate 83.1)
5–15 cm tall; with harsh hairs; leaves lanceolate; corolla with short tube and flat spreading lobes, measuring 5–7 mm in diameter, blue, with yellow scales at the entrance to the throat. Grassland, stabilized scree; stony, medium soils; 1600–2900 m; common. Mountain plant of Central and Southern Europe. F3, R3, N3, H3, D3, L4, T1, K3. Flowering time: 6–8.

e. **Scorpion grass,** *Eritrichium* Schrader
King of the Alps, *Eritrichium nanum* (L.) Schrader (Plate 83.2)
1–6 cm tall; silky tomentose; leaves oval, up to 1 cm long; corolla with a short tube and flat spreading lobes, measuring 5–8 mm in diameter, bright-blue, with yellow scales at the entrance to the throat; in contrast to the forget-me-not, the king of the Alps has one leaf at the base of each flower, and its fruits have winged and toothed margins. Rock crevices; substratum poor in calcium; 2500–3200 m; rather rare (occurs only in the inner ranges). Alpine plant. F3, R2, N2, H2, D2, L5, T1, K3. Flowering time: 7–8.
Protected: *CH/Ao,* L, *So/F.*

52nd family: **mint family,** *Labiatae (Lamiaceae)*

Aromatic; stem quadrangular; leaves cross-wise opposite; flowers arranged whorl-like in axils of the leaves, often forming a terminal group; corolla zygomorphic (two petals form the upper lip whereas the lower lip is mostly trilobed); stamens 4, inserted on the corolla; ovary superior, 4-lobed, with 2 stigmas. The family is represented in the Alps by more than 50 species.

a. **Germander,** *Teucrium* L.
   Mountain germander, *Teucrium montanum* L.   (Plate 83.3)
   Creeping semi-shrub 5–10 cm tall; leaves narrowly lanceolate, leathery, whitely tomentose underneath; corolla without upper lip, the lower lip 5-lobed with a large median part, yellowish-white. Rocky slopes, open grassland; dry, stony, calciferous soils; 600–2200 m; not common. Central European plant. F1, R4, N2, H2, D3, L4, T3, K4. Flowering time: 6–8.

b. **Dragonhead,** *Dracocephalum* L.
   Dragonhead of Ruysch, *Dracocephalum ruyschiana* L.   (Plate 83.4)
   10–30 cm tall; leaves narrowly lanceolate; corolla with a sickle-shaped upper lip and emarginate median segment of the lower lip, 2.5–3 cm long, blue-violet. Meadows, pastures; dry soils; 1400–2200 m; rather rare. Eurosibirian plant. F2, R3, N2, H3, D4, L4, T2, K4. Flowering time: 7–8.
   Protected: R. *CH/Ti/Li.*

c. **Horminum,** *Horminum* L.
   Pyrenean horminum, *Horminum pyrenaicum* L.   (Plate 84.1)
   10–25 cm tall; leaves in a basal rosette, oval, obtusely dentate; inflorescence unilateral; corolla with truncate to emarginate upper lip and emarginate median segment of the lower lip, violet. Pastures, meadows; stony, meagre, calcium-rich soils; 1200–2300 m; rare (the Grisons, the southernmost ranges). Mountain plant of Central and Southern Europe (western). F3, R5, N2, H3, D3, L4, T2, K4. Flowering time: 6–7.
   Protected: *TI.*

d. **Mint,** *Mentha* L.
   Horse mint, *Mentha longifolia* (L.) Huds. *(M. silvestris* L.)
                                               (Plate 84.2)
   30–80 cm tall; with a pungent smell of peppermint; leaves lanceolate, dentate, whitely tomentose underneath; inflorescence spicate; corolla with 4-lobed margin, 3–4 mm long, lilac to pink. Flushes, pastures, banks of streams; intermittently humid, base-, and nitrogen-rich soils; 500–1800 m; rather common. Eurosibirian plant. F4w, R4, N4, H3, D5, L3, T3, K3. Flowering time: 7–9.

e. Bugle, *Ajuga* L.

Pyramidal bugle, *Ajuga pyramidalis* L.   (Plate 84.3)
10–20 cm tall; plant densely leafed, pyramid-shaped; leaves oval, those in the inflorescence mostly red-violet; corolla with a short, straight, bilobed upper lip, and an emarginate median segment of the lower lip, 1–1.8 cm long, blue. Pastures; meagre soils poor in calcium; 1300–2500 m; rather common. North European-Alpine plant. F2, R2, N2, H4, D4, L4, T2, K3. Flowering time: 6–7.

f. Selfheal, *Prunella* L.

Large selfheal, *Prunella grandiflora* (L.) Scholler   (Plate 84.4)
5–30 cm tall; leaves oval, smooth-edged or shallowly notched; inflorescence head-like; corolla with helmet-shaped upper lip and a large, dentate median segment of the lower lip, 2–2.5 cm long, blue-violet. Light woods, open grassland; dry, meagre, calciferous soils; 500–2100 m; not common. Central European plant. F2, R4, N2, H3, D4, L4, T3, K4. Flowering time: 6–9.

g. Betony, *Betonica* L.

Fox-tail betony, *Betonica alopecuros* L.   (Plate 85.1)
Differs from the dense-flowered betony in the following characters: up to 50 cm tall; corolla 12–15 cm long, pale-yellow. Light woods, grassy slopes; stony, calcium-rich soils; 800–1900 m; rather rare (only in the southern ranges, and also in the Sefinen valley in the Bernese Oberland). Mountain plant of Central and Southern Europe (southern). F3, R5, N3, H4, D3, L3, T3, K3. Flowering time: 6–7.
Protected: R.

Dense-flowered betony, *Betonica hirsuta* L. *(Stachys densiflora* Benth.)   (Plate 85.2)
10–30 cm tall; leaf rosettes with long-petiolate, narrowly oval leaves which are cordate at the base and obtusely dentate; inflorescence head-like; corolla with helmet-shaped upper lip and a large, emarginate median segment of the lower lip, 1.5–2.2 cm long, red. Grassy slopes, dwarf shrub stands; meagre, dry soils; 1500–2300 m; rather rare (occurs only in the western and southern ranges). Mountain plant of Central and Southern Europe (western). F2, R3, N2, H3, D3, L3, T2, K2. Flowering time: 7–8.

h. Hemp-nettle, *Galeopsis* L.

Narrow-leaved hemp-nettle, *Galeopsis angustifolia* Ehrh. (Plate 85.3)
10–30 cm tall; leaves narrowly lanceolate, smooth-edged, or at most with 4 small teeth; corolla with tube enlarged in the distal part, helmet-shaped upper lip, and a dentate median segment of the lower lip, 1–2.2 cm long, purple; a small, upright, hollow tooth on each side of the entrance to the throat. Boulder fields, scree; dry, stony, calciferous soils; 600–1700 m; not common. Central European plant. F2, R5, N2, H2, D2, L4, T3, K4. Flowering time: 6–8.

216

Large-flowered hemp-nettle, *Galeopsis speciosa* Miller (Plate 85.4)
20–70 cm tall; coarsely and stiffly hairy; stem swollen at the nodes; leaves broadly lanceolate, toothed; corolla similar to *Galeopsis angustifolia* but 2.2–3 cm long yellow, with emarginate or truncate, deep violet-speckled median segment of the lower lip. Forest clearings, hedges, roadsides; nutrient-rich soils; 600–1900 m; rare (only in the eastern ranges). Plant of the eastern Europe. F3, R3, N5, H3, D4, L3, T3, K4. Flowering time: 7–9.

i. **Woundwort,** *Stachys* L.
Limestone woundwort, *Stachys alpina* L. (Plate 86.1)
60–100 cm tall; no basal rosette; leaves short-petiolate, oval, cordate at the base, dentate, pilose with short hairs; corolla with helmet-shaped upper lip, and large, bilobed median segment of the lower lip, 1.5–1.8 cm long, brown-purple, with coarse and stiff hairs outside. Light forests, tall-herb stands, resting places of animals; base-, and nitrogen-rich soils; 600–2000 m; not common. Plant of Central Europe. F3, R4, N4, H4, D4, L3, T3, K2. Flowering time: 7–9.

k. **Calamint,** *Satureja* L.
Alpine calamint, *Satureja alpina* (L.) Scheele (Plate 86.2)
10–20 cm tall; leaves small, oval, with a few teeth; corolla with flat, emarginate upper lip, and large, emarginate median segment of the lower lip, 1.2–2 cm long, purple-violet. Rocky slopes, open grassland; stony, dry, meagre soils; 800–2300 m; rather common. Mountain plant of Central and Southern Europe (southern). F2, R3, N2, H2, D3, L4, T3, K4. Flowering time: 7–8.

l. **Thyme,** *Thymus* L.
Wild thyme, *Thymus polytrichus* A. Kerner *(Th. serpyllum* auct.)
(Plate 86.3)
3–10 cm tall; flowering shoots growing from aboveground stolons; stem with short white hairs distributed all round; leaves small, leathery; corolla with almost flat, emarginate upper lip, and broad median segment of the lower lip, 3–6 mm long, purple. Pastures, scree, cliffs; stony, dry, meagre soils; 600–2900 m; rather common. Mountain plant of Central and Southern Europe. F2, R4, N2, H2, D2, L4, T2, K4. Flowering time: 6–8.
The Alpine flora includes many further species of thyme, difficult to distinguish between.

m. **Scullcap,** *Scutellaria* L.
Alpine scullcap, *Scutellaria alpina* L. (Plate 86.4)
10–40 cm tall; leaves oval, truncate or cordate; calyx with a single 2–5 mm long scale in the distal part; corolla with 3-lobed, blue-violet upper lip (larger segment helmet-shaped), and undivided, whitish lower lip 2.5–3 cm long. Scree, open grassland; stony, calciferous soils; 1500–2300 m; rare (occurs only in the SW ranges, northwards up to the Fribourg Alps). Mountain plant of Central and Southern Europe (southern). F2, R5, N2, H2, D2, L5, T2, K4. Flowering time: 6–8.

217

53rd family: **figwort family,** *Scrophulariaceae*

Leaves opposite or alternate; corolla zygomorphic or virtually actinomorphic, united; stamens mostly 5; ovary superior, undivided; stigma 1, undivided or bilobed. The family is represented in the Alps by about 100 species.

a. **Speedwell,** *Veronica* L.

Leaves mostly opposite; calyx 4- or 5-partite; corolla with a short tube and 4 spreading lobes; stamens 2. The Alpine flora includes more than 20 species of the genus.

Rock speedwell, *Veronica fruticans* Jacq. *(V. saxatilis* Scop.)
(Plate 87.1)
5–10 cm tall; stem woody at the base; leaves oval; inflorescence 1–10-flowered; calyx 5-partite, without glandular hairs; corolla measuring 10–15 mm in diameter, blue. Grassy slops, pastures; stony, dry soils mostly poor in calcium; 1000–2800 m; not common. North European-Alpine plant. F2, R3, N2, H2, D3, L4, T2, K4. Flowering time: 6–7.

Shrubby speedwell, *Veronica fruticulosa* L.   (Plate 87.2)
Differs from the rock speedwell as follows: inflorescence 5–20-flowered; calyx with glandular hairs; corolla pink with darker veins. Rock crevices, scree; stony, calcium-rich soils; 800–2400 m; not common. Mountain plant of Central and Southern Europe. F2, R5, N2, H2, D1, L4, T2, K4. Flowering time: 6–7.

Daisy-leaved speedwell, *Veronica bellidioides* L.   (Plate 87.3)
5–20 cm tall; leaves grouped rosette-like at the base, oval; inflorescence 3–10-flowered, umbel-like; calyx 4-partite, with glandular hairs; corolla measuring 6–9 mm in diameter, violet-blue. Grassland; meagre, humous soils; 1800–2800 m; rather common (esp. in the inner ranges). Mountain plant of Central and Southern Europe. F2, R1, N2, H4, D4, L4, T1, K3. Flowering time: 7–8.

Alpine speedwell, *Veronica alpina* L.   (Plate 87.4)
2–15 cm tall; leaves not in a rosette, oval; inflorescence 5–20-flowered umbel-like; calyx mostly 5-partite, sparsely pilose but without glandular hairs; corolla measuring 5–7 mm in diameter, blue. Snow-patches, scree, resting places of animals; humid, humous soils poor in bases; 1500–3000 m; rather common. Arctic-Alpine plant. F4, R2, N3, H4, D3, L4, T1, K2. Flowering time: 7–8.

Leafless speedwell, *Veronica aphylla* L.   (Plate 88.1)
2–8 cm tall; leaves grouped rosette-like at the base, oval, mostly toothed in the distal part, with sparse hairs; flowers 2–4, terminal, on a leafless stem; calyx 4-partite, with glandular hairs; corolla measuring 6–8 mm in diameter, lilac with darker veins. Scree, open grassland; calcium-rich, meagre, humous soils; 1500–2800 m; rather common. Mountain plant of Central and Southern Europe. F3, R5, N2, H4, D3, L4, T1, K3. Flowering time: 7–8.

Tender speedwell, *Veronica tenella* All. (Plate 88.2)
5–15 cm tall; forms loose tufts; leaves rounded to oval, smooth-edged or obtusely dentate, glabrous; calyx 4-partite, with glandular hairs; corolla measuring 6–8 mm in diameter, blue with darker veins. Resting places of animals, flushes, roadsides; humid, nutrient-rich soils; 1400–2500 m; rather common. Eurosibirian-North American plant. F4, R3, N4, H3, D4, L3, T2, K2. Flowering time: 6–9.

b. **Toadflax,** *Linaria* Miller
Alpine toadflax, *Linaria alpina* (L.) Miller (Plate 88.3)
2–10 cm tall; creeping; leaves in groups of 3–4, verticillate, narrowly lanceolate, fleshy, glabrous, bluish; flowers in a few-flowered, short raceme; calyx 5-partite; corolla with short tube spurred at the base, the upper lip bipartite, the lower one tripartite, blue to violet, with orange-yellow or paler palate. Scree; humid, base-rich, stony soils; 1200–3000 m (occasionally at lower altitudes when seeds brought down the mountain with water). Mountain plant of Central and Southern Europe. F4, R4, N2, H1, D2↑, L5, T1, K3. Flowering time: 6–8.
Protected: *NE, SO.*

c. **Balsam,** *Erinus* L.
Alpine balsam, *Erinus alpinus* L. (Plate 88.4)
5–20 cm tall; forms loose tufts; leaves in a basal rosette, oval to ligulate, smooth-edged or with single teeth, sparsely pilose; calyx 5-partite, with glandular hairs; corolla virtually actinomorphic, with short tube and 5 emarginate, flat spreading lobes, measuring 0.8–1.2 cm in diameter, lilac to violet-red. Rock crevices, coarse scree; calciferous substratum; 600–2200 m; not common (occurs above all in the western ranges). Mountain plant of Central and Southern Europe (western) F2, R5, N2, H2, D1, L4, T2, K3. Flowering time: 6–9.
Protected: *BL, SO.*

d. **Mullein,** *Verbascum* L.
Frequently tomentose; leaves oval, entire; flowers single, or in spicate bunches in axils of the upper leaves; calyx 5-partite; corolla almost actinomorphic, with short tube and flat spreading lobes. The genus is represented in the Alps by about 10 species, mostly difficult to distinguish between.

Thick-leaved mullein, *Verbascum crassifolium* DC. (Plate 89.1)
30–150 cm tall; cauline leaves often slightly decurrent; corolla measuring 1.5–3 cm in diameter, yellow. Bushes, pastures, rocky slopes; dry, nutrient-rich soils poor in bases; 1000–2000 m; not common. Plant of the western Alps. F2, R2, N4, H3, D3, L4, T2, K3. Flowering time: 6–7.

e. **Foxglove,** *Digitalis* L.
Flowers in unilateral, spicate racemes; calyx 5-partite; corolla with a long, campanulate tube constricted near the base, shortly 5-lobed; lobes unequal, recurved. There are only 3 species in the Alps; the **red foxglove** *(Digitalis purpurea* L.), cultivated in our gardens, occurs solely in the western Alps.

219

Big-flowered foxglove, *Digitalis grandiflora* Miller *(D. ambigua* Murr.) (Plate 89.2)
30–80 cm tall; corolla 3–4 cm long with the distal part measuring 1.5–2 cm in diameter, yellow with light-brown network inside, not bearded. Forest clearings, pastures, bushes; stony, nutrient-rich soils; 800–1900 m; not common. Eurosibirian plant. F3, R3, N4, H4, D3, L3, T3, K3. Flowering time: 6–8.
Protected: AG, *BL, GE, NW, OW, SH, TG,* ZH/*B*/Ti.

Small yellow foxglove, *Digitalis lutea* L. (Plate 89.3)
40–80 cm tall; corolla 2–2.5 cm long, with the distal part measuring 5–8 mm in diameter, light-yellow, bearded inside. Light woods, bushes; base-rich soils; 600–1600 m; not common. Plant of Central Europe. F3, R4, N3, H4, D4, L3, T3, K2. Flowering time: 6–8.
Protected: AG, GE, *NW, OW, SH, TG,* ZH/*B*/Ti.

f. **Tozzia,** *Tozzia* L.
Alpine tozzia, *Tozzia alpina* L. (Plate 89.4)
Biennial hemiparasite[15]; 15–50 cm tall; leaves opposite, lanceolate, with few teeth; calyx 4-partite; corolla with short tube and 5 spreading lobes (indistinctly two-lipped), measuring 6–8 mm in diameter, yellow with purple-dotted lower lip. Tall-herb stands, banks of streams; humid, base-, and nutrient rich soils; 1200–2400 m; not common. Mountain plant of Central and Southern Europe. F4, R4, N4, H3, D4, L2, T2, K2. Flowering time: 6–7.

g. **Cow-wheat,** *Melampyrum* L.
Annual hemiparasite[15]; leaves opposite, lanceolate; calyx 4-partite; corolla with tube enlarged in the distal part, and 2-lipped margin; the upper lip helmet-shaped, the lower one 3-partite, with palate. The genus is represented in the Alps by about 6 species.

Wood cow-wheat, *Melampyrum silvaticum* L. (Plate 90.1)
8–25 cm tall; corolla 6–10 mm long, yellow, with open mouth. Woods, dwarf shrub stands; acid, meagre, humous soils; 800–2400 m; common. North European-Alpine plant. F3, R1, N2, H5, D4, L2, T2, K3. Flowering time: 7–9.

Common cow-wheat, *Melampyrum pratense* L. (Plate 90.2)
10–50 cm tall; corolla 10–20 mm long, white to yellow with dark-yellow palate; mouth closed by the palate. Light woods, dwarf shrub stands, pastures; acid, meagre, humous soils; 600–2200 m; rather common. Eurosibirian plant. F3, R1, N2, H4, D4, L3, T3, K3. Flowering time: 7–9.

h. **Yellow-rattle,** *Rhinanthus* L.
Annual hemiparasite[15]; leaves opposite, lanceolate, toothed; calyx laterally flattened, strongly enlarged when old, 4-toothed; corolla with

[15] *Hemiparasites* have green leaves and are thus able to synthesize sugar, but depend upon other plants for water and nutrients. They tap off the water from roots of their hosts through specialized suckers. Farmers do not welcome hemiparasites (esp. yellow-rattle) in their meadows, because these plants do not have a good feed value and also diminish the yield of a given plot.

long tube and 2-lipped margin; the upper lip helmet-shaped in the terminal part, with a single, short, violet or whitish tooth on either side; the lower lip 3-partite. The Alpine flora includes about 6 species.

Hairy yellow-rattle, *Rhinanthus alectorolophus* (Scop.) Pollich *(Rh. hirsutus* Lam.) (Plate 90.3)
10–50 cm tall; calyx tomentose; corolla 18–23 mm long, yellow; leaves in the inflorescence sharply toothed. Meadows, flushes; intermittently humid, base-rich soils; 400–1900 m; rather common. Plant of Central Europe. F3w, R4, N3, H4, D4, L4, T3, K3. Flowering time: 6–7.

Narrow-leaved yellow-rattle, *Rhinanthus angustifolius* Gmelin *(Rh. subalpinus* [Stern.] Sch. and Th., *Rh. aristatus* Čelak.) (Plate 90.4)
8–50 cm tall; leaves in the inflorescence with 1–3 mm long, awned teeth at the base; calyx glabrous; corolla 13–20 mm long, yellow. Meadows, pastures, scree; intermittently humid, base-rich, meagre soils; 800–2600 m; rather common. Mountain plant of Central and Southern Europe (eastern). F3w, R4, N2, H2, D4, L4, T2, K3. Flowering time: 7–9.

i. **Bartsia,** *Bartsia* L.
Alpine bartsia, *Bartsia alpina* L. (Plate 91.1)
Perennial hemiparasite[15]; 5–20 cm tall; leaves opposite, oval, obtusely dentate, hairy; calyx 4-partite; corolla with long tube enlarged in the distal part, and 2-lipped margin, 1.5–2.5 cm long, deep violet; the upper lip helmet-shaped, the lower one 3-partite. Meadows, pastures, flushes; intermittently humid, humous soils; 1200–2800 m; rather common. Arctic-Alpine plant. F4w, R3, N3, H4, D4, L4, T1, K3. Flowering time: 6–8.

k. **Eye-bright,** *Euphrasia* L.
Annual hemiparasite[15]; leaves opposite, dentate; calyx 4-partite; corolla with tube and 2-lipped margin; the upper lip emarginate; the lower lip longer than the upper one, 3-partite, with emarginate lobes. The genus is represented in the Alps by about 15 species.

Common eye-bright, *Euphrasia rostkoviana* Hayne (Plate 91.2)
5–25 cm tall; stem mostly with glandular hairs in the upper part; corolla 8–14 mm long, white with darker veins, and a yellow palate. Meadows, pastures, fens; intermittently humid, meagre, humous soils; 400–2600 m; rather common. North European-Alpine plant. F4w, R3, N2, H4, D5, L3, T2, K3. Flowering time: 6–10.

Alpine eye-bright, *Euphrasia alpina* Lam. (Plate 91.3)
5–15 cm tall; stem without glandular hairs; corolla 9–15 mm long, lilac or light-blue with darker veins, and a yellow spot on the palate. Grassland; dry, meagre soils poor in calcium; 1800–2700 m; not common (occurs nearly exclusively in the inner ranges). Mountain plant of Central and Southern Europe (western). F2, R2, N2, H3, D4, L5, T1, K4. Flowering time: 7–9.

Dwarf eye-bright, *Euphrasia minima* L.   (Plate 91.4)
2–10 cm tall; stem without glandular hairs; corolla 5–7 mm long, with light-blue, lilac, or reddish upper lip, and yellow or whitish to lilac lower lip (less often the whole corolla yellow). Grassland, pastures; meagre soils poor in calcium; 1500–3000 m; rather common. Mountain plant of Central and Southern Europe. F3, R2, N2, H4, D4, L4, T1, K3. Flowering time: 7–9.

1. **Lousewort,** *Pedicularis* L.
Perennial hemiparasite[15]; leaves in a basal rosette; cauline leaves mostly alternate, pinnately divided to the mid-vein; flowers in a spike; calyx 5-partite or two-lipped; corolla with a long tube enlarged in the distal part, with helmet-shaped upper lip, and large, 3-partite lower lip. The genus is represented in the Alps by more than 20 species, and includes some typical mountain plants.

Foliated lousewort, *Pedicularis foliosa* L.   (Plate 92.1)
20–40 cm tall; leaves 2-pinnatisect; leaves in the inflorescence longer than the flowers; calyx with smooth-edged lobes; corolla 20–28 mm long, light-yellow, the upper lip rounded in the distal part, the lower lip glabrous. Tall-herb stands, tall-growing meadows; humid, base-, and nutrient-rich soils; 1200–2400 m; not common (occurs above all in the northern ranges). Mountain plant of Central and Southern Europe. F4, R4, N4, H3, D5, L3, T2, K2. Flowering time: 6–7.

Skinned lousewort, *Pedicularis recutita* L.   (Plate 92.2)
20–40 cm tall; leaves 2-pinnatisect; leaves in the inflorescence shorter than the flowers; calyx with smooth-edged lobes; corolla 12–15 mm long, deep brown-red, with the upper lip acute in the distal part, the lower lip glabrous. Tall-herb-stands, swamps; intermittently humid, nutrient-rich soils; 1200 2500 m; not common (occurs above all in the eastern ranges). Plant of the eastern Alps. F4w, R3, N4, H4, D5, L3, T2, K2. Flowering time: 6–7.
Protected: *F.*

Arched lousewort, *Pedicularis gyroflexa* Vill.   (Plate 92.3)
15–25 cm tall; leaves 2-pinnatisect; leaves in the inflorescence shorter than the flowers; calyx with irregularly dentate lobes; corolla 24–32 mm long, red, with the upper lip narrowed into a 2–3 mm long spur in the distal part; the lower lip with ciliated margins. Rock crevices, rocky slopes; calcium-rich substratum; 1400–2800 m; very rare (in Switzerland only at the Gr. St. Bernard, and in the southern Ticino). Mountain plant of Central and Southern Europe (western). F2, R5, N2, H3, D2, L5, T2, K4. Flowering time: 6–7.
Protected: R. *TI.*

Beaked lousewort, *Pedicularis rostrato-spicata* Crantz *(P. incarnata* Jacq.)   (Plate 92.4)
15–40 cm tall; leaves 2-pinnatisect; leaves in the inflorescence shorter than the flowers; calyx lobes with short teeth; corolla 12–16 mm long, light-purple, with the upper lip narrowed into a 4–5 mm long spur in

the distal part; the lower lip glabrous. Meadows, pastures, grassy slopes; stony, base-rich soils; 2000–2700 m; rare (mostly in the inner ranges). Alpine plant. F2, R4, N2, H4, D3, L4, T1, K3. Flowering time: 6–7.

Kerner's lousewort, *Pedicularis kerneri* D. T. (Plate 93.1)
5–15 cm tall; leaf segments dentate; leaves in the inflorescence shorter than the flowers; calyx lobes deeply dentate; corolla 16–24 mm long, purple, with the upper lip narrowed into a 3.5–5 mm long spur in the distal part; the lower lip glabrous. Grassland, coarse scree; stony, meagre soils poor in calcium; 1800–3000 m; not common (almost exclusively in the inner ranges). Mountain plant of Central and Southern Europe (western). F2, R2, N2, H3, D3, L5, T1, K4. Flowering time: 7–8.

Capitate lousewort, *Pedicularis rostrato-capitata* Crantz
Differs from the preceding as follows: up to 20 cm tall; leaves 2-pinnatisect, the leaf segments divided to the mid-vein; the lower lip with ciliate margin. Grassy slopes, rocky ledges; dry, calcium-rich, stony soils; 1600–2800 m; rare (in Switzerland only the Speer and the eastern Grisons). Plant of the eastern Alps. F2, R5, N2, H4, D3, L4, T1, K4. Flowering time: 7–8.

Fern-leaved lousewort, *Pedicularis aspleniifolia* Flörke
Differs from Kener's lousewort as follows: up to 8 cm tall; calyx lobes less deeply dentate; corolla 13–18 mm long. Stabilized scree; base-rich soils; 2000–2800 m; rare (in Switzerland only in the Lower Engadine). Plant of the eastern Alps. F3, R4, N2, H3, D2, L5, T1, K2. Flowering time: 7–8.
Protected: R.

Tuberous lousewort, *Pedicularis tuberosa* L. (Plate 93.2)
10–25 cm tall; leaves 2-pinnatisect; leaves in the inflorescence shorter than the flowers; calyx with finely dentate lobes; corolla 14–20 mm long, light-yellow, with the upper lip narrowed into a 3.5–4.5 mm long spur in the distal part; the lower lip glabrous. Meadows, pastures; dry, meagre soils poor in bases; 1300–2700 m; rather common. Mountain plant of Central and Southern Europe (western). F2, R2, N2, H4, D4, L4, T2, K3. Flowering time: 6–8.

Ascending lousewort, *Pedicularis ascendens* Schleicher *(P. barrelieri* Rchb.)
Similar to the tuberous lousewort, but with smooth-edged calyx lobes. Meadows, pastures; stony, calcium-rich soils; 1000–2200 m; rare (in Switzerland only west of the Gotthard massif). Plant of the western Alps. F2, R4, N2, H4, D3, L4, T2, K3. Flowering time: 7–8.

Oeder's lousewort, *Pedicularis oederi* Vahl *(P. versicolor* Wahlenb.)
(Plate 93.3)
4–15 cm tall; leaf segments finely dentate; leaves in the inflorescence shorter than the flowers; calyx with smooth-edged lobes; corolla 18–30 mm long, light-yellow with purple spots on either side of the upper lip; the upper lip slightly acute in the distal part; the lower lip

glabrous. Open grassland; stony, meagre, calcium-rich soils; 1400–2500 m; not common (occurs above all in the northern ranges). Arctic-Alpine plant. F3, R5, N2, H5, D3, L4, T1, K3. Flowering time: 6–7.

Whorled lousewort, *Pedicularis verticillata* L. (Plate 93.4)
5–20 cm tall; cauline leaves in groups of 3–4, verticillate (in all other species opposite!); calyx with smooth-edged, short teeth; corolla 12–16 mm long, purple, with the upper lip truncate in the distal part; the lower lip glabrous. Pastures, grassland; humid, base-rich, meagre soils; 1400–2800 m; rather common. Arctic-Alpine plant. F4, R4, N2, H4, D3, L4, T1, K3. Flowering time: 6–7.

54th family: **broomrape family,** *Orobanchaceae*

a. **Broomrape,** *Orobanche* L.
Root-parasites («broomrapes») with underground tubers attached to roots of the host plant; they take up water, nutrients, and sugar from their host; have no green leaves but brown to red scales; flowers zygomorphic, in spicate inflorescences; corolla with broad tube and two-lipped margin. Broomrapes are partly depended on specific host plants. The family is represented in the Alps by about 20 species occurring above all in warmer areas (the Central and Southern Alps); they are very difficult to determine.

Purple broomrape, *Orobanche purpurea* Jacq. (Plate 94.1)
15–30 cm tall; calyx 4–5-partite; corolla 18–28 mm long, lilac with darker veins. Parasitic on yarrow, thistles, and plants of the mint family. Grassland; dry, meagre soils; 600–1600 m; rare (occurs nearly exclusively in the central and southern valleys). Plant of the Mediterranean region. F2, R3, N2, H3, D4, L4, T4, K4. Flowering time: 6–7.

55th family: **butterwort family,** *Lentibulariaceae*

a. **Butterwort,** *Pinguicula* L.
Leaves in a basal rosette, oval, glandular, sticky on the upper surface; flowers singly on long stems, zygomorphic; calyx 5-partite; corolla with a spur; the upper lip 2-partite, the lower one 3-partite; throat hairy; ovary 1, superior. The Alpine flora includes only a few species of the genus.
Insects become glued to the glandular leaf surface and are digested by the plant. The butterworts take up in this way some part of nutrients (esp. proteins) and are thus able to grow in meagre soils.

Alpine butterwort, *Pinguicula alpina* L. (Plate 94.2)
5–15 cm tall; lower lip of the calyx deeply 2-partite, with not spreading lobes; corolla white with 1–3 yellow spots on the median segment of the lower lip. Fens, grassland; intermittently humid, base-rich soils;

600–2600 m; not common. Eurosibirian plant. F4w, R4, N2, Hx, D5, L4, T2, K4. Flowering time: 6–7.
Protected: *AG*, NE, *TG*, *ZH*.

Common butterwort, *Pinguicula vulgaris* L. (Plate 94.3)
5–20 cm tall; lower lip of the calyx 2-partite at most to the middle, with not spreading lobes; corolla violet with 1–3 white spots on the lower lip. Fens; intermittently wet, base-rich soils; 400–1800 m; not common. Eurosibirian-North American plant. F4w, R4, N2, H4, D5, L4, T3, K3. Flowering time: 6–7.
Protected: *AG*, NE, *TG*, *ZH*.

Hairy-spurred butterwort, *Pinguicula leptoceras* Rchb. (Plate 94.4)
5–15 cm tall; lower lip of the calyx 2-partite virtually to the base, with spreading lobes; corolla blue-violet with 1–3 white spots on the lower lip. Grassland; intermittently wet soils; 1200–2500 m; not common (occurs above all in the inner ranges). Alpine plant. F4w, R3, N2, H4, D5, L4, T2, K3. Flowering time: 7–8.

56th family: **plantain family,** *Plantaginaceae*

a. **Plantain,** *Plantago* L.
Leaves with parallel main veins, sheath-like enlarged at the base; flowers in spikes, small; calyx 4-partite; corolla with short tube and 4-partite margin, membranous, whitish to brown; ovary superior; fruit in form of a capsule. The genus is represented in the Alps by about 8 species.

Alpine plantain, *Plantago alpina* L. (Plate 95.1)
5–15 cm tall; leaves narrowly lanceolate, 3-veined; stem pilose, with clinging hairs; spikes 1.5–3 cm long; stamens yellow. Pastures, meadows; meagre soils poor in bases; 1300–2500 m; rather common. Mountain plant of Central and Southern Europe (western). F3, R2, N2, H4, D4, L4, T2, K3. Flowering time: 5–7.

Black plantain, *Plantago atrata* Hoppe *(P. montana* Lam.)
Differs from the alpine plantain as follows: leaves 3–7-veined; stem with spreading, 1.5–2 mm long hairs; spikes 0.5–1.5 cm long; stamens whitish. Pastures, grassland, scree; medium soils with late-lying snow; 1300–2500 m; rather common. Mountain plant of Central and Southern Europe. F3, R3, N3, H4, D4, L4, T2, K2. Flowering time: 5–7.

Medium plantain, *Plantago media* L. (Plate 95.2)
20–40 cm tall; leaves broadly lanceolate, 5–9-veined; stem pilose, with clinging hairs; spikes 2–8 cm long; stamens lilac. Pastures, meadows; dry, base-rich, meagre soils; 300–2200 m; rather common. Eurosibirian plant. F2, R4, N2, H3, D4, L4, T3, K4. Flowering time: 6–7.

57th family: globularia family, *Globulariaceae*

a. Globularia, *Globularia* L.

Leaves opposite, glabrous; flowers grouped in heads; calyx 5-toothed; corolla with short tube and 2-lipped margin (the upper lip 2-partite, the lower one 3-partite); ovary superior; fruit in form of a nut. The Alpine flora includes 4 species of the genus.

Heart-leaved globularia, *Globularia cordifolia* L.   (Plate 95.3)
3–10 cm tall; stem woody at the base, prostrate; leaves oval or paddle-shaped; heads measuring 1-1.5 cm in diameter, blue. Rock crevices, coarse scree; not common. Mountain plant of Central and Southern Europe. F1, R5, N2, H2, D1, L5, T2, K4. Flowering time: 5–7.

Bald-stemmed globularia, *Globularia nudicaulis* L.   (Plate 95.4)
10–25 cm tall; stem not woody, upright; basal leaves narrowly oval; heads measuring 1.5–2.5 cm in diameter, blue. Grassy slopes, pastures; dry, stony, calcium-rich soils; 1000–2400 m; not common. Mountain plant of Central and Southern Europe (western). F2, R5, N2, H3, D3, L4, T2, K3. Flowering time: 6–7.

58th family: bedstraw family, *Rubiaceae*

a. Bedstraw, *Galium* L.

Stem mostly 4-angled, segmented by verticillate leaves; flowers actinomorphic; calyx 4-partite; corolla with short tube and 4 spreading lobes; ovary inferior; fruit didymous (formed of two similar parts attached to each other by a small portion of their surface). The genus is represented in the Alps by about 15 species, partly difficult to distinguish from each other.

Dwarf bedstraw, *Galium anisophyllum* Vill. *(G. pumilum* auct.)
(Plate 96.1)
5–15 cm tall; form loose tufts; middle leaves in whorls of 7–9, narrowly lanceolate; cymes axillary in the upper whorl, few- to multi-flowered, distinctly longer than the leaves; fruit stalks upright. Meadows, pastures, coarse scree; stony, dry, meagre soils; 1200–2800 m; rather common. Mountain plant of Central and Southern Europe. F2, R3, N2, H3, D3, L4, T2, K3. Flowering time: 6–8.

Swiss bedstraw, *Galium helveticum* Weigel   (Plate 96.2)
3–5 cm tall; forms dense tufts and trails over the ground; middle leaves in whorls of 6–7, narrowly lanceolate; cymes in axils of the upper leaves, one- to few-flowered, hardly longer than the leaves; fruit stalks recurved. Scree; stony, calcium-rich soils; 1800–2600 m; not common (occurs above all in the northern ranges). Alpine plant. F3, R5, N2, H2, D2↑, L5, T1, K3. Flowering time: 7–8.

59th family: **honeysuckle family,** *Caprifoliaceae*

Plants woody; leaves mostly opposite; calyx small, often indistinct; corolla 5-partite; ovary inferior. The family is represented in the Alps by about 12 species, mostly shrubs.

a. **Twinflower,** *Linnaea* L.

Northern twinflower, *Linnaea borealis* L.   (Plate 96.3)
5–15 cm tall; stem filiform, creeping; leaves small, rounded; flowers mostly in pairs, nodding; corolla funnel-shaped, 7–10 mm long, white, often tinged pink. Coniferous woods; acid, humous soils; 1300–2200 m; not common (occurs mostly in the inner ranges). Eurosibirian-North American plant. F3, R1, N1, H5, D4, L2, T2, K3. Flowering time: 7–8.
Protected: *Ao, L, So.*

b. **Honeysuckle,** *Lonicera* L.
Shrubs; two flowers mostly with united ovaries on the common stem; corolla zygomorphic, with 4-partite upper lip and entire lower lip; fruit in form of a double berry.

Blue-berried honeysuckle, *Lonicera coerulea* L.
(Plate 96.4; Fig. 35B, p.   )
60–150 cm tall; leaves 2–5 cm long, 1.5–2 times as long as broad; flowers on the common peduncle about 1 cm long; flowers yellowish; fruit blue. Light woods, bushes; meagre soils poor in bases; 1200–2400 m; rather common (esp. in the inner ranges). North European-Alpine plant. F3, R2, N2, H4, D4, L3, T2, K3. Flowering time: 6–7.

Black-berried honeysuckle, *Lonicera nigra* L.   (Fig. 35A, p.   )
60–150 cm tall; leaves 3–6 cm long, 2–3 times as long as broad; flowers on the common peduncle 3–4 cm long. Forests, bushes; medium soils; 600–2000 m; rather common. Mountain plant of Central and Southern Europe. F3, R3, N3, H4, D4, L2, T2, K3. Flowering time: 6.

Alpine honeysuckle, *Lonicera alpigena* L.   (Fig. 35C, p.   )
30–180 cm tall; larger leaves over 6 cm long, 2–3 times as long as broad; flowers on the common long stem; flowers yellow at the base, red-brown above; fruit deep red. Forests, bushes; base- and nutrient-rich, humous soils; 800–2000 m; not common. Mountain plant of Central and Southern Europe. F3, R4, N3, H4, D4, L2, T2, K3. Flowering time: 5–6.

c. **Elder,** *Sambucus* L.

Red-berried elder, *Sambucus racemosa* L.   (Fig. 36D, p.   )
Bush up to 4 m tall; leaves pinnately divided, with 3–5 lanceolate, dentate leaflets; flowers actinomorphic, small, in compact panicles, yellow-green; berry-like fruits red. Forests, bushes; nitrogen-rich soils; 600–2200 m; common. Plant of Central Europe. F3, R3, N4, H3, Dx, L3, T3, K3. Flowering time: 5–6.
The berries are slightly poisonous, but become edible when cooked and make an excellent jelly.

60th family: **valerian family,** *Valerianaceae*

a. **Valerian,** *Valeriana* L.

Plants often with small, only female flowers; leaves opposite; frequently with a peculiar smell, particularly evident when dry, and very attractive to cats; inflorescence short, paniculate; corolla often almost actinomoorphic, cylindrical, with mostly 5-partite margin; ovary inferior; calyx forming a pappus in fruits, its 10–25 feathery bristles promoting dispersal by the wind. The genus is represented in the Alps by about 10 species.

Mountain valerian, *Valeriana montana* L.   (Plate 97.1)
10–50 cm tall; leaves oval, mostly truncate at the base; smooth-edged or indistinctly toothed; cauline leaves entire; corolla 3.5–6 mm long, white to pink. Scree, cliffs, banks of torrents; stony, calcium-rich soils; 1000–2600 m; rather common. Mountain plant of Central and Southern Europe. F3, R5, N2, H3, D2, L3, T2, K3. Flowering time: 5–7.

Three-leaved valerian, *Valeriana tripteris* L.   (Plate 97.2)
10–50 cm tall; leaves oval, cordate at the base, distinctly toothed; cauline leaves tripartite to the base; corolla 3.5–6 mm long, white to pink. Rock crevices, coarse scree; stony soils; 800–2200 m; rather common. Mountain plant of Central and Southern Europe. F3, R3, N2, H3, Dx, L3, T2, K3. Flowering time: 5–7.

Spikenard, *Valeriana celtica* L.   (Plate 97.3)
5–20 cm tall; leaves narrowly lanceolate, smooth-edged; corolla 1–3 mm long, yellowish, purple to brown-red outside. Open grassland, pastures; stony, humous soils poor in calcium; 2000–2800 m; exceedingly rare (in Switzerland only in the southern Wallis; in the eastern Alps occurs a closely related taxon). Graian-Pennine plant. F2, R2, N2, H4, D2, L4, T1, K3. Flowering time: 7–8.
Protected: R*. R. (Ti)/F.

Dwarf valerian, *Valeriana supina* L.   (Plate 97.4)
3–12 cm tall; leaves rounded, ciliate, smooth-edged; corolla 2–5 mm long, pink. Scree; calcium-rich substratum; 2200–2800 m; rather rare (in Switzerland only in the eastern Grisons). Plant of the eastern Alps. F3, R5, N2, H2, D2, L4, T1, K3. Flowering time: 7–8.

Willow-leaved valerian, *Valeriana saliunca* All.
Differs from the dwarf valerian as follows: leaves narrowly oval, glabrous; corolla 4–5.5 mm long. Scree, pastures; base-rich, stony soils; 1800–2600 m; rare (in Switzerland only the Wallis and the Fribourg Alps). Mountain plant of Central and Southern Europe (western). F2, R4, N2, H2, D2, L4, T1, K3. Flowering time: 7–8.
Protected: R*.

228

Rock valerian, *Valeriana saxatilis* L. (Fig. 50)
5–30 cm tall; leaves lanceolate, their margins and the upper surface
with single hairs; flowers 1–4 mm long, white. Rock crevices, coarse
scree; limestone and dolomite; 800–2400 m; rare (only the northeastern
and southern ranges). Mountain plant of Central and Southern Europe
(eastern). F2, R5, N2, H3, D1, L4, T2, K3. Flowering time: 6–7.
Protected: R.

Fig. 50. Rock valerian *(Valeriana saxatilis)*. ⅓× (from *6.1.k.*).

61st family: **teasel family,** *Dipsacaceae*

Leaves opposite; flowers in a compact, head-, or spadix-like inflorescence enveloped in bracts; calyx often consisting only of bristles,
encircled by membranous epicalyx; corolla 4-, or 5-partite, united,
zygomorphic; ovary inferior. The family is represented in the Alps by
about 15 species.

a. **Small teasel,** *Cephalaria* Schrader
 Alpine small teasel, *Cephalaria alpina* (L.) Schrader (Fig. 51)
60–100 cm tall; leaves pinnately divided; heads measuring 2.5–5 cm
in diameter; corolla yellowish-white, densely hairy outside. Tall-herb
stands, bushes; base-, and nutrient-rich soils; 800–2000 m; rare (occurs
mostly in the southern and western ranges). Plant of the western Alps.
F3w, R4, N4, H3, D5, L3, T3, K4. Flowering time: 7–8.
Protected: R.

Fig. 51. Alpine small teasel *(Cephalaria alpina)*. ⅓ × (from *6.1.k.*).

b. **Scabious,** *Scabiosa* L.

Bright scabious, *Scabiosa lucida* Vill. (Plate 98.1)

10–35 cm tall; lower leaves entire, the upper ones pinnately divided, virtually glabrous, and slightly shiny; heads measuring 2.5–4 cm in diameter; calyx bristles 5–8 mm long, black; corolla red to blue-violet, 5-lobed. Grassy slopes, meadows; stony, base-rich soils; 1500–2700 m; rather common. Mountain plant of Central and Southern Europe. F2, R4, N2, H3, D3, L4, T2, K3. Flowering time: 7–8.

c. **Scabious,** *Knautia* L.
  Wood scabious, *Knautia silvatica* (L.) Duby   (Plate 98.2)
  20–100 cm tall; leaves entire, with coarse and stiff hairs; heads measuring 2.5–4 cm in diameter; calyx bristles 2–3 mm long, light-brown; corolla violet, 4-lobed. Tall-herb stands, light woods, bushes; medium soils; 600–2200 m; common. Eurosibirian plant. F3, R3, N3, H3, D4, L3, T3, K3. Flowering time: 6–9.

62nd family: **bellflower family,** *Campanulaceae*

Plants mostly with milky sap; leaves alternate, entire; flowers actinomorphic, with 5 calyx lobes and 5-partite, united corolla; ovary inferior. The family is represented in the Alps by more than 50 species, some of them very typical mountain plants.

a. **Bellflower,** *Campanula* L.
  Flowers single, or in inflorescences (racemes, spikes, or panicles, rarely heads); corolla bell-, or funnel-shaped; stamens hairy, encircling the style. The Alpine flora includes about 30 species of the genus.

Tufted bellflower, *Campanula thyrsoides* L.   (Plate 98.3)
  10–40 cm tall; leaves narrowly lanceolate, with coarse and stiff hairs; flowers in a compact spike; calyx sinus obtuse; corolla light-yellow, 1.5–2.5 cm long. Meadows; dry, base-rich soils; 1500–2400 m; not common. Mountain plant of Central and Southern Europe (eastern). F2, R4, N2, H3, D4, L4, T2, K3. Flowering time: 6–7.
  Protected: *AI, NW, OW,* SG, *TI/Li/L.*

Spiked bellflower, *Campanula spicata* L.   (Plate 98.4)
  20–70 cm tall; leaves narrowly lanceolate, with coarse and stiff hairs; flowers in a loose spike; calyx sinus obtuse; corolla blue-violet, 1.2–2.5 cm long. Scree, cliff steppes; dry, stony soils; 400–1700 m; rather rare (occurs in the Central and Southern Alps). Mountain plant of Central and Southern Europe (southern). F1, R3, N2, H3, D3, L4, T4, K4. Flowering time: 6–7.
  Protected: L.

Broad-leaved bellflower, *Campanula latifolia* L.   (Plate 99.1)
  50–120 cm tall; leaves oval to lanceolate, hairy, dentate; flowers in a loose, upright raceme, nodding; calyx sinus acute; corolla violet-blue or white, 3–3.5 cm long. Tall-herb stands, woods; humid, nutrient-rich, humous soils; 800–1600 m; rather rare (occurs above all in the Northern Alps). Eurosibirian plant. F4, R3, N4, H4, D4, L2, T3, K2. Flowering time: 6–8.
  Protected: *GL,* SG/L.

Rhomboid-leaved bellflower, *Campanula rhomboidalis* L. (Plate 99.2)
  25–50 cm tall; cauline leaves oval to broadly lanceolate; flowers in a few-flowered raceme, nodding; calyx sinus obtuse; corolla blue-violet, 1.2–2 cm long. Meadows, tall-herb stands; nutrient-rich soils;

1000–2200 m; rather common (only west of the Hinterrhein area). Mountain plant of Central and Southern Europe (western). F3, R3, N4, H4, D4, L3, T2, K3. Flowering time: 6–7.
Protected: L.

Bearded bellflower, *Campanula barbata* L. (Plate 99.3)
10–30 cm tall; leaves narrowly oval to lanceolate, with coarse and stiff hairs; flowers in a unilateral, few-flowered raceme, nodding; calyx sinus with cordate, recurved appendages; corolla blue-lilac to blue (rarely white). Pastures, dwarf shrub stands; meagre soils poor in calcium; 1200–2600 m; rather common. Scandinavian-Alpine plant. F3, R2, N2, H4, D4, L4, T2, K3. Flowering time: 7–8.
Protected: L.

Scheuchzer's bellflower, *Campanula scheuchzeri* Vill. (Plate 99.4)
5–30 cm tall; cauline leaves narrowly lanceolate; flowers single, or in a few-flowered raceme, nodding before the flowers open; calyx sinus obtuse; corolla blue-violet, 1.5–2.5 cm long. Meadows, pastures, scree; stony, medium soils; 1400–3000 m; common. Mountain plant of Central and Southern Europe. F3, R3, N3, H3, D3, L4, T2, K3. Flowering time: 7–8.
Protected: L.

Mt. Cenis bellflower, *Campanula cenisia* L. (Plate 100.1)
1–5 cm tall, creeping; leaves rounded-oval; flowers single; calyx sinus obtuse; corolla light-blue, very broadly bell-shaped, measuring 1.5–2.5 cm in diameter. Coarse scree; calciferous substratum; 2500–3100 m; rather rare (occurs above all in the inner ranges). Plant of the western Alps. F3, R4, N2, H1, D2, L5, T1, K3. Flowering time: 7–8.
Protected: SG, *TI*/L.

Small bellflower, *Campanula cochleariifolia* Lam. (Plate 100.2)
5–15 cm tall; lower cauline leaves lanceolate, roughly toothed; flowers single, or in few-flowered racemes, nodding; calyx sinus obtuse; corolla light-blue, 1–2 cm long. Scree, rock crevices, boulder fields; stony, humid, base-rich soils; 700–3000 m; rather common. Mountain plant of Central and Southern Europe. F4, R4, N2, H2, D2↑, L4, T2, K3. Flowering time: 6–8.
Protected: L.

Incised bellflower, *Campanula excisa* Schleicher (Plate 100.3)
5–12 cm tall; leaves very narrowly lanceolate; flowers single, or grouped in twos and threes, nodding; calyx sinus obtuse; corolla light-violet-blue, with emarginate sinus between lobes, 1.5–2.5 cm long. Coarse scree, boulder fields, rock crevices; substratum poor in calcium (nearly exclusively upon para-gneiss); 2000–2800 m; very rare (in Switzerland only in the southern Wallis and NW Ticino). Graian-Pennine plant. F2, R2, H2, D2, L4, T1, K3. Flowering time: 7–8.

232

b. **Rampion,** *Synotoma* Schulz

Tassel rampion, *Synotoma comosum* (L.) Schulz *(Physoplexis comosa* [L.] Schur, *Phyteuma comosum* [L.])　　　　　　(Plate 100.4)
8–20 cm tall; leaves petiolate, reniform, toothed; flowers in a headlike inflorescence; corolla globular to cylindrical but strongly contracted at the mouth, ending in a bill, white to lilac with a dark-violet bill, 1.5–3 cm long. Rock crevices; limestone and dolomite; 500–1600 m; very rare (occurs only in the Southern Alps, east of the Swiss border). Plant of the Southern Alps. F3, R5, N2, H2, D1, L4, T3, K3. Flowering time: 7–8.
Protected: *Bz, L, Tn.*

c. **Rampion,** *Phyteuma* L.
Flowers in a compact spike, or head; corolla cylindrical, united at the base and in the terminal part; stamens encircling the style. The genus is represented in the Alps by about 18 species.

Oval-headed rampion, *Phyteuma ovatum* Honckeny *(Ph. Halleri* All.)
　　　　　　　　　　　　　　　　　　　　　　　(Plate 101.1)
30–80 cm tall; basal leaves cordate, about as long as wide, dentate; flowers in obovate, later often cylindrical, spike; bracts as long or longer as the width of the spike; corolla 1–1.5 cm long, curved in the subterminal/terminal part of the spike, deep violet. Tall-herb stands, meadows; humid, nutrient-rich soils; 1200–2100 m; not common. Mountain plant of Central and Southern Europe. F4, R4, N4, H4, D4, L3, T2, K2. Flowering time: 6–7.

Spiked rampion, *Phyteuma spicatum* L.　　　　　　(Plate 101.2)
Differs from the preceding in the yellowish-white corolla with green tips. Woods, meadows; medium, humous soils; 400–1600 m; rather common. Plant of Central Europe. F3, R3, N3, H4, D4, L2, T3, K2. Flowering time: 6.

Round-headed rampion, *Phyteuma orbiculare* L.　　　(Plate 101.3)
10–40 cm tall; basal leaves oval to lanceolate, rounded or cordate at the base, 1.5–5 times as long as wide, dentate; flowers in a spherical head; bracts as long or longer as the width of the head; corolla 1–1.5 cm long, nearly straight, or curved about the middle part of the head, blue. Meadows, pastures; base-rich, meagre soils; 500–2500 m; rather common. Plant of Central Europe. F3w, R4, N2, H3, D4, L4, T2, K3. Flowering time: 6–7.
Protected: *BL.*

Betony-leaved rampion, *Phyteuma betonicifolium* Vill. (Plate 101.4)
20–60 cm tall; basal leaves cordate, acute, 3–8 times as long as wide, toothed; flowers in a cylindrical spike; bracts mostly shorter than the width of the spike; corolla 0.7–1.2 cm long, straight, blue-violet. Meadows, pastures; meagre soils poor in calcium; 1000–2600 m; rather common. Alpine plant. F3, R2, N2, H4, D4, L3, T2, K3. Flowering time: 6–8.

233

Globularia-leaved rampion, *Phyteuma globulariifolium* Sternb. and Hoppe (*Ph. pauciflorum* auct.)   (Plate 102.1)

1–5 cm tall; basal leaves narrowly oval, or lanceolate, 2–4 times as long as wide, smooth-edged, or with 3–5 teeth at the tip; flowers in a few-flowered head; bracts oval about as long as the head; corolla ca. 1 cm long, curved about the middle of the head, blue. Open grassland, hilltops; acid, wind-exposed soils; 2200–3200 m; not common. Mountain plant of Central and Southern Europe (western). F2, R2, N2, H3, D3, L5, T1, K4. Flowering time: 7–8.

Dwarf rampion, *Phyteuma humile* Schleicher   (Plate 102.2)

3–8 cm tall; basal leaves gramineous, more than 15 times as long as wide; flowers in a multi-flowered head; bracts 4–7 times as long as wide, as long, or longer than the head, with teeth at the base; corolla 1–1.5 cm long, curved about the middle of the head, blue-violet. Rock crevices; substratum poor in calcium, snow-free in winter; 2200–3200 m; exceedingly rare (only in the Monte Rosa massif). Pennine plant. F2, R2, N2, H3, D1, L5, T1, K4. Flowering time: 7–8.
Protected: R*. R.

Rhaetic rampion, *Phyteuma hedraianthifolium* R. Schulz

Differs from the dwarf rampion as follows: bracts 10–20 times as long as wide, mostly twice as long as the head, with spaced teeth. Rock crevices; substratum poor in calcium, snow-free in winter; 2000–3000 m; rare (in Switzerland only the Upper Engadine, the Puschlav, and the Bergell area). Rhaetic-Bergamo plant. F2, R2, N2, H3, D1, L5, T1, K4. Flowering time: 7–8.
Protected: R.

Hemispherical rampion, *Phyteuma hemisphaericum* L. (Plate 102.3)

5–15 cm tall; differs from the dwarf rampion in the bracts which are 2–4 times as long as wide, and mostly smooth-edged. Grassland, pastures, rock crevices; dry soils poor in calcium; 1700–3000 m; rather common (above all in the inner ranges). Mountain plant of Central and Southern Europe (western). F2, R2, N2, H3, D4, L4, T1, K3. Flowering time: 7–8.

Scheuchzer's rampion, *Phyteuma scheuchzeri* All.   (Plate 102.4)

Differs from the round-headed rampion as follows: leaves 2–8 times as long as wide, acute; bracts 8–30 times as long as wide, ¼ longer than the width of the head; corolla nearly straight. Rock crevices; 600–2200 m; not common (occurs only in the Central and Southern Alps). Plant of the Southern Alps. F2, R3, N2, H2, D1, L4, T3, K4. Flowering time: 5–7.

63rd family, composite family, or daisy family, *Compositae (Asteraceae)*

Leaves mostly alternate; flowers in a head enveloped in bracts (see Fig. 28, composite head); calyx mostly filiform (pappus); corolla tubular or ligulate (in the latter, the corolla tube is prolonged only along one side as a strap-shaped «ligule»); stamens 5, united into a tube, epipetalous; ovary inferior. The composite plants represent undoubtedly the largest family in the Alpine flora, more than 200 species occurring in various places.

a. **Adenostyle,** *Adenostyles* Cass.
Basal leaves large, toothed; heads few-flowered, in an umbel-like panicle; all flowers tubular; pappus white, consisting of 2–3 rows of equally long bristles.

Hedge-leaved adenostyle, *Adenostyles alliariae* (Gouan) Kerner
(Plate 103.1)
60–150 cm tall; leaves cordate to reniform, tomentose underneath, irregularly toothed; teeth longer than wide; heads 3–6-flowered; flowers red-lilac. Tall-herb stands, woods, bushes; nutrient-rich, humous soils; 1000–2600 m; common. Mountain plant of Central and Southern Europe. F4, R3, N4, H4, D4, L2, T2, K2. Flowering time: 7–9.

Glabrous-leaved adenostyle, *Adenostyles glabra* (Miller) DC. *(A. alpina* Bluff and Fing.)
Differs from the preceding as follows: 30–80 cm tall; leaves hairy underneath only on the veins, not tomentose; teeth mostly wider than long; heads mostly 3-flowered. Scree, forest on steep slopes; stony, calcium-rich soils; 900–2200 m; rather common. Mountain plant of Central and Southern Europe. F4, R4, N3, H3, D2, L2, T2, K2. Flowering time: 6–8.

White-leaved adenostyle, *Adenostyles leucophylla* (Willd.) Rchb. *(A. tomentosa* [Vill.] Sch. and Th.)
(Plate 103.2)
10–40 cm tall; leaves reniform to cordate, densely tomentose underneath, rather regularly toothed; teeth about as wide as long; heads 12–24-flowered; flowers flesh-red. Scree, boulder fields; substratum poor in calcium; 2200–2900 m; rather rare (occurs only in the inner ranges). Plant of the western Alps. F4, R2, N2, H2, D2, L5, T1, K3. Flowering time: 7–8.

b. **Arnica,** *Arnica* L.
Mountain arnica, *Arnica montana* L.
(Plate 103.3)
20–40 cm tall; leaves oval, smooth-edged, the lower ones opposite (alternate in all other composite plants occurring in the Alps!); heads 1–3 per stem, measuring 5–8 cm in diameter; the outer flowers ligulate, the inner ones tubular, deep yellow. Pappus bristles in a single row. Pastures, light woods, mires; meagre, humous soils poor in bases; 800–2600 m; rather common. North European-Alpine plant. F3w, R2, N2, H4, D4, L4, T2, K3. Flowering time: 6–8.
Protected: *AI,* AR, *NE,* NW, OW, SG, *ZH*/Ao.

c. **Goldenrod,** *Solidago* L.
Alpine goldenrod, *Solidago alpestris* Waldst. and Kit. (Plate 103.4)
6–40 cm tall; leaves lanceolate, 4–6 times as long as wide; heads few-flowered, in a compact, terminal panicle, outer flowers ligulate, the

inner ones tubular; heads measuring 1.5–2 cm in diameter, yellow; pappus bristles in 1–2 rows. Grassland, pastures, dwarf shrub stands; stony, humous soils poor in calcium; 1300–2700 m; common. Mountain plant of Central and Southern Europe. F3, R2, N2, H4, D3, L3, T2, K3. Flowering time: 7–9.

The **common goldenrod** *(Solidago virga-aurea* L.) occurring at lower altitudes (esp. in forests) has leaves 3–4 times as long as wide, and more but smaller heads than the alpine goldenrod.

d. Groundsel, or ragwort, *Senecio* L.

Heads multi-flowered; outer flowers ligular, the inner ones tubular; all flowers of the same colour, yellow to orange; involucre bracts in two rows; outer bracts very short, the inner ones all of an equal length; pappus bristles in a single row. The genus is represented in the Alps by about 20 species.

Hoary groundsel, *Senecio incanus* L. (Plate 104.1)
1–15 cm tall; leaves pinnately divided almost to the midrib, whitely tomentose; heads 3–15, in an umbel-like raceme, measuring 1–2 cm in diameter, yellow. Grassland; dry, stony soils poor in calcium; 2000–3000 m; rather common (occurs only in the inner ranges west of the Gotthard massif.) Mountain plant of Central and Southern Europe (western). F2, R1, N2, H4, D3, L5, T1, K4. Flowering time: 7–8.

Carniol groundsel, *Senecio carniolicus* Willd. (Plate 104.2)
Differs from the preceding in the leaves which are pinnately divided halfway to the midrib or only a little farther, and have a grey tomentum (not white). Grassland; dry, stony soils poor in calcium; 1800–3000 m; rather common (occurs only in the inner ranges, east of the line Parpan–Bergell; isolated populations at the Furka). Mountain plant of Central and Southern Europe (eastern). F2, R1, N2, H3, D3, L5, T1, K4. Flowering time: 7–8.

The plants intermediary between *Senecio incanus* and *S. carniolicus,* which occur in the area of Misox (E Ticino) and around the Lake of Como, represent the **insubric groundsel** *(Senecio insubricus* Chenev.)
Protected: R.

One-headed groundsel, *Senecio uniflorus* All. *(S. halleri* Dandy)
(Plate 104.3)
Differs from the hoary groundsel as follows: leaves pinnately divided at most to the midrib; heads single, measuring 2–3 cm in diameter. Coarse scree, open grassland; stony soils poor in calcium; 2200–3000 m; rather rare (in Switzerland only in the southern ranges of the Wallis between Simplon and Zermatt). Graian-Pennine plant. F2, R2, N2, H3, D3, L5, T1, K4. Flowering time: 7–8.
Protected: R.

Rock groundsel, *Senecio rupester* Waldst. and Kit. (Plate 104.4)
20–60 cm tall; unpleasantly smelling; leaves with sparse cobwebby hairs, pinnately divided beyond the middle; heads numerous, grouped in an irregular, umbel-like panicle, measuring 2–3 cm in diameter, yellow. Gravel pits, roadsides, resting places of animals; stony,

nutrient-rich soils; 600–2400 m; rather common (esp. in the eastern part, expanding westwards along the roads). Mountain plant of Central and Southern Europe (eastern). F3, R3, N4, H2, D3, L4, T2, K4. Flowering time: 6–8.

Orange groundsel, *Senecio capitatus* (Wahlenb.) Steudel *(S. aurantiacus* auct.) (Plate 105.1)
15–30 cm tall; leaves tomentose on both sides, oval to lanceolate, smooth-edged, or sinuate-dentate; heads few, grouped head-like, measuring 2–3 cm in diameter, orange-red. Grassy slopes, meadows; stony, calciferous soils; 1200–2400 m; rare (occurs above all in the outer ranges). Eurasiatic mountain plant. F2, R4, N2, H4, D3, L4, T2, K3. Flowering time: 6–7.
Protected: R. *FR.*

Abrotanum-leaved groundsel, *Senecio abrotanifolius* L. (Plate 105.2)
10–40 cm tall; leaves glabrous, or sparsely hairy, 1–2-pinnatisect; heads in a loose, umbel-like panicle, measuring 2.5–4 cm in diameter, yellow-orange to orange-red. Dwarf shrub stands, pastures; stony, dry soils poor in calcium; 1600–2600 m; rather rare (occurs above all in the inner ranges). Plant of the eastern Alps. F2, R2, N3, H4, D3, L4, T2, K4. Flowering time: 7–9.

Alpine groundsel, *Senecio alpinus* (L.) Scop. *(S. cordifolius* Clairv.) (Plate 105.3)
30–100 cm tall; leaves grey tomentose underneath, broadly oval, cordate at the base, toothed; heads 6–20, in an umbel-like panicle, measuring 2–3.5 cm in diameter, yellow. Resting places of animals, banks of streams; humid, nutrient-rich soils; 800–2000 m; rather common (esp. in the northern ranges). Plant of the eastern Alps. F4w, R4, N5, H4, D5, L3, T2, K2. Flowering time: 7–8.

Fuchs's groundsel, or **alpine ragwort,** *Senecio fuchsii* Gmelin (Plate 105.4)
60–120 cm tall; leaves glabrous or sparsely hairy, lanceolate, 5–10 times as long as wide in the upper third of the stem; heads numerous, in an umbel-like panicle, measuring 2.5–3 cm in diameter, yellow. Involucre 2–3 mm thick. Woods, bushes, forest clearings; nutrient-rich, humous soils; 800–1800 m; rather common. Central European plant. F3, R3, N4, H4, D4, L3, T3, K2. Flowering time: 7–9.

Wood groundsel, *Senecio nemorensis* L.
Differs from the preceding by the leaves 3–5 times as long as wide in the upper third of the stem, and the involucre 3–4 mm thick. Tall-herb stands, bushes, resting places of animals; humid, nutrient-rich soils; 1200–2200 m; rather common. Eurosibirian plant. F4, R3, N4, H4, D4, L3, T2, K2. Flowering time: 7–9.

Leopard's-bane groundsel, *Senecio doronicum* L. (Plate 106.1)
20–50 cm tall; leaves with loose greyish tomentum underneath, oval to lanceolate, sinuate-dentate; heads mostly 1–5, measuring 3.5–6 cm in diameter, yellow. Open grassland, scree, pastures; base-rich, stony soils;

237

1500–2600 m; rather common. Mountain plant of Central and Southern Europe. F3, R4, N2, H3, D3, L4, T1, K4. Flowering time: 7–8.

d. Leopard's-bane, *Doronicum* L.

Differs from the groundsel in the involucre consisting of two rows of bracts, both rows of nearly the same length. The Alpine flora includes about 6 species of the genus.

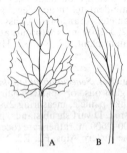

Fig. 52. Large-flowered leopard's-bane *(Doronicum grandiflorum)*. B: Clusius's leopard's-bane *(Doronicum clusii)*. ⅓ ×.

Large-flowered leopard's-bane, *Doronicum grandiflorum* Lam.
(Plate 106.2; Fig. 52A)
10–40 cm tall; leaves oval, truncate or cordate at the base, with glandular hairs; heads mostly single, measuring 4–8 cm in diameter, yellow. Scree; stony, base-rich soils; 1800–2800 m; not common. Mountain plant of Central and Southern Europe. F3, R4, F4, N3, H2, D2↑, L5, T1, K3. Flowering time: 7–8.

Clusius's leopard's-bane, *Doronicum clusii* (All.) Tausch (Fig. 52B)
Differs from the preceding in the leaves which have no glandular hairs and mostly narrow into petiole, only rarely being truncate and never cordate. Scree, boulder fields; soils poor in calcium; 2000–3000 m; not common (occurs nearly exclusively in the inner ranges). Mountain plant of Central and Southern Europe. F3, R2, N2, H3, D2, L5, T1, K3. Flowering time: 7–8.

Fleabane, *Erigeron* L.

Heads multi-flowered; outer flowers ligulate, the inner ones tubular; ligulate flowers white, lilac, or purple, tubular flowers yellowish to reddish; involucral bracts arranged like tiles on a roof; pappus bristles in a single row. The genus is represented in the Alps by about 8 species, difficult to distinguish between.

Alpine fleabane, *Erigeron alpinus* L. (Plate 106.3)
3–30 cm tall; leaves lanceolate, hairy on both sides; heads 1–5, rarely up to 10 per stem, measuring 1.5–2 cm in diameter; involucre sparsely pilose (not whitely tomentose); ligulate flowers pink to purple.

Meadows, pastures; dry, meagre soils; 1400–2600 m; rather common. Mountain plant of Central and Southern Europe. F2, R3, N2, H3, D4, L4, T2, K3. Flowering time: 7–8.

One-flowered fleabane, *Erigeron uniflorus* L. (Plate 106.4)
Differs from the preceding as follows: up to 15 cm tall; leaves hairy at most on margins; heads single; involucre whitely tomentose; ligulate flowers mostly white. Open grassland, ridges; stony, wind-exposed soils; 1800–3200 m; rather common. Arctic-Alpine plant. F2, R3, N2, H4, D3, L5, T1, K4. Flowering time: 7–8.

f. **Aster,** *Aster* L.
Alpine aster, *Aster alpinus* L. (Plate 107.1)
5–20 cm tall; leaves hairy, narrowly oval to lanceolate, smooth-edged; heads single, measuring 3–4.5 cm in diameter, outer flowers ligulate, blue-violet. Pappus bristles in 2–3 rows. Open grassland, rocky ledges; stony, base-rich, meagre soils; 900–2800 m; not common. Eurosibirian-North American plant. F2, R4, N2, H4, D3, L4, T2, K4. Flowering time: 6–8.
Protected: *AI,* AR, *GL,* GR, *NE, NW, OW,* SG, *SO,* SZ, UR/Vo.

g. **Alpine daisy,** *Bellidiastrum* Cass.
Micheli's daisy, *Bellidiastrum michelii* Cass. (Plate 107.2)
5–25 cm tall; leaves oval, obtusely dentate, sparsely pilose (esp. underneath); heads single on leafless stems, measuring 2–4 cm in diameter, outer flowers ligulate, white; pappus bristles in 2–3 rows. Pastures, unstable slopes, flushes; intermittently humid, base-rich soils; 600–2600 m; rather common. Mountain plant of Central and Southern Europe (eastern). F3w, R4, N2, H3, D5, L3, T2, K3. Flowering time: 6–7.
Protected: GE.

h. **Edelweiss,** *Leontopodium* Cass.
Edelweiss, *Leontopodium alpinum* Cass. (Plate 107.3)
5–20 cm tall; leaves lanceolate, tomentose (esp. underneath); heads 2–10, grouped umbel-like, surrounded by whitely tomentose leaves forming a star-shaped envelope; outer flowers filiform, the inner ones tubular, yellowish. Open grassland, rocky ledges, steep slopes; dry, base-rich, meagre, stony soils; 1600–2800 m; rather rare. Mountain plant of Central and Southern Europe. F2, R4, N2, H4, D3, L4, T1, K4. Flowering time: 7–8.
Protected: *AI, AR, BE, FR,* GL, GR, LU, NW, OW, *SG,* SZ, *TI,* UR/*B*/*Ti,* Vo/Li/Ao, *Bz,* L, *So, Tn.*

i. **Ox-eye,** *Buphthalmum* L.
Yellow ox-eye, *Buphthalmum salicifolium* L. (Plate 107.4)
20–60 cm tall; leaves narrowly lanceolate, sparsely hairy; heads single, terminal, measuring 3–6 cm in diameter, yellow, outer flowers ligulate; pappus short, united, dentate. Light woods, meadows; inter-

mittently dry, base-rich soils; 400–2100 m; not common. Mountain plant of Central and Southern Europe (eastern). F2w, R4, N2, H3, D5, L3, T3, K4. Flowering time: 6–9.
Protected: BL, TG, ZH.

k. **Pussytoes,** *Antennaria* Gaertner
Heads terminal, in an umbel-like group; outer flowers filiform, the inner ones tubular; involucral bracts arranged like tiles on a roof; pappus bristles thickened above like the antennae of a butterfly. The Alpine flora includes two species of the genus.

Common pussytoes, *Antennaria dioeca* (L.) Gaertner   (Plate 108.1)
5–20 cm tall; with stolons; basal leaves oval, hairy (esp. underneath); heads 3–12, measuring 4–7 mm in diameter; involucre of female heads dark-red, pink, or white, that of male heads mostly white. Pastures, heaths; dry, meagre soils poor in bases; 1000–2600 m; rather common. Eurosibirian-North American plant. F2, R2, N2, H4, D4, L4, T2, K3. Flowering time: 6–7.
Protected: *BL, SH.*

Carpathian pussytoes, *Antennaria carpatica* (Wahlenb.) Bluff and Fingerh.   (Plate 108.2)
Differs from the preceding as follows: no stolons; lower leaves narrowly lanceolate; outer involucral bracts brown. Grassland, hilltops; dry, humous, wind-exposed soils; 2000–2800 m; not common. Mountain plant of Central and Southern Europe. F2, R3, N2, H4, D4, L4, T1, K4. Flowering time: 7–8.

l. **Cudweed,** *Gnaphalium* L.
Leaves mostly narrowly lanceolate, smooth-edged, tomentose (esp. underneath); heads small, often in spicate inflorescences; outer flowers filiform, the inner ones tubular; bracts of involucres arranged like tiles on a roof. The genus is represented in the Alps by 4 species.

Wood cudweed, *Gnaphalium silvaticum* L.   (Plate 108.3)
10–40 cm tall; leaves virtually glabrous above, mostly 1-veined; heads in a multi-headed spike; the lowest leaves in the spike shorter than the spike itself; involucral bracts with brown scarious margins; flowers brownish. Forest clearings, forest roads, pastures; soils poor in calcium; 600–2400 m; rather common. Eurosibirian-North American plant. F3, R2, N3, H4, D4, L3, T3, K3. Flowering time: 6–8.

Norwegian cudweed, *Gnaphalium norvegicum* Gunnerus
Differs from the preceding as follows: leaves mostly 2-veined; the lowest leaves in the spike mostly longer than the spike itself; involucral bracts deep brown to the very margin. Light woods, pastures, dwarf shrub stands; humous soils poor in calcium; 1400–2600 m; not common. Eurosibirian-North American plant. F3, R2, N3, H4, D4, L3, T2, K2. Flowering time: 7–8.

Dwarf cudweed, *Gnaphalium supinum* L.   (Plate 108.4)
2–10 cm tall; leaves tomentose on both sides; heads 1–6; involucral bracts with brown scarious margins, mostly acute; flowers brownish. Snow-patches, pastures; humid soils poor in calcium, with late-lying snow; 1600–3000 m; rather common (esp. in the inner ranges). Arctic-Alpine plant. F4, R2, N2, H4, D4, L5, T1, K2. Flowering time: 7–8.
Protected: *NW.*

Hoppe's cudweed, *Gnaphalium hoppeanum* Koch
Differs from the preceding in the involucral bracts which have deep brown margin and are more or less obtuse. Open grassland; base-rich soils; 1700–2800 m; not common. Mountain plant of Central and Southern Europe. F3, R4, N2, H4, D4, L4, T1, K3. Flowering time: 7–8.

m.Wormwood of **mugwort,** *Artemisia* L.
Leaves pinnately or palmately divided; heads small, spherical to ovoid, measuring up to 6 mm in diameter; involucral bracts arranged like tiles on a roof; all flowers tubular, no ligulate flowers; no pappus. The Alpine flora includes about 10 species of the genus.

Genipi wormwood, *Artemisia genipi* Weber *(A. spicata* Wulf.)
(Plate 109.1)
5–15 cm tall; aromatic; basal leaves palmately or pinnately divided, with 3–5 lobes, grey tomentose (hairs similar to the compass needle); cauline leaves pinnately divided; heads 5–30, in a slightly nodding spike, 8–20-flowered; flowers yellow. Coarse scree, rocky crevices; stony, calciferous soils; 2400–3000 m; rather rare (occurs above all in the inner ranges). Mountain plant of Central and Southern Europe (western). F2, R4, N2, H2, D2, L5, T1, K4. Flowering time: 7–8.
Protected: *CH/Ti.*

Noble wormwood, *Artemisia mutellina* Vill. *(A. laxa* [Lam.] Fritsch)
(Plate 109.2)
Differs from the preceding as follows: leaves always palmately divided; heads 3–20, in axils of the upper leaves, with long pedicles. Coarse scree, rock crevices; stony soils; 1800–2800 m; not common (occurs above all in the inner ranges). Mountain plant of Central and Southern Europe (western). F3, R3, N2, H2, D2, L5, T1, K4. Flowering time: 7–8.
Protected: *CH/B/Ti, Vo/Li.*

Glacial wormwood, *Artemisia glacialis* L.   (Plate 109.3)
Differs from the genipi wormwood as follows: leaves always palmately divided; heads 3–10, in a head-like, terminal group, 30–40-flowered. Coarse scree, rock crevices; stony soils poor in calcium; 2200–3000 m; rare (in Switzerland only in the southern ranges of the Wallis). Plant of the western Alps. F3, R2, N2, H2, D2, L5, T1, K4. Flowering time: 7–8.
Protected: *R. CH.*

n. **Yarrow** or **sneezewort,** *Achillea* L.

Heads in an umbrella-like, umbel-like racemes or panicles; involucral bracts arranged like tiles on a roof; marginal flowers ligulate, the inner ones tubular and mostly yellowish-white; no pappus. The genus is represented in the Alps by about 15 species.

Dwarf yarrow, *Achillea nana* L. (Plate 109.4)
5–15 cm tall; aromatic; leaves pinnately divided, with dentate lobes, densely tomentose; heads 5–20 per stem, very shortly pedicellate, measuring 0.6–1 cm in diameter; ligulate flowers white, their ligules about ½ as long as the involucre. Scree slopes, alluvial areas; stony soils poor in bases; 1800–3000 m; not common (occurs above all in the inner ranges). Plant of the western Alps. F3, R2, N2, H2, D2, L5, T1, K3. Flowering time: 7–8.

Clavena's yarrow, *Achillea clavenae* L. (Plate 110.1)
Differs from the preceding as follows: up to 25 cm tall; leaves mostly with smooth-edged lobes, hairy with silky clinging hairs; heads measuring 1–1.8 cm in diameter, rather long-pedicellate; ligulas in the ligulate flowers longer than the involucre. Rock crevices, coarse scree; calciferous substratum; 1700–2500 m; rather rare (in Switzerland only the southern Ticino). Plant of the eastern Alps. F2, R5, N2, H2, D1, L5, T1, K4. Flowering time: 6–7.
Protected: E. *TI.*

Musk yarrow, *Achillea moschata* Wulfen (Plate 110.3)
Differs from the dwarf yarrow as follows: up to 20 cm tall; leaves mostly with smooth-edged lobes, sparsely pilose with short hairs, or glabrous; heads with rather long peduncles, measuring 0.9–1.4 cm in diameter; ligulas in the ligulate flowers longer than the involucre. Coarse scree, grassy slopes; stony soils poor in calcium; 1700–3000 m; rather common (mostly in the inner ranges). Plant of the eastern Alps. F3, R2, N2, H3, D2, L5, T1, K3. Flowering time: 7–8.

Black yarrow, *Achillea atrata* L. *(A. halleri* Crantz) (Plate 110.4)
Differs from the dwarf yarrow as follows: up to 25 cm tall; leaves sparsely pilose; heads measuring 1.2–1.8 cm in diameter, 3–10 per stem; ligula in the ligulate flowers longer than the involucre. Scree; calcium-rich substratum; 1700–2800 m; rather common. Plant of the eastern Alps. F3, R5, N2, H2, D2↑, L5, T1, K3. Flowering time: 7–8.

Large-leaved yarrow, *Achillea macrophylla* L. (Plate 110.2)
40–100 cm tall; leaves large, pinnately divided, with lanceolate, toothed segments; heads 6–50 per stem, with rather long peduncles, measuring 1–1.3 cm in diameter; ligulate flowers white, their ligula longer than the involucre. Tall-herb stands, green alder thicket; nutrient-rich, humous soils; 1400–2000 m; rather common. Mountain plant of Central and Southern Europe (western). F3, R3, N4, H4, D4, L3, T2, K2. Flowering time: 7.

Erect yarrow, *Achillea stricta* Schleicher (Plate 111.1)
20–80 cm tall; leaves large, 2–3-pinnate (with 1.2–2 mm wide midrib); heads 15–35 per stem, with rather short peduncles, measuring 6–8 mm in diameter; ligulate flowers pink to purple, their ligula about half as long as the involucre. Meadows, bushes; nutrient-rich soils; 1000–2500 m; not common (occurs only in the central and southern Alpine valleys). Mountain plant of Central and Southern Europe (eastern). F3, R3, N4, H4, D4, L4, T2, K3. Flowering time: 7–8.
The closely related **common yarrow** *(Achillea millefolium* L.) differs from the erect yarrow in the narrower leaf midribs, and often white ligulate flowers. It frequently occurs at lower altitudes, but is also able to grow up to the timberline and may hybridize with the erect yarrow.

o. **Marguerite,** *Chrysanthemum* L.
Heads rather large; involucral bracts arranged like tiles on a roof; marginal flowers ligulate, the inner ones tubular and yellow; no pappus. The Alpine flora includes about 8 species of the genus.

Mountain marguerite, *Chrysanthemum adustum* (Koch) Fritsch *(Ch. montanum* All. p.p.) (Plate 111.2)
15–30 cm tall; leaves narrowly oval in outline, with 6–20 teeth on either side; heads mostly single, measuring 3.5–7 cm in diameter; involucral bracts with black-brown margins; ligulate flowers white. Grassy slopes, scree; intermittently dry, base-rich soils; 600–2300 m; rather common. Mountain plant of Central and Southern Europe. F3w, R4, N2, H2, D4, L3, T2, K3. Flowering time: 6–8.
The closely related **common marguerite** *(Ch. leucanthemum* L.) occurs at lower altitudes.

Alpine marguerite, *Chrysanthemum alpinum* L. (Plate 111.3)
5–15 cm tall; basal leaves broadly oval in outline, pinnately divided, comb-shaped with 2–5 lobes on either side; heads single, measuring 2–4 cm in diameter; involucral bracts with dark-brown margins; ligulate flowers white. Grassland, scree, snow-patches; soils poor in calcium; 1600–3200 m; rather common (above all in the inner ranges). Mountain plant of Central and Southern Europe (western). F3, R2, N2, H4, D4, L5, T1, K3. Flowering time: 7–8.

Haller's marguerite, *Chrysanthemum halleri* Suter *(Ch. atratum* auct.) (Plate 111.4)
Differs from the preceding as follows: 10–20 cm tall; leaves narrowly oval, with 3–7 narrowly lanceolate segments on either side; heads measuring up to 5 cm in diameter; involucral bracts with black margins. Scree; stony, calcium-rich soils; 1600–2600 m; not common (occurs above all in the eastern part of the Alps). Plant of the eastern Alps. F3, R5, N2, H2, D2, L5, T1, K3. Flowering time: 7–8.

p. **Butterbur,** *Petasites* Miller
Basal leaves large, triangular to reniform; dentate; stem with scale-shaped leaves; heads in short compact racemes; involucral bracts in 2–3 rows, all of the same length; all flowers tubular; pappus bristles in a single row.

Paradoxal butterbur, *Petasites paradoxus* (Retz.) Baumg. *(P. niveus* [Vill.] Baumg.) (Plate 112.1)
10–30 cm tall when flowering, up to 60 cm tall when bearing fruit; leaves appearing at the end of the flowering period, triangular to oval, at first grey-tomentose but later becoming glabrous above, with persistent white tomentum underneath (also on the veins); cauline leaves red-brown to violet; flowers reddish. Scree, banks of torrents; calcium-rich substratum; 800–2300 m; rather common. Mountain plant of Central and Southern Europe. F4w, R5, N3, H2, D2↑, L5, T2, K3. Flowering time: 4–6.

White butterbur, *Petasites albus* (L.) Gaertner (Plate 112.2)
Differs from the preceding as follows: leaves appearing after flowering, rounded to reniform, with persistent grey tomentum underneath (veins nearly glabrous; cauline leaves pale green; flowers mostly yellowish-white. Forests; intermittently humid, nutrient-rich soils; 500–1900 m; common. Eurosibirian plant. F4w, R3, N4, H4, D5, L2, T3, K3. Flowering time: 3–5.

q. **Coltsfoot,** *Tussilago* L.
Coltsfoot, *Tussilago farfara* L. (Plate 112.3)
5–15 cm tall when flowering, up to 30 cm tall when bearing fruit; leaves appearing after flowering, cordate, dentate, whitely tomentose on both sides at first, later becoming glabrous above; stem with small, scale-shaped leaves, with only a single head; head measuring 2–3 cm in diameter; involucral bracts in a single row; outer flowers ligulate, yellow; pappus bristles in numerous rows. Sliding slopes, gravel pits, roadsides, scree; intermittently dry, base-rich soils; 200–2400 m; common. Eurosibirian plant. F3w, R4, N3, H2, D5, L4, T3, K3. Flowering time: 4–7.

r. **Purple coltsfoot** or **alpine coltsfoot,** *Homogyne* Cass.
Purple coltsfoot or **alpine coltsfoot,** *Homogyne alpina* (L.) Cass. (Plate 112.4)
10–30 cm tall; basal leaves small, rounded to reniform, leathery, deep green above, sinuate-dentate; heads single, measuring 1.5–2.5 cm in diameter; involucral bracts in one row; all flowers tubular, reddish. Pastures, dwarf shrub stands; humous soils; 1300–2800 m; common. Mountain plant of Central and Southern Europe. F3, R3, N2, H4, D4, L3, T2, K2. Flowering time: 6–7.

s. **Knapweed,** *Centaurea* L.
Involucral bracts arranged like tiles on a roof, with scarious appendages; all flowers tubular; marginal flowers often larger than the inner ones; pappus missing or consisting of very short bristles. The genus is represented in the Alps by about 20 species.

Alpine knapweed, *Centaurea alpestris* Hegetschw. (Plate 113.1)
20–60 cm tall; leaves 1–2-pinnatisect, with narrow oval segments; heads 1–4 per stem, measuring 4–6 cm in diameter, purple; involucral bracts with large, black, triangular, fringed appendages which conceal

the bracts of the next row. Meadows; dry, base-rich soils; 1200–2500 m; not common. Mountain plant of Central and Southern Europe. F2, R4, N3, H3, D4, L4, T2, K3. Flowering time: 7–8.

Nerved knapweed, *Centaurea nervosa* Willd. (Plate 113.3)
10–40 cm tall; leaves lanceolate, sinuate, often grey-pilose; heads single, measuring 4–6 cm in diameter, purple; involucral bracts with feathery, light-brown appendages more than 1 cm long. Meadows, pastures, bushes; soils poor in calcium; 1200–2300 m; not common. Mountain plant of Central and Southern Europe (eastern). F3, R2, N3, H3, D4, L4, T2, K3. Flowering time: 7–8.

Mountain knapweed, *Centaurea montana* L.
10–60 cm tall; leaves lanceolate, smooth-edged, decurrent, sparsely tomentose; heads mostly single, measuring 4–6 cm in diameter; outer flowers blue, the inner ones reddish; involucral bracts with black, fringed margin. Woods, meadows; base-rich soils; 600–2000 m; rather common (esp. in the northern ranges). Mountain plant of Central and Southern Europe. F3, R4, N3, H3, D4, L3, T2, K2. Flowering time: 6–7.
Protected: AG, *AI*, BL, NW, *OW*, SG, TG, ZH.

t. **Giant knapweed,** *Rhaponticum* Lam.
Scarious giant knapweed, *Rhaponticum scariosum* Lam. *(Centaurea rhapontica* L.) (Plate 113.2)
40–100 cm tall; leaves very large, oval, acute, cordate at the base, toothed, whitely tomentose underneath; heads single, measuring 5–11 cm in diameter, purple-red; only tubular flowers present; bracts with round, brown appendages 0.5–1 cm wide. Tall-herb stands, meadows, scree; stony, nutrient-rich soils; 1400–2400 m; rather rare. Alpine plant. F3, R3, N4, H2, D2, L4, T2, K3. Flowering time: 7–8.
Protected: *GL*/Li/*F*.

u. **Carline thistle,** *Carlina* L.
Silver thistle, *Carlina simplex* Waldst. and Kit. *(C. acaulis* L. p.p.)
(Plate 114.1)
5–20 cm tall; leaves in rosette, pinnately divided, prickly; open heads measuring 5–12 cm in diameter; involucral bracts radially curved backwards; silver-white inside; only tubular flowers present; flowers whitish to reddish; pappus bristles feathery, 9–11. Pastures, bushes; dry, meagre soils; 800–2600 m; rather common. Mountain plant of Central and Southern Europe. F2, R3, N2, H3, D4, L4, T2, K3. Flowering time: 7–9.
Protected: *AG*, BE, BL, BS, JU, NW, OW, *SH*, UR, ZH/*Ao*.

v. **Plume-thistle,** *Cirsium* Miller
Leaves prickly-ciliate; involucral bracts ending in prickles; only tubular flowers present; pappus bristles feathery, in numerous rows. The genus is represented in the Alps by about 12 species.

245

Thorny thistle, *Cirsium spinosissimum* (L.) Scop.　　(Plate 114.2)
20–50 cm tall; whole stem leafy; leaves lanceolate, pinnately divided, stiff, with prickles; heads measuring 1–2 cm in diameter, in a head-like group, enveloped in pale-green, prickly leaves; corolla light-yellow. Pastures, resting places of animals, banks of streams, scree; intermittently humid, nutrient-rich soils; 1700–2800 m; rather common. Alpine plant. F4w, R3, N4, H3, D4, L4, T1, K3. Flowering time: 7–8.

Stemless thistle, *Cirsium acaule* (L.) Scop.　　(Plate 114.3)
5–10 cm tall; leaves in basal rosette, lanceolate, pinnately divided, prickly; heads measuring 2.5–4.5 cm in diameter, single, virtually sessile; corolla purple-red. Pastures; intermittently dry, base-rich soils; 800–2300 m; rather common (esp. the Northern and Central Alps). Plant of Central Europe. F2w, R4, N3, H4, D4, L4, T2, K3. Flowering time: 7–9.

Woolly thistle, *Cirsium eriophorum* (L.) Scop.　　(Plate 114.4)
60–150 cm tall; leaves pinnately divided, lanceolate, with prickly hairs above, whitely tomentose underneath; leaf segment ending in a strong prickle; heads measuring 4–7 cm in diameter, single, terminal, with dense cobwebby tomentum outside; corolla purple-red to blue-violet. Pastures, resting places of animals; dry, base-, and nutrient-rich soils; 1000–2000 m; rather rare. Plant of Central Europe. F2, R4, N4, H3, D4, L4, T2, K3. Flowering time: 7–9.
Protected: Li.

Melancholy thistle, *Cirsium helenioides* (L.) Hill *(C. heterophyllum* [L.] Hill)　　(Plate 115.1)
60–120 cm tall; leaves lanceolate, entire, or the middle leaves pinnatisect in the distal part; leaves not prickly, whitely tomentose underneath; heads measuring 2.5–4 cm in diameter, 1–3 per stem; corolla purple-red. Bushes, meadows; stony, humid, nutrient-rich soils; 1200–2200 m; rather common (esp. in the inner ranges). Eurosibirian plant. F4, R3, N4, H3, D3, L3, T2, K4. Flowering time: 7–8.

w.**Thistle,** *Carduus* L.
Differs from the plume-thistle as follows: stem winged by decurrent leaves; pappus bristles rough, not feathery. The Alpine flora includes about 6 species of the genus.

Great marsh thistle, *Carduus personata* (L.) Jacq.　　(Plate 115.2)
50–150 cm tall; leaves large, oval, the lower ones pinnately divided, sparsely tomentose underneath; heads measuring 1.5–2.5 cm in diameter, terminal, in a ball-like group; corolla purple-red. Meadows, tall-herb stands, resting places of animals; humid, base-, and nutrient-rich soils; 800–2000 m; rather common. Mountain plant of Central and Southern Europe. F4, R4, N5, H4, D5, L3, T2, K2. Flowering time: 6–8.

Smooth-stemmed thistle, *Carduus defloratus* L.　　(Plate 115.3)
15–60 cm tall; leaves lanceolate, sinuate to pinnately divided, mostly glabrous on both sides; heads measuring 2–3 cm in diameter, single, terminal; stem below the head without prickles; corolla purple-red.

Scree, grassy slopes, pastures; dry, mostly base-rich soils; 800–2600 m; rather common (esp. in the northern ranges). Mountain plant of Central and Southern Europe. F2, R4, N2, H2, D3, L4, T2, K3. Flowering time: 6–8.

Plants occurring in the southern ranges are much more prickly; they also grow in soils not very rich in bases.

x. **Sawwort,** Saussurea DC.
Plants without prickles; leaves entire, tomentose underneath; involucral bracts arranged like tiles on a roof; all flowers tubular; pappus bristles in two rows, the inner ones feathery. There are 4 species of the genus in the Alps.

Tomentose sawwort, Saussurea discolor (Willd.) DC.   (Plate 115.4)
10–30 cm tall; leaves narrowly triangular, with long tips, cordate at the base, irregularly toothed, whitely tomentose underneath; heads 3–8, in an umbel-like group, measuring 0.8–1.2 cm in diameter; corolla light-violet to purple. Rock crevices, grassy slopes; stony, calcium-rich soils; 1500–2600 m; rather rare (very rare in the Northern Alps). Eurasiatic mountain plant. F2, R4, N2, H2, D1, L4, T2, K4. Flowering time: 7–8.

Protected: GL.

Alpine sawwort, Saussurea alpina (L.) DC.
Differs from the preceding as follows: leaves lanceolate, mostly entire, sparsely grey-tomentose underneath; corolla violet-red. Open grassland; wind-exposed, humous soils; 1600–2800 m; rather rare (occurs above all in the inner ranges). Arctic-Alpine plant (European). F3, R3, N3, H4, D3, L5, T1, K4. Flowering time: 7–8.

Protected: GL.

Sow-thistle, Cicerbita Wallr.
Blue sow-thistle, Cicerbita alpina (L.) Wallr. (Mulgedium alpinum [L.] Less.)   (Plate 116.1)
50–150 cm tall; with milky sap; leaves pinnately divided, with large, triangular segments; heads in a narrow panicle, pedicels with glandular hairs, measuring 1.6–2.4 cm in diameter; all flowers ligulate, blue-violet; pappus bristles rough, in a single row. Tall-herb stands, forests; humid, nutrient-rich soils; 1300–2100 m; rather common. North European-Alpine plant. F4, R3, N4, H4, D4, L3, T2, K2. Flowering time: 7–8.

z. **Cat's-ear,** Hypochoeris L.
One-headed cat's-ear, Hypochoeris uniflora Vill.   (Plate 116.2)
15–40 cm tall; with milky sap; leaves oval to lanceolate, sinuate, with sparse, rough hairs on both sides; heads single, measuring 3.5–5 cm in diameter; involucre densely pilose, with black hairs; all flowers ligulate, yellow; pappus bristles feathery, in a single row. Meadows, pastures; intermittently dry, humous soils poor in calcium; 1500–2600 m; rather common (above all in the inner ranges). Mountain plant of Central and Southern Europe (eastern). F3w, R2, N2, H4, D4, L4, T2, K3. Flowering time: 7–8.

za. **Hawkbit,** *Leontodon* L.

Plants with milky sap; leaves in basal rosette; heads single, terminal, on stem, or on branches; involucral bracts arranged like tiles on a roof; all flowers ligulate, yellow; pappus bristles in two rows, the inner ones feathery. The genus is represented in the Alps by about 10 species.

Swiss hawkbit, *Leontodon helveticus* Mérat *(L. pyrenaicus* auct.)
(Plate 116.3)

5–30 cm tall; leaves narrowly oval to lanceolate, sinuate to almost smooth-edged, hairy on both sides (hairs simple); stem one-headed, with numerous scale-like leaves; heads measuring 2–3 cm in diameter; involucre sparsely pilose with spreading hairs. Pastures, grassland; meagre soils poor in bases; 1700–3000 m; common (esp. in the inner ranges). Mountain plant of Central and Southern Europe. F3, R2, N2, H4, D4, L4, T1, K3. Flowering time: 7–8.

Rough hawkbit, *Leontodon hispidus* L. (Plate 116.4)

8–30 cm tall; leaves narrowly oval to lanceolate, smooth-edged or sinuate, glabrous or pilose (hairs 2–4-partite); stem one-headed with 0–3 scale-shaped cauline leaves; heads measuring 2–3 cm in diameter; involucre sparsely pilose with short hairs. Meadows, pastures; medium soils; 300–2700 m; common. Plant of Central Europe. F3, R3, N3, H3, D4, L4, T3, K4. Flowering time: 6–8.

Hyoseroid hawkbit, *Leontodon hyoseryoides* Welw.

Differs from the preceding in the basal leaves which are deeply pinnatisect. Scree, boulder fields; stony, base-rich substratum; 800–2500 m; not common. Mountain plant of Central and Southern Europe. F3w, R4, N3, H1, Dx↑, L4, T2, K3. Flowering time: 7–8.

Mountain hawkbit, *Leontodon montanus* Lam. (Plate 117.1)

Differs from the rough hawkbit as follows: up to 10 cm tall; leaves glabrous, or pilose underneath (hairs simple); involucre densely pilose with black, spreading hairs. Scree; calcium-rich substratum; 2000–2800 m; not common. Alpine plant. F3, R5, N2, H1, D2↑, L5, T1, K2. Flowering time: 7–8.

zb. **Dandelion,** *Taraxacum* Zinn.

Alpine dandelion, *Taraxacum alpinum* (Hoppe) Hegetschw.
(Plate 117.2)

5–20 cm tall; with milky sap; leaves sinuate to pinnately divided; stem hollow, leafless, single-headed; involucral bracts in two rows, glabrous, or woolly-white; all flowers ligulate, yellow; pappus bristles rough. Meadows, scree; humid, nutrient-rich soils; 1800–3000 m; rather common. Mountain plant of Central and Southern Europe. F4, R3, N4, H2, D3, L4, T1, K2. Flowering time: 6–9.

At lower altitudes, particularly in nutrient-rich meadows, occurs the **common dandelion** *(Taraxacum officinale* Weber). Alpine dandelion differs from this taxon in the broader outer bracts of the involucre (1–1⅓ times as broad as the inner ones).

248

zc. **Hawk's-beard,** *Crepis* L.

Plants with milky sap; leaves mostly in basal rosette; involucral bracts mostly in two rows; all flowers ligulate; pappus bristles rough, in many rows; fruits tapered or beak-shaped above. The genus is represented in the Alps by about 15 species.

Hawk's-beard of Mt. Triglav, *Crepis terglouensis* (Hacquet) Kerner
(Plate 117.3)

2–6 cm tall; leaves sinuate-pinnatisect at least half to the midrib, with broad triangular segments, glabrous; involucre densely pilose with black spreading hairs; head single, measuring 3–5 cm in diameter, yellow. Scree; stony, calcium-rich, wind-exposed soils; 2000–2700 m; rare (occurs above all in the northern ranges). Plant of the eastern Alps. F3, R4, N2, H2, D2, L5, T1, K4. Flowering time: 7–8.

Dwarf hawk's-beard, *Crepis pygmaea* L. (Plate 117.4)

4–15 cm tall; leaves broadly oval, truncate or cordate at the base, glabrous, or whitely tomentose; head single, measuring 1.5–2.5 cm in diameter, yellow; involucre whitely tomentose. Scree; stony, calcium-rich soils; 2000–2600 m; rare (occurs mostly in the inner ranges). Mountain plant of Central and Southern Europe (western). F3, R5, N2, H1, D2, L5, T1, K3. Flowering time: 7–8.

Mountain hawk's-beard, *Crepis pontana* (L.) D. T. (Plate 118.1)

26–60 cm tall; leaves broadly lanceolate, sinuate, encircling stem with the rounded base, almost glabrous; head 1 per stem, measuring 4–5 cm in diameter, yellow; involucre pilose with green and white hairs. Meadows; base-rich, humous soils; 1400–2400 m; not common (occurs above all in the northern ranges). Mountain plant of Central and Southern Europe (eastern). F3, R4, N3, H4, D4, L4, T2, K2. Flowering time: 7–8.

Golden hawk's-beard, *Crepis aurea* (L.) Cass. (Plate 118.2)

5–25 cm tall; leaves oval to lanceolate, sinuate to pinnatisect, glabrous; head 1 per stem, measuring 2–3 cm in diameter, orange-yellow to fire-red; involucre pilose with black, spreading hairs. Pastures, meadows; nutrient-rich, humous soils; 1200–2700 m; rather common. Mountain plant of Central and Southern Europe (eastern). F3, R3, N4, H4, D4, L4, T2, K3. Flowering time: 6–8.

Larger hawk's-beard, *Crepis conyzifolia* (Gouan) D. T. (Plate 118.3)

25–60 cm tall; basal leaves present at the time of flowering, lanceolate, sinuate, pilose; cauline leaves encircling stem with two acute lobes; heads 1–9 per stem, measuring 3–5 cm in diameter, yellow; involucre with long, yellow hairs, frequently also with short, white hairs and short glandular ones. Pastures, meadows; humous soils poor in calcium; 1400–2700 m; rather common (esp. in the inner ranges). Eurasiatic mountain plant. F3, R2, N3, H4, D4, L4, T2, K3. Flowering time: 7–8.

Pyrenean hawk's-beard, *Crepis blattarioides* (L.) Vill. *(C. pyrenaica* [L.] Greuter)
20–60 cm tall; basal leaves absent at the time of flowering; cauline leaves lanceolate, sinuate, hairy, encircling stem with acute lobes; heads 2–6 per stem, measuring 3–5 cm in diameter, yellow; involucre with short, yellowish to black hairs as well as short, curly ones (no glandular hairs). Meadows, tall-herb stands; humid, base-, and nutrient-rich soils; 1000–2200 m; not common (occurs above all in the northern ranges). Mountain plant of Central and Southern Europe. F4, R4, N4, H4, D4, L3, T2, K2. Flowering time: 6–8.

Jacquin's hawk's-beard, *Crepis jacquinii* Tausch   (Plate 118.4)
5–20 cm tall; leaves lanceolate, the first ones entire, the later ones dentate to (on stem) deeply pinnatisect, with narrow lanceolate segments perpendicular to the leaf axis; head single, measuring 2–3 cm in diameter, yellow; involucre grey-tomentose with long, black hairs. Open grassland, scree; stony, calcium-rich soils; 1700–2800 m; not common (occurs nearly exclusively east of the line: Rhine valley – Lake of Como). Mountain plant of Central and Southern Europe (eastern). F3, R5, N2, H4, D3, L5, T1, K4. Flowering time: 7–8.

zd. **Lettuce,** *Prenanthes* L.

Hare lettuce, *Prenanthes purpurea* L.   (Plate 119.1)
30–100 cm tall; with milky sap; leaves narrowly oval, almost smooth-edged, encircling stem with the cordate base; heads numerous, in loose panicles, 2–5-flowered; involucral bracts in two rows, glabrous; all flowers ligulate, violet to purple; pappus bristles rough, in two rows. Woods, tall-herb stands; medium soils; 400–2000 m; rather common. Plant of Central Europe. F3, R3, N3, H4, D4, L2, T3, K3. Flowering time: 7–9.

ze. **Hawkweed,** *Hieracium* L.

Differs from the hawk's-beard *(Crepis)* in the mostly yellowish pappus and the fruits not tapered above. The Alpine flora includes about 20 species of the genus. The reproduction in hawkweeds being mostly asexual, numerous microspecies and fixed hybrids render an exact determination exceedingly difficult.

Mouse-ear hawkweed, *Hieracium pilosella* L.   (Plate 119.2)
5–30 cm tall; stoloniferous; basal leaves narrowly oval to lanceolate, smooth-edged, with long simple hairs above, whitely tomentose below; stem one-headed, with numerous, long, simple hairs in the lower part; heads measuring 1.5–2 cm in diameter, yellow; involucral bracts with stellate, glandular, and frequently also simple hairs. Meadows, pastures; dry, meagre soils; 300–3000 m; rather common. Eurosibirian plant. F2, R3, N2, H3, D4, L4, T3, K4. Flowering time: 6–9.

Prenanth hawkweed, *Hieracium prenanthoides* Vill.   (Plate 119.3)
25–70 cm tall; no stolons; all leaves cauline at the time of flowering, lanceolate, encircling stem with the broadly cordate base, sparsely pilose (simple hairs); stem bearing 6–30 heads, mostly glabrous the

lower part, with long, simple, glandular hairs in the upper part; heads measuring 1–2 cm in diameter, yellow; involucral bracts with few simple hairs, and numerous glandular hairs. Woods, tall-herb stands, bushes; nutrient-rich, humous soils; 1200–2200 m; rather common. Eurosibirian plant. F3, R3, N4, H4, D4, L2, T2, K3. Flowering time: 7–9.

Orange hawkweed, *Hieracium aurantiacum* L. (Plate 119.4)
20–40 cm tall; stoloniferous; basal leaves narrowly oval to lanceolate, smooth-edged, or with single fine teeth, with long simple hairs on both sides, and also with stellate hairs underneath; stem bearing 2–12 heads, with long, dark hairs; heads in an umbel-like group, measuring 1–2 cm in diameter, yellow-orange to brown-red; involucral bracts with stellate hairs, and with simple dark hairs as well. Meadows, pastures; meagre soils poor in calcium; 1300–2200 m; not common. North European-Alpine plant. F3, R2, N2, H4, D4, L4, T2, K3. Flowering time: 6–8.
Protected: *Li.*

Woolly hawkweed, *Hieracium villosum* L. (Plate 120.1)
10–30 cm tall; no stolons; basal leaves lanceolate to ligulate, smooth-edged, or with single teeth, with long, white, simple hairs; stem bearing 1–4 heads, with long, simple white hairs throughout the whole length; heads measuring 2–3.5 cm in diameter, yellow; involucral bracts with many, silky, long, simple hairs. Meadows, open grassland; stony, calcium-rich soils; 1200–2600 m; rather common. Mountain plant of Central and Southern Europe (eastern). F3, R5, N2, H3, D3, L4, T2, K3. Flowering time: 7–8.

Whitish hawkweed, *Hieracium intybaceum* Vill. *(H. albidum* Vill.)
(Plate 120.2)
5–30 cm tall; leaves narrowly lanceolate, irregularly dentate (teeth 1–6 mm long and narrow) with many glandular hairs on both sides and therefore sticky; stem bearing 1–6 heads, with many, often dark, glandular hairs, and with single stellate hairs in the upper part; heads measuring 2.5–4 cm in diameter, yellowish-white; involucral bracts with many glandular hairs. Open grassland, scree; stony, dry soils poor in bases; 1600–2700 m; not common (occurs above all in the inner ranges). Alpine plant. F2, R2, N2, H3, D2, L4, T2, K4. Flowering time: 7–8.

Statice-leaved hawkweed, *Hieracium staticifolium* All. (Plate 120.3)
15–30 cm tall; stoloniferous; basal leaves very narrowly lanceolate, smooth-edged, or with single fine teeth, glabrous or floccose; stem bearing 1–5 heads, floccose in the upper part; heads measuring 2–3 cm in diameter, light-yellow; bracts floccose. Scree, banks of torrents; stony, intermittently dry, base-rich soils; 800–2400 m; not common. Mountain plant of Central and Southern Europe (eastern). F2w, R3, N2, H1, D2, L4, T3, K4. Flowering time: 7–8.

Alpine hawkweed, *Hieracium alpinum* L. (Plate 120.4)
5–20 cm tall; no stolons; basal leaves lanceolate, mostly smooth-edged, with many simple hairs,and also many short glandular hairs,

251

particularly on margins; stem single-headed, with mostly dark, simple hairs, and short glandular hairs throughout the whole length; heads measuring 2–3.5 cm in diameter, yellow; involucral bracts with long, silky hairs, and short glandular hairs. Open grassland, dwarf shrub stands; humous soils poor in calcium; 1700–3000 m; rather common (esp. in the inner ranges). Arctic-Alpine plant. F3, R1, N2, H4, D4, L4, T1, K3. Flowering time: 7–8.

Glanduliferous hawkweed, *Hieracium glanduliferum* Hoppe
Differs from the preceding in the leaves without glandular hairs. Open grassland, rocky ledges; stony, acid, humous soils; 2100–2800 m; rather common (esp. in the inner ranges). Mountain plant of Central and Southern Europe. F2, R1, N2, H4, D3, L5, T1, K4. Flowering time: 7–8.

Protected: *NW, OW.*

References

The following pages present some works pertinent to particular chapters of this book. For more information, or different interpretations, the reader is referred to these publications.

1. Origin and formation of the Alpine flora (see also Part 6)

a. *Favarger C., 1975:* Cytotaxonomie et histoire de la flore orophile des Alpes et de quel-ques autres massifs montagneux d'Europe. Lejeunia 77, 455.

b. *Frenzel B. (eds.), 1972:* Vegetationsgeschichte der Alpen. Ber. Dtsch. Bot. Ges. *85*, 1–192.

c. *Hantke R., 1978–1983:* Eiszeitalter. Die jüngste Erdgeschichte der Schweiz und ihrer Nachbargebiete. 3 vol. Thun (Ott).

d. *Jerosch Marie C., 1903:* Geschichte und Herkunft der schweizerischen Alpenflora. Leipzig (Engelmann), 223 pp.

e. *Kral F., 1979:* Spät- und postglaziale Waldgeschichte der Alpen auf Grund der bisherigen Pollenanalyse. Veröff. Inst. Waldbau Univ. Bodenkultur, Wien. 175 pp.

f. *Lüdi W., 1953:* Die Pflanzenwelt des Eiszeitalters im nördlichen Vorland der Schweizer Alpen. Veröff. Geobot. Inst. Rübel *27*, 208 pp.

g. – *1955:* Die Vegetationsentwicklung seit dem Rückzug der Gletscher in den Alpen. Ber. Geobot. Forsch. Inst. Rübel *1954*, 36–68.

h. *Mägdefrau K., 1968:* Palaeobiologie der Pflanzen. 4th ed. Stuttgart (Fischer), 443 pp.

i. *Welten M., 1982:* Vegetationsgeschichtliche Untersuchungen in den westlichen Schweizer Alpen: Bern-Wallis. (Birkhäuser), Basle, Boston, Stuttgart, 104 pp.

k. *Zoller H. and Kleiber H., 1971:* Überblick der spät- und postglazialen Vegetationsgeschichte in der Schweiz. Boissiera *19*, 113–128.

2. Distribution of Alpine plants (see also Part 6)

a. *Dansereau P., 1957:* Biogeography. New York (Ronald), 394 pp.

b. *Furrer E., 1942:* Kleine Pflanzengeographie der Schweiz. 2nd ed., Zurich (Schulthess).

c. *Good R., 1953:* The geography of the flowering plants. 2nd ed., London (Longmans et al.), 452 pp.

d. *Merxmüller H., 1952:* Untersuchungen zur Sippengliederung und Arealbildung in den Alpen. München (Ver. Schutze Alpenpflanzen und -Tiere), 105 pp.

e. *Welten M. and Sutter R., 1982:* Verbreitungsatlas der Farn- und Blütenpflanzen der Schweiz. (Birkhäuser), Basle, Boston und Stuttgart. 2 vol., 752 pp., 696 pp.

3. Climate and soil of the Alps (see also Parts 4 and 6)

a. *Aulitzki H., 1963:* Grundlagen und Anwendung des vorläufigen Wind-Schnee-Ökogrammes. Mitt. Forstl. Bundes-Vers.anst. Mariabrunn, *60*, 765–834.

b. *Cadisch J., 1953:* Geologie der Schweizer Alpen. 2nd ed., Basle (Wepf), 480 pp.

c. *Franz H., 1980:* Untersuchungen an alpinen Böden in den hohen Tauern 1974–1978. Stoffdynamik und Wasserhaushalt. Veröff. Österr. MaB-Hochgebirgspr. Hohe Tauern, Innsbruck, 3 vol.

d. *Hegg O., 1977:* Mikroklimatische Wirkung der Besonnung auf die phänologische Entwicklung und auf die Vegetation in der alpinen Stufe der Alpen. In Dierschke H. (ed.): Vegetation und Klima. Intern. Ver. Vegetk. 249–270.

e. *Imhof E., 1965:* Schweizerischer Mittelschulatlas. Zurich (Orell-Füssli).

f. *Liniger H., 1958:* Vom Bau der Alpen. Thun (Ott), 236 pp.

g. *Lundegardh H., 1957:* Klima und Boden. 5th ed., Jena (Fischer), 584 pp.
h. *Maurer J. et al., 1909:* Das Klima der Schweiz. Frauenfeld (Huber), 2 vol., 302 and 217 pp.
i. *Primault B., 1981:* Indices de chaleur. Doc. Suisse Agrométéor. *201.*
k. *Schroeter C., 1926:* Das Pflanzenleben der Alpen. 2nd ed., Zurich (Raustein), 1288 p.
l. *Schüepp M., 1960–1963:* Lufttemperatur. Klimatologie der Schweiz. Part C. suppl. Ann. SMZA.
m. *Uttinger H., 1949:* Die Niederschlagsmengen in der Schweiz. 1901–1940. Zurich (SMZA).

4. Alpine plants and their environment

a. *Backhuys W., 1968:* Der Elevationseffekt bei einigen Alpenpflanzen der Schweiz. Blumea *16,* 273–320.
b. *Billings W. D., 1974:* Adaptations and origins of alpine plants. Arctic and Alpine Res. *3,* 129–142.
c. *– 1979:* Aspects of the ecology of alpine and subalpine plants. In Webber P.J. (ed.): High Altitude Geoecology. AAAS Selected Symposium *17,* 97–125.
d. *– and Mooney H. A., 1968:* The ecology of arctic and alpine plants. Biol. Rev. *43,* 481–530.
e. *Bliss L. C., 1971:* Arctic and alpine plant life cycles. Ann. Rev. Ecol. Syst. *2,* 405–438.
f. *Braun-Blanquet J., 1958:* Über die obersten Grenzen pflanzlichen Lebens im Gipfelbereich des Schweizerischen Nationalparks. Ergebn. Wiss. Unters. Schweiz. Nationalpark *6,* 119–142.
g. *Brzoska W., 1977:* Stoffproduktion und Energiehaushalt von Nivalpflanzen. In Ellenberg H.: Ökosystemforschung. Berlin (Springer), 225–233.
h. *Caldwell M. M., 1968:* Solar ultraviolet radiation as an ecological factor for alpine plants. Ecol. Monogr. *38,* 243–268.
i. *Cernusca A. (ed.), 1977:* Alpine Grasheide Hohe Tauern. Ergebnisse der Ökosystemstudie 1976. Innsbruck (Univ. Verlag Wagner), 175 pp.
k. *Franz H., 1979:* Ökologie der Hochalpen. Stuttgart (Ulmer), 495 pp.
l. *Landolt E., 1967:* Gebirgs- und Tieflandsippen von Blütenpflanzen im Bereich der Schweizer Alpen. Bot. Jb. *86,* 463–480.
m. *– 1977:* Beziehungen zwischen Vegetation und Umwelt in den Alpen. In Wolkinger F. (ed.): Natur und Mensch im Alpenraum, Graz (L. Boltzmann-Inst.), 27–44.
n. *Larcher W., 1973:* Ökologie der Pflanzen. Stuttgart (Ulmer), UTB *232.*
o. *– 1980:* Klimastress im Gebirge – Adaptationstraining und Selektionsfilter für Pflanzen. Rhein.-Westf. Akad. Wiss. Vortr. N *291,* 49–88.
p. *– 1983:* Ökophysiologische Konstitutionseigenschaften von Gebirgspflanzen. Ber. Dtsch. Bot. Ges. *96,* 73–85.
q. *– and Wagner J., 1976:* Temperaturgrenzen der CO_2-Aufnahme und Temperaturresistenz der Blätter von Gebirgspflanzen im vegetationsaktiven Zustand. Öcol. Plant, *11,* 361–374.
r. *Moser W., 1977:* Licht, Temperatur und Photosynthese an der Station «Hoher Nebelkogel». In: Ellenberg H.: Ökosystemforschung. Berlin (Springer), 203–223.
s. *Nägeli W., 1969:* Waldgrenze und Kampfzone in den Alpen. Hespa Mitt. (Luzern) *19* (1), 44 pp.
t. *Pisek A., 1963:* An den Grenzen des Pflanzenlebens im Hochgebirge. Jb. Ver. Schutze Alpenpflanzen und -Tiere *28,* 112–129.
u. *Tranquillini W., 1979:* Physiological ecology of the alpine timberline. Ecol. Studies *31,* 137 pp.
v. *Ulmer W., 1937:* Über den Jahresgang der Frosthärte einiger immergrüner Arten der alpinen Stufe, sowie der Zirbe und Fichte. Jb. Wiss. Bot. *84,* 553–592.
w. *Walter H., 1962:* Standortslehre. 2nd ed., Stuttgart (Ulmer), 566 pp.

5. Vegetation of the Alps

a. *Albrecht J., 1969:* Soziologische und ökologische Untersuchungen alpiner Rasengesellschaften, insbesondere an Standorten auf Kalk-Silikat-Gesteinen. Diss. Bot. *5.* Lehre (Cramer) 91 pp.

b. *Braun-Blanquet J., 1913:* Die Vegetationsverhältnisse der Schneestufe in den Rätisch-Lepontischen Alpen. Nouv. Mém. Soc. Helv. Sc. Nat. *48,* 347 pp.

c. – *1948/50:* Übersicht der Pflanzengesellschaften Rätiens. Vegetatio *1,* 29–41, 129–146, 285–316; *2,* 20–37, 214–237, 341–360.

d. – *1954:* La végétation alpine et nivale des Alpes françaises. Montpellier, 72 pp.

e. – *1958:* Über die obersten Grenzen pflanzlichen Lebens im Gipfelbereich des Schweizerischen Nationalparks. Ergebn. Wiss. Unters. Schweiz. Nationalpark *6,* 119–142.

f. – *1964:* Pflanzensoziologie. 3rd ed., Wien (Springer), 865 pp.

g. – , *Pallmann H. and Bach R., 1954:* Pflanzensoziologische und bodenkundliche Untersuchungen im Schweizerischen Nationalpark und seinen Nachbargebieten. Ergebn. Wiss. Unters. Schweiz. Nationalpark *28,* 200 pp.

h. *Dietl W., 1972:* Die Vegetationskartierung als Grundlage für die Planung einer umfassenden Alpenverbesserung im Raume Glaubenbüelen (Obwalden). Alpwirtsch. Landsch.pfl. Glaubenbüelen, Obwalden, 6–153.

i. *Ellenberg H. and Klötzli F., 1972:* Waldgesellschaften und Waldstandorte der Schweiz. Mitt. Eidg. Anst. Forstl. Vers.w. *48,* 587–930.

k. *Gigon A., 1971:* Vergleich alpiner Rasen auf Silikat und Karbonboden. Veröff. Geobot. Inst. ETH, Stiftung Rübel, *48,* 163 pp.

l. *Hartmann H., 1971:* Die azidophilen Pflanzengesellschaften in der alpinen Stufe des westlichen Rätikons und der Schesaplanagruppe. Jber. Nat. Ges. Graubünden, Chur, *94,* 1–81.

m. *Jenny-Lips H., 1930:* Vegetationsbedingungen und Pflanzengesellschaften auf Felsschutt. Beih. Bot. Centralblatt *46,* 119–296.

n. *Kuoch R., 1954:* Wälder der Schweizer Alpen im Verbreitungsgebiet der Weisstanne. Mitt. Schweiz. Anst. forst. Vers.w. *30,* 133–260.

o. *Landolt E., 1983:* Probleme der Höhenstufen in den Alpen. Botanica Helvetica *93,* 255–268.

p. *Marschall F., 1947:* Die Goldhaferwiese (Trisetetum flavescentis) der Schweiz. Beitr. Geob. Landesaufnahme Schweiz *26,* 168 pp.

q. *Mayer H., 1974:* Wälder des Ostalpenraumes. Stuttgart (Fischer), 344 pp.

r. *Moor M., 1954:* Fichtenwälder im Schweizer Jura. Vegetatio *5/6,* 542–552.

s. *Oberdorfer E., 1977ff.:* Süddeutsche Pflanzengesellschaften. 4vol., 2nd ed., Jena (Fischer).

t. *Ozenda P. and Wagner H., 1975:* Les séries de végétation de la chaîne alpine et leurs équivalences dans les autres systèmes phytogéographiques. Doc. Cartogr. Ecol *16,* 49–64.

u. *Saxer A., 1955:* Die Fagus-Abies- und Piceagürtelarten in der Kontaktzone der Tannen- und Fichtenwälder der Schweiz. Beitr. Geob. Landesaufnahme Schweiz *37,* 1–198.

v. *Schmid E., 1944/51:* Vegetationskarte der Schweiz. 4 parts. Berne (Huber).

w. *Schwarz U., 1955:* Die natürlichen Fichtenwälder des Juras. Beitr. Geob. Landesaufnahme Schweiz *35,* 1–143.

x. *Vetterli L., 1982:* Alpine Rasengesellschaften auf Silikatgestein bei Davos. Veröff. Geobot. Inst. ETH, Stiftung Rübel, *76,* 92 pp.

y. *Zollitsch B., 1966:* Soziologische und ökologische Untersuchungen auf Kalkschiefern in hochalpinen Gebieten. Ber. Bayer., Bot. Ges. *40,* 38 pp.

z. *Zumbühl G., 1983:* Pflanzensoziologisch-ökologische Untersuchungen von gemähten Magerrasen bei Davos. Veröff. Geobot. Inst. ETH, Stiftung Rübel, *81,* 101 pp.

6. Alpine plants, and general works

The list presented here includes more important publications dealing with Alpine areas of Switzerland as well as the Swiss Jura. The works listed also contain some data relating to the preceding chapters of our book. Publications marked with asterisks give complete lists of species and their localities from particular areas.

6.1. Central Europe, Switzerland, and the Alps

a. *Becherer A., 1972:* Führer durch die Flora der Schweiz. Basle (Schwabe), 207 pp.

b. **Binz A., 1980:* Schul- und Exkursionsflora für die Schweiz. 17th ed. (revised by A. Becherer and Ch. Heitz), Basle (Schwabe), 422 pp.

c. *Birkenhauer J., 1980:* Die Alpen. UTB *955,* 231 pp.

d. Christ H., 1882: Das Pflanzenleben der Schweiz. 2nd ed., Zurich (Schulthess), 488 pp.
e. Ellenberg H., 1982: Vegetation Mitteleuropas mit den Alpen in ökologischer Sicht. 3rd ed., Stuttgart (Ulmer), 989 pp.
f. Favarger C., 1958 and 1959: Flora und Vegetation der Alpen (I. alpine belt and II. subalpine belt). Neuchâtel (Delachaux & Niestlé), 280 and 304 pp.
g. *Fenaroli L., 1955: Flora delle alpi. Milan (Martello), 369 pp.
h. *Hegi G., 1906/31: Illustrierte Flora von Mitteleuropa. (2nd ed. from 1935), Munich (Lehmann now Hanser). 6 large volumes.
i. – 1977: Alpenflora. 18th ed. (revised by H. Merxmüller and H. Reisigl), Munich (Parey), 194 pp.
k. *Hess H.E., Landolt E. and Hirzel R., 1976–1980: Flora der Schweiz und angrenzender Gebiete. 3 vol., 2nd ed., Basle (Birkhäuser), 2690 pp.
l. – 1984: Bestimmungsschlüssel zur Flora der Schweiz. 2nd ed., Basle, Stuttgart (Birkhäuser), 657 pp.
m. Jenny-Lips H., 1948: Vegetation der Schweizer Alpen. Zurich (Büchergilde Gutenberg), 240 pp.
n. Landolt E., 1977: Ökologische Zeigerwerte zur Schweizer Flora. Veröff. Geobot. Inst. ETH, Stiftung Rübel, *64,* 208 pp.
o. Lippert W., 1981: Fotoatlas der Alpenblumen. Munich (Gräfe and Unzer), 259 pp.
p. Rübel E. and Schroeter C., 1923: Pflanzengeographischer Exkursionsführer für eine botanische Exkursion durch die Schweizer Alpen. Zurich (Rascher) 85 pp.
q. Scharfetter R., 1938: Das Pflanzenleben der Ostalpen. Vienna, 419 pp.
r. Schroeter C., 1926: Das Pflanzenleben der Alpen. 2nd ed., Zurich (Raustein), 1288 pp.
s. –1956: Taschenflora des Alpenwanderers. 28th ed. (revised by W. Lüdi), Zurich (Raustein), 92 pp.
t. Thommen E., 1983: Taschenatlas der Schweizer Flora. 6th ed. (revised by A. Becherer and A. Antonietti), Basle (Birkhäuser), 352 pp.
u. Tutin T.G. and Heywood V.H., 1964–1980: Flora Europaea. 5 vol.

6.2. Jura

*Aubert S., 1901: La Flore de la Vallée de Joux. Bull. Soc. Vaud. Sci. Nat. *36,* 323–741.
– und Luquet A., 1930: Etudes phytogéographiques sur la chaîne Jurassienne. Recherches sur les associations végétales du Mont Tendre. Revue Géographie Alpine *1930,* 50 pp.
Béguin C., 1972: Contribution à l'étude phytosociologique et écologique du Haut-Jura. Beitr. Geobot. Landesaufn. Schweiz. *54,* 190 pp.
*Briquet J., 1894: Le Mont Vuache. Etude de floristique. Bull. Trav. Soc. Bot. Genève *7,* 24–146, 232–234.
*Durand T. and Pittier H., 1881–1886: Catalogue de la flore vaudoise, Lausanne, 250 pp.
Fauconnet Ch., 1867: Herborisations à Salève. Genève et Bâle, 195 pp.
*Favre J., 1924: La Flore du cirque de Moron et des hautes Côtes du Doubs. Bull. Soc. Neuch. Sc. Nat. *49,* 130 pp.
*Godet C.H., 1853: Flore du Jura. Neuchâtel, 872 pp.
*– 1869: Supplément à la flore du Jura suisse et français. Neuchâtel, 220 pp.
*Graber A., 1924: La flore des gorges de l'Areuse et du Creux-du-Van. Bull. Soc. Neuchâtel. Sci. Nat. *48,* 25–365.
*Grenier Ch., 1865–1875: Flore de la Chaîne Jurassique. Paris, 1001 pp.
Ischer A., 1935: Les tourbières de la Vallée des Ponts-de-Martel. Bull. Soc. Neuchâtel. Sci. Nat. *60,* 77–164.
*Kummer G., 1937–1946: Die Flora des Kantons Schaffhausen mit Berücksichtigung der Grenzgebiete. Mitt. Naturf. Ges. Schaffhausen, 936 pp.
*Lüscher H., 1918: Flora des Kantons Aargau. Aarau, 217 pp.
Magnin A., 1904: Monographies botaniques de 74 lacs Jurassienne. Paris, 426 pp.
Moor M., 1942: Die Pflanzengesellschaften der Freiberge (Berner Jura). Ber. Schweiz. Bot. Ges. *52,* 363–422.
– 1955: L'étude de la végétation dans le Jura et en Ajoie. Rec. Etudes Trav. Sci. *1955,* 189–206.

256

– and *Schwarz U.*, *1957:* Die kartographische Darstellung der Vegetation des Creux du Van-Gebietes. Beitr. Geobot. Landesaufn. Schweiz *37*, 114 pp.

*Parmentier P., *1894:* Flore nouvelle de la chaîne jurassique et de la Haute-Saône. Autun, 307 pp.

Pfadenhauer J., *1973:* Versuch einer vergleichend-ökologischen Analyse der Buchen-Tannen-wälder des Schweizer Jura (Weissenstein und Chasseral). Veröff. Geobot. Inst. ETH, Stiftung Rübel *50*, 60 pp.

*Probst R., *1949:* Verzeichnis der Gefässkryptogamen und Phanerogamen des Kantons Solothurn und der angrenzenden Gebiete. Solothurn, 587 pp.

Richard J. L., *1961:* Les forêts acidophiles du Jura. Beitr. Geobot. Landesaufn. Schweiz *38*, 164 pp.

– *1972:* La végétation des crêtes rocheuses du Jura. Ber. Schweiz. Bot. Ges. *82*, 68–112.

Rikli M., *1907:* Das Lägerngebiet. Ber. Schweiz. Bot. Ges. *17*, 5–83.

Spinner H., *1918:* La distribution verticale et horizontale des végétaux vasculaires dans le Jura Neuchâtelois. Mém. Univ. Neuchâtel *2*, 200 pp.

– *1932:* Le Haut-Jura neuchâtelois nord-occidental. Beitr. Geobot. Landesaufn. Schweiz *17*, 197 pp.

Zoller H., *1958:* Die Vegetation und Flora des Schaffhauser Randens. Mitt. Naturf. Ges. Schaffhausen *26*, 1–36.

6.3. Northern Alps

*Amberg K., *1916:* Der Pilatus in seinen pflanzengeographischen und wirtschaftlichen Verhält-nissen. Luzerne, 267 pp.

*Aregger J., *1958:* Flora der Talschaft Entlebuch und der angrenzenden Gebiete Obwaldens. Ebikon (Aregger), 296 pp.

*Baumgartner G., *1900:* Das Churfirstengebiet in seinen pflanzengeographischen und wirt-schaftlichen Verhältnissen. Jber. St. Gall. Naturw. Ges. *1899/1900*, 147–390.

Beauverd G., *1931:* Le massif de la Tournette. Bull. Soc. Bot. Genève *23*, 418.

*Bettschart A., *1982 (ed):* Die Karstlandschaft des Muotatales. Ber. Schwyz. Natf. Ges. *8*, 100 pp.

Bolleter R., *1920:* Vegetationsstudien aus dem Weisstannental. Jb. St. Gall. Naturw. Ges. *57*, suppl., 140 pp.

*Briquet J., *1889:* Notes floristiques sur les Alpes lémaniennes. Bull. Trav. Soc. Bot. Genève *5*, 191–220.

*Dörr E. and Müller L., *1964ff.:* Flora des Allgäus. In Fortsetzungen. Ber. Bayer. Bot. Ges. *37ff.*

*Durand T. and Pittier H., *1887:* Catalogue de la flore vaudoise. Lausanne, 250 pp.

*Dutoit D., *1934:* Contribution à l'étude de la végétation du Massif de Naye sur Montreux. Mém. Soc. Vaud. Sci. Nat. *47*, 365–413.

*Fischer L., *1876:* Verzeichnis der Gefässpflanzen des Berner Oberlandes. Mitt. Naturf. Ges. Bern *1875*, 1–196.

*Gander M., *1888:* Flora Einsidlensis. Einsiedeln, 136 pp.

Gilomen H., *1941:* Die Flora der westschweizerischen Kalkalpen. Mitt. Natf. Ges. Bern. *1941*, 29 pp.

Hegg O., *1965:* Untersuchungen zur Pflanzensoziologie und Ökologie im Naturschutzgebiet Hohgant (Berner Voralpen). Beitr. Geobot. Landesaufn. Schweiz *46*, 188 pp.

*Hegi G., *1900–1902:* Das obere Tösstal und die angrenzenden Gebiete, floristisch und pflan-zengeographisch dargestellt. Bull. Herb. Boissier *1*, 179–212, 337–352, 533–548, 637–652, 689–736, 793–824, 913–944, 1041–1072, 1153–1200, 1233–1300; *2*, 49–108, 185–216.

Hess E., *1921:* Forstbotanische Monographie des Oberhasli von Interlaken bis zur Grimsel. Berne, 92 pp.

Höhn W., *1930:* Bilder aus der Pflanzenwelt des Haslitales. Meiringen (Brügger), 39 pp.

*Jaquet F., *1929:* Catalogue raisonné des plantes vasculaires du canton de Fribourg et des contrées limitrophes. Mém. Soc. Fribourg. Sci. Nat. *5*, 381 pp.

– and *Buser R.*, *1907:* Contribution à l'étude de la flore fribourgeoise IX. Mém. Soc. Frib. Sci. Nat. *2*, H. 4.

257

*Kägi H., 1920: Die Alpenpflanzen des Mattstock-Speer-Gebietes und ihre Verbreitung ins Zürcher Oberland. Jb. St. Gall. Naturw. Ges. *56*, 45–254.

Lienert L. and Wallimann H., 1963: Pflanzengeographie von Obwalden. Sarnen, 390 pp.

Lüdi W., 1921: Die Pflanzengesellschaften des Lauterbrunnentales und ihre Sukzession. Beitr. Geobot. Landesaufn. Schweiz *9*, 350 pp.

– 1933: Pflanzengeographische Streifzüge im Hohgantgebiet. Mitt. Naturf. Ges. Bern *1933*, 135–188.

Merz W., 1966: Flora des Kantons Zug. Mitt. Naturf. Ges. Luzern *20*, 368 pp.

Murr J., 1923–1926: Neue Übersicht über die Farn- und Blütenpflanzen von Vorarlberg und Liechtenstein. Bregenz, 507 pp.

Perrier de la Bathie E., 1917, 1928: Catalogue raisonné des plantes vasculaires de Savoie. Bd. I und II. Le Carriol (Lot.).

Rhiner J., 1893/1895: Die Gefässpflanzen der Urkantone und von Zug. Ber. St. Gall. Naturw. Ges. *1891/92*, 147–271, *1892/93*, 175–260, *1893/94*, 111–207.

Roth A., 1912, 1913: Das Murgtal und die Flumser-Alpen. Jb. St. Gall. Naturw. Ges. *52*, 1–183.

– 1919: Die Vegetation des Walenseegebietes. Beitr. Geobot. Landesaufn. Schweiz *7*, 60 pp.

Schmid H., 1906: Wodurch unterscheidet sich die Alpenflora des Kronberggebietes von derjenigen des Gäbris? Jahrb. Natw. Ges. St. Gallen *1906*, 25 pp.

Schnyder A., 1930: Floristische und Vegetationsstudien im Alviergebiet. Vierteljahrsschr. Naturf. Ges. Zürich *75*, suppl. *17*, 188 pp.

Schroeter C., 1895: Das St. Antönienthal im Prättigau in seinen wirtschaftlichen und pflanzengeographischen Verhältnissen. Zurich 272 pp.

– and Nägeli O., 1919: Die Flora der Mythen. In Müller H.: Die Mythen. Sektion Mythen SAC *1919*. 24–30.

Schweingruber F., 1972: Die subalpinen Zwergstrauchgesellschaften im Einzugsgebiet der Aare (schweizerische nordwestliche Randalpen). Mitt. Schweiz. Anst. Forstl. Versuchsw. *48*, 200–505.

– 1974: Föhrenwälder im Berner Oberland und am Vierwaldstättersee. Ber. Schweiz. Bot. Ges. *83*, 175–204.

Villaret P., 1956: Etude floristique de la vallée d'Anzeindaz. Lausanne, 264 pp.

Vogt M., 1920: Pflanzengeographische Studien im Obertoggenburg. Jb. St. Gall. Naturw. Ges. *57*, 170–298.

Wartmann J. and Schlatter T., 1881–1888: Kritische Übersicht über die Gefässpflanzen der Kantone St. Gallen und Appenzell. Ber. St. Gall. Naturw. Ges. *1879/80*, 61–238; *1882/83*, 159–328; *1886/87*, 247–461.

Widmer R., 1966: Die Pflanzenwelt des Appenzellerlandes. Appenzeller Hefte Herisau *4*, 60 pp.

Winteler R., 1927: Studien über Soziologie und Verbreitung der Wälder, Sträucher und Zwergsträucher des Sernftales. Viertelj.schr. Natf. Ges. Zürich *72*, 185 pp.

Wirz-Luchsinger H., 1958: Beiträge zur Kenntnis der Flora und Vegetation des hintern Linthtales und des Tödigebietes. Mitt. Naturf. Ges. Glarus *10*, 291 pp.

Wirz J., 1893–1896: Flora des Kantons Glarus. Glarus, 40 + 176 + 72 pp.

6.4. Central Alps

Becherer A., 1956: Florae Vallesiacae Supplementum. Supplement zu Henri Jaccards Catalogue de la Flore valaisanne. Denkschriften Schweiz. Naturf. Ges. *81*, 1–556.

Beger H., 1922: Assoziationsstudien in der Waldstufe des Schanfigg. Jb. Naturf. Ges. Graubünden *1921/22*. suppl., 147 pp.

Binz A., 1907–1908: Das Binnental und seine Flora. Ber. Realschule Basel *1907–1908*, 46 pp.

Braun-Blanquet J., 1917: Aus dem Schanfigg – Die Pflanzenwelt der Plessuralpen. Chur, 38 pp.

– 1918: Eine Pflanzengeographische Exkursion durchs Unterengadin und in den Nationalpark. Beitr. Geobot. Landesaufn. Schweiz *4*, 80 pp.

– 1961: Die inneralpine Trockenvegetation. Stuttgart. Geobot. Selecta *1*, 273 pp.

- *and Richard F., 1949:* Groupements végétaux et sols du bassin de Sierre. Bull. Soc. Murith. Valais *66,* 106–134.

*- *and Rübel E., 1932–1935:* Flora von Graubünden. Veröff. Geobot. Inst. Rübel *7,* 1695 pp.

- *and Thellung A., 1921:* Observations sur la végétation et sur la flore des environs de Zermatt. Bull. Soc. Murith. *41,* 18–55.

**Brunies S. E., 1906:* Die Flora des Ofengebietes. Jber. Naturf. Ges. Graubündens *48,* 1–326.

Campell E. and Trepp N., 1968: Vegetationskarte des schweizerischen Nationalparks. Erg. Wiss. Unters. Schw. Nat. Park. *11/58,* 1–42.

**Candrian M., 1928:* Katalog der Oberengadiner Flora. Jber. Naturf. Ges. Graubündens *66,* suppl., 174 pp.

**Capeder E., 1904:* Exkursions- und Schulflora von Chur und Umgebung mit Berücksichtigung des anschliessenden Gebietes von Arosa. Chur, 372 + 63 pp.

Correvon H., 1900: La vallée de Tourtemagne en Valais. Jahrbuch SAC. *35,* 187–202.

**Dalla Torre v. K. W. and Sarntheim v. L., 1900–1913:* Die Farn- und Blütenpflanzen von Tirol, Vorarlberg und Liechtenstein. 6 Bde. (4 parts). Innsbruck.

Derks K., 1928: Die Flora von Klosters. Klosters, 44 pp.

**Favre E., 1875:* Guide du botaniste sur le Simplon. Bull. Murith. *5/6,* 318 pp.

Flütsch P., Horvat J. and Öfelein H., 1930: Über die Pflanzengesellschaften der alpinen Stufe des Berninagebietes. Jber. Naturf. Ges. Graubündens *68,* 56 pp.

Frey E., 1922: Die Vegetationsverhältnisse der Grimselgegend im Gebiet der zukünftigen Stauseen. Mitt. Naturf. Ges. Bern *6,* 196 pp.

Frey H., 1934: Die Walliser Felsensteppe. Diss. Zurich. 218 pp.

Furrer E., 1914: Vegetationsstudien im Bormiesischen. Vierteljahresschr. Naturf. Ges. Zurich *59,* 78 pp.

*- *and Longa M., 1915:* Flora von Bormio. Beih. Bot. Centralbl. *33* (II), 110 pp.

Gams H., 1927a: Von den Follaterres zur Dent de Morcles: Vegetationsmonographie aus dem Wallis. Beitr. Geobot. Landesaufn. Schweiz *15,* 760 pp.

Giacomini V. and Pignatti S., 1955: Flora e vegetazione dell'alta Valle del Braulio. Mem. Soc. It. Sci. Nat. Milano *11,* 47–238.

-, *Pirola A. and Wikus E., 1964:* I pascoli di altitudine dello Spluga. Delpinoa, n.s. *4,* 233–304.

**Grisch A., 1907:* Beiträge zur Kenntnis der pflanzengeographischen Verhältnisse der Ber-günerstöcke. Beih. Bot. Centralbl. *2, 22,* 255–316.

Guyot H., 1920: Le Valsorey. Beitr. Geobot. Landesaufn. Schweiz. *8,* 155 pp.

Hager P. K., 1916: Verbreitung der wildwachsenden Holzarten im Vorderrheintal (Kanton Graubünden). Berne, 331 pp.

Hegi G., 1913: Zur Flora des Silsersees im Oberengadin. Ber. Schw. Bot. Ges. *22,* 213, 221.
1928: Zur Flora von Maloja. Vierteljahresschr. Naturf. Ges. Zürich *73,* suppl. 15, 233–251.

Heuer I., 1949: Untersuchungen an Föhrenwaldbeständen des Pfynwaldes. Beitr. Geobot. Landesaufn. Schweiz *28,* 185 pp.

**Jaccard H., 1895:* Catalogue de la flore valaisanne. Neue Denkschr. Schweiz. Naturf. Ges. *34,* 472 pp.

**Jäggli M., 1940:* Flora del S. Bernardino. Boll. Soc. Ticinese Sci. Nat. *35,* 1–203 (2nd ed 1983).

**Käser M., 1885:* Die Flora des Avers. Jb. SAC *20,* 364–393.

*- *and Sulger Buel C., 1917:* Flora von Samnaun. Jb. St. Gall. Naturw. Ges. *54,* 132–208.

Keller R., 1904: Vegetationsskizzen aus den Grajischen Alpen. Winterthur, 279 pp.

**Killias E., 1888:* Die Flora des Unterengadins. Jber. Naturf. Ges. Graubündens *31,* suppl., 266 pp.

Lüdi W., 1950: Die Pflanzenwelt des Aletschwald-Reservates bei Brig (Wallis). Bull. Murith. *67,* 122–178.

**Pannatier J., 1902:* La florule du Val des Dix. Bull. Murith. *31,* 116–149.

Richard J. L., 1968: Les groupements végétaux de la réserve d'Aletsch. Beitr. Geobot. Landesaufn. Schweiz *51,* 305.

Rübel E., 1912: Pflanzengeographische Monographie des Berninagebietes. Bot. Jb. *47,* 616 pp.

**Schibler W., 1937:* Flora von Davos. Jber. Naturf. Ges. Graubündens *74,* suppl., 216 pp.

Schmid E., 1930: Vegetationskarte der oberen Reusstäler. Beitr. Geobot. Landesaufn. Schweiz *16,* 64 pp.

–, *1936:* Die Reliktföhrenwälder der Alpen. Beitr. Geobot. Landesaufn. Schweiz *21,* 190 pp.

Steiger E., 1906: Beiträge zur Kenntnis der Flora der Adula-Gebirgsgruppe. Verh. Naturf. Ges. Basel *18,* 131–370, 465–755.

Tissière P.G., 1868: Guide du botaniste sur le Grand St-Bernard. Bull. Murith. (Suppl.) *1,* 177 pp.

Vaccari L., 1904–1911: Catalogue raisonné des plantes vasculaires de la Vallée d'Aosta. Bd. 1. Aoste, 635 pp.

Zoller H., 1964: Flora des schweizerischen Nationalparks und seiner Umgebung. Ergebn. Wissensch. Unters. Schweiz. Nationalpark *9,* 408 pp.

–, 1974: Flora und Vegetation der Innalluvionen zwischen Scuol und Martina. Ergebn. Wissensch. Unters. Schweiz. Nationalpark *12,* 209 pp.

6.5. Southern Alps

Bär J., 1914: Die Flora des Val Onsernone. Boll. Soc. Tic. Sci. Nat. *11,* 413 pp.

– *1918:* Die Vegetation des Val Onsernone (Kt. Tessin). Beitr. Geobot. Landesaufn. Schweiz *5,* 80 pp.

Becherer A., 1950: Beiträge zur Flora des Puschlav. Jb. Naturf. Ges. Graubündens *82,* 131–177.

– *1960:* Die Flora des Tessin und des Comerseegebietes im Lichte der neueren Erforschung. Bauhinia *1,* 261–281.

– *1965:* Zur Flora des Bernhardinpasses. Bauhinia *2,* 275–287.

Bertolani-Marchetti D., 1954–1955: Ricerche sulla vegetazione della Valsesia I, II. Nuovo G. Bot. Ital. N.S. *61,* 515–578; *62,* 283–334.

Braun-Blanquet J. and Rübel E., 1932–1935: Flora von Graubünden. Veröff. Geobot. Inst. Rübel, 7, 1695 pp.

Brockmann H., 1907: Die Flora des Puschlav und ihre Pflanzengesellschaften. Leipzig (Engelmann), 438 pp.

Chenevard P., 1910: Catalogue des plantes vasculaires du Tessin. Mém. Inst. Nat. Genevois *21,* 533 pp.

Furrer E., 1953: Botanische Skizze vom Pizzo Corombe (Colombe), einem Dolomitberg im Nordtessin. Ber. Geobot. Forsch. Inst. Rübel *1952,* 54–72.

Giacomini V., 1960: Il paesaggio vegetale della Provincia di Sondrio. Flora et Vegetatio Ital. *3,* 132 pp.

Geilinger G., 1908: Die Grignagruppe am Comersee. Beih. Bot. Centralbl. *24,* 119–420.

Hofer H.R., 1967: Die wärmeliebenden Felsheiden Insubriens. Bot. Jb. *87,* 176–251.

Jäggli M., 1908: Monografia floristica del Monte Camoghè. Boll. Soc. Ticinese Sci. Nat. *4,* 1–249.

–, 1940: Flora del S. Bernardino. Boll. Soc. Ticinese Sci. Nat. *35,* 1–203 (2nd ed. 1983).

Keller R., 1903: Beiträge zur Kenntnis der Flora des Bleniotales. Bull. Herb. Boissier II, *3,* 371–386, 461–487.

Massara G.F., 1834: Prodomo della Flora Valtellinese. Sondrio, 219 pp.

Oberdorfer E., 1964: Der insubrische Vegetationskomplex, seine Struktur und Abgrenzung gegen die submediterrane Vegetation in Oberitalien und in der Südschweiz. Beitr. Naturk. Forsch. Südw. Deutsch. *23,* 141–187.

Pitschmann H. and Reisigl H., 1957: Endemische Blütenpflanzen der Südalpen zwischen Luganersee und Etsch. Veröff. Geobot. Inst. ETH, Stiftung Rübel, *35,* 44–68.

Pitschmann H., Reisigl H. and Schiechtl. H., 1965: Flora der Südalpen vom Gardasee zum Comersee. 2nd ed. Stuttgart, 299 pp.

Rodegher E. and Venanzi G., 1894: Prospetto della Flora della Provincia di Bergamo. Treviglio, 146 pp.

Rossi P., 1926: Nuovo contributo alla Flora delle Grigne. II. Phanerogamae. Nuovo G. Bot. Ital. *33,* 252–339.

Rossi S., 1883: Studi sulla Flora Ossolana. Domodossola, 112 pp.

Schroeter C. and Rikli M., 1904: Botanische Exkursionen im Bedretto-, Formazza- und Bosco-Tal. Zürich (Raustein) 92 pp.

260

6.6. Endangered plants and plant protection

a. *Bayerisches Landesamt für Umweltschutz 1974:* Rote Liste bedrohter Farn- und Blüten-pflanzen in Bayern. Schriftreihe Naturschutz und Landschaftspflege. München, 8 pp.

b. *Filipello S., Peccenini S. G. and Bergamo S., 1979:* Repertorio delle specie della flora italiana sottoposte a vincolo di protezione nella legislazione nazionale e regionale. Pavia (Consiglio Naz. Ric.).

c. *Landolt E., 1982:* Geschützte Pflanzen der Schweiz. 3rd ed., Basle (SBN).

d. *–, Fuchs H. P., Heitz Ch. and Sutter R., 1982:* Bericht über die gefährdeten und seltenen Gefässpflanzenarten der Schweiz («Rote Liste»). Ber. Geobot. Inst. ETH, Stiftung Rübel, 49, 195–218.

e. *Lucas G. L., and Walters S. M., 1982:* List of rare, threatened and endemic plants in Europe. IUCN, Morges. 357 pp. (auch Conseil de l'Europe, Coll. Sauvegarde de la Nature *27*).

f. *Müller Th. and Kast D., 1969:* Die geschützten Pflanzen Deutschlands. Stuttgart (Schwäb. Alpver.). 17 pp.

g. *Plank St., 1975:* Gesetzlich geschützte Pflanzen in Österreich. Graz (L. Boltzmann-Institut). 50 pp.

h. *Gesetz vom 21. Dez. 1966 betr. die Abänderung des Naturschutzgesetzes.* Liechtenstein. Landesgesetzblatt 1967, *5*, 4 pp.

i. Listes des espèces végétales protégées sur l'ensemble du territoire national. Jour. Off. Rép. Française 1982, N. C. 4559–4562.

Common names of plants included in colour Plates

Latin	*German*	*French*	*Italian*	*Rhaeto-Romanic*
Achillea	Schafgarbe	Achillée	Achillea	Iva
A. atrata	Schwarze S.	A. noirâtre	A. nerastra	I. trapartida (stgira)
A. clavenae	Bittere S.	A. de Clavena	A. di Clavena	I. da Clavena
A. macrophylla	Grossblättrige S.	A. à grandes feuilles	A. a larghe foglie	I. fegliada
A. moschata	Moschus-S., Iva	A. musquée	A. moscata, Erba rota	I.-femna
A. nana	Zwerg-S.	A. naine	A. nana	I. pitschna
A. stricta	Steife S.	A. dressée	A. eretto	I. airia
Aconitum	Eisenhut	Aconit	Aconito	Tustgin
A. lycoctonum	Gelber E., Wolfswurz	A. Tue-Loup	Luparia	T. mellen
A. napellus	Blauer E.	A. Napel, Casque de Jupiter	A. napello	T. blau
A. paniculatum	Rispen-E.	A. panicule	A. a pannocchia	T. paniclà
Adenostyles	Alpendost, Drüsengriffel	Adénostyle	Adenostile	Cuderitscha
A. alliariae	Grauer A.	A. à feuilles d'Alliaire	A. grigia	C. alpina
A. leucophylla	Filziger A.	A. à feuilles blanches	A. lanuginosa	C. alva
Ajuga pyramidalis	Pyramiden-Günsel	Bugle pyramidale	Bugola piramidale	Bigiola piramida
Alchemilla	Frauenmantel	Alchémille	Alchemilla	Ruanaida
A. alpina	Silbermantel	A. des Alpes	A. alpina	R. alpina
A. pentaphyllea	Fünfblatt-F.	A. à cinq folioles	A. a 5 fogliole	R. da tschintg fegls
A. vulgaris	Gewöhnlicher F.	A. vulgaire	A. comune	R. cumina
Allium	Lauch	Ail	Aglio	Agl
A. schoenoprasum	Schnittlauch	Ciboulette, Civette	A. verdazzurro	Tschaguglin
A. victorialis	Allermannsharnisch	Herbe à neuf chemises	A. serpentino	Agl chaun
Androsace	Mannsschild	Androsace	Androsace, Gelsomino	Androsa
A. alpina	Alpen-M.	A. des Alpes	A. alpina	A. alpina
A. brevis	Charpentiers M.	A. de Charpentier	A. di Charpentier	A. curta
A. carnea	Fleischroter M.	A. couleur de chair	A. carnicina	A. charnera
A. chamaejasme	Zwerg-M.	A. Petit Jasmin	A. nana cigliata	A. jasmin
A. helvetica	Schweizer M.	A. de Suisse	A. elvetica	A. helvetica
A. lactea	Milchweisser M.	A. couleur de lait	A. lattea	A. da latg

Latin	*German*	*French*	*Italian*	*Rhaeto-Romanic*
A. obtusifolia	Stumpfblättriger M.	A. à feuilles obtuses	A. ottusifolia	A. mutta
A. vandellii	Vandellis M.	A. de Vandelli	A. di Vandelli	A. da Vandelli
A. villosa	Zottiger M.	A. velue	A. appenninica	A. pailusa
A. vitaliana	Goldprimel	Douglasia	A. gialla, Primula d'oro	A. vitaliana
Anemone	Anemone, Windröschen	Anémone	Anemone	Anemone
A. baldensis	Monte Baldo-A.	A. du Mont Baldo	A. fragolino	A. baldensia
A. narcissiflora	Narzissenblütige A.	A. à fleurs de Narcisse	A. a fiore di Narciso	A. narcissa
Antennaria	Katzenpfötchen	Antennaire	Antennaria	Maimora
A. carpatica	Karpaten-K.	A. des Carpathes	A. carpathica	M. carpatica
A. dioeca	Zweihäusiges K.	A. dioïque	A. dioica	M. cumina
Anthyllis	Wundklee	Anthyllide	Antillide	Traifegl balsam
A. alpestris	Alpen-W.	A. des Alpes	Vulneraria alpestre	T. b. alpester
A. cherleri	Cherlers W.	A. de Cherler	A. di Cherler	T. b. da Cherler
Aquilegia	Akelei	Ancolie	Aquilegia	Aquilegia
A. alpina	Alpen-A.	A. des Alpes	A. alpina	A. alpina
A. vulgaris	Gewöhnliche A.	A. vulgaire	Amor nascosto	A. vulgara
Arabis	Gänsekresse	Arabette	Arabetta	Arabina
A. alpina	Alpen-G.	A. des Alpes	A. delle Alpi	A. alpina
A. coerulea	Bläuliche G.	A. bleuâtre	A. cerulea	A. blaua
A. jacquinii	Bach-G.	A. de Jacquin	A. di Jacquin	A. d'ual (da Jacquin)
A. pumila	Zwerg-G.	A. naine	A. nana	A. nanina
A. turrita	Turm-G.	A. Tourette	A. maggiore	A. turetta
Arctostaphylos	Bärentraube	Raisin d'Ours	Grappolo orsino	Garvais
A. alpina	Alpen-B.	R. des Alpes	Uva d'orso alpina	G. alpin
A. uva-ursi	Immergrüne B.	R. commun	Uva orsina	G. d'urs
Arenaria biflora	Zweiblütiges Sandkraut	Sabline à deux fleurs	Arenaria biflora	Arnera da duas flurs
Armeria alpina	Alpen-Grasnelke	Arméria des Alpes	Armeria alpina	Armeria alpina
Arnica montana	Arnika	Arnica	Arnica montana, Tabacco	Arnica da muntogna
Artemisia	Edelraute, Beifuss, Wermut	Armoise	Artemisia, Assenzio	Assens
A. genipi	Schwarze E.	A. Genepi	Erba del Genepi	A. Genepi
A. glacialis	Gletscher-E.	A. des glaciers	A. dei ghiacci	A. da glatscher
A. mutellina	Echte E.	A. lâche, Genépi vrai	Genepì bianco	A. mastgel
Asphodelus albus	Affodil	Asphodèle blanc	Asfodelo bianco	Asfodela alva

Latin	German	French	Italian	Rhaeto-Romanic
Aster alpinus	Alpen-Aster	Aster des Alpes	Astro delle Alpi	Astra alpina
Astragalus	Tragant	Astragale	Astragolo	Astragl
A. alpinus	Alpen-T.	A. des Alpes	A. alpino	A. alpin
A. australis	Südlicher T.	A. austral	A. australe	A. dal sid
A. frigidus	Gletscherlinse	Phaque des regions froides	A. gelido	A. da glatscher
A. penduliflorus	Alpenlinse	Ph. des Alpes	A. a fiori penduli	A. pendus
Astrantia	Sterndolde	Astrance	Astranzia	Astranza
A. major	Grosse S.	A. grande	A. maggiore	A. gronda
A. minor	Kleine S.	A. petite	A. minore	A. pitschna
Athamanta cretensis	Augenwurz	Athamante de Crète	Atamanta di Creta	Atamanta da Creta
Bartsia alpina	Bartschie	Bartsie des Alpes	Clinopodio alpino, Bartsia	Bartschia alpina
Bellidiastrum michelii	Alpenmasslieb	Fausse Pâquerette	Margheritaccia di Micheli	Belastra da Michel
Betonica	Betonie	Bétoine, Epiaire	Betonica	Chalesch-spina
B. alopecuros	Fuchsschwanz-B.	B. Queue de renard	B. bianca	C.-s. mellen
B. hirsuta	Rauhaarige B.	B. à fleurs denses	B. irsuta	C.-s. pailus
Biscutella levigata	Brillenschötchen	Lunetière lisse	Biscutella	Biscutella glischa
Blechnum spicant	Rippenfarn	Blechnum Spicant	Lonchite minore	Felesch lantschetta
Botrychium lunaria	Mondraute	Botrychium Lunaire	Botrichio Erba lunaria	Glinetta cumina
Buphthalmum salicifolium	Gewöhnliches Ochsenauge	Buphthalme à feuilles de Saule	Asteroide salicina	Egls bov salesch
Bupleurum	Hasenohr	Buplèvre	Bupleuro	Uregliada
B. ranunculoides	Hahnenfuss-H.	B. Fausse Renoncule	B. ranuncoloide	U. ranunchel
B. stellatum	Stern-H.	B. étoilé	B. stellato	U. stailada
Calluna vulgaris	Heidekraut	Fausse Bruyère	Brugo, Grecchia	Brutg vulgar
Caltha palustris	Sumpf-Dotterblume	Populage	Calta, Farferugine	Flur paintg da pall
Callianthemum coriandrifolium	Korianderblättrige Schmuckblume	Callianthème à feuilles de Coriandre	Ranuncolo con foglie di Coriandro	Ranunchel dal Chatschadur
Campanula	Glockenblume	Campanule	Campanula, Campanella	Brunsina
C. barbata	Bärtige G.	C. barbue	C. barbuta	B. pailusa
C. cenisia	Mont Cenis-G.	C. du Mont Cenis	C. del Cenisio	B. da Cenis
C. cochleariifolia	Kleine G.	C. menue	C. con foglie a cucchiaio	B. pitschna
C.excisa	Ausgeschnittene G.	C. incisée	C. incisa	B. tagliada
C. latifolia	Breitblättrige G.	C. à larges feuilles	C. a larghe foglie	B. lada

265

Latin	German	French	Italian	*Rhaeto-Romanic*
C. rhomboidalis	Rautenblättrige G.	C. rhomboidale	C. romboidale	B. romboida
C. scheuchzeri	Scheuchzers G.	C. de Scheuchzer	C. di Scheuchzer	B. da Scheuchzer
C. spicata	Ährige G.	C. en épi	C. spigata	B. spiada
C. thyrsoides	Strauss-G.	C. en thyrse	C. tirsoide	B. puschlada
Cardamine	Schaumkraut	Cardamine	Cardamine, Billeri	Cardamina
C. alpina	Alpen-S.	C. des Alpes	C. delle Alpi	C. alpina
C. amara	Bitteres S.	C. amère	C. amara	C. amara
C. heptaphylla	Fieder-Zahnwurz	C. à sept folioles	Dentaria pennata	C. da set fegls
C. resedifolia	Resedenblättriges S.	C. à feuilles de Réséda	C. a foglie di Reseda	C. reseda
C. rivularis	Bach-S.	C. des ruisseaux	C. delle ripe	C. d'ual
Carduus	Distel	Chardon	Cardo	Chardun
C. defloratus	Berg-D.	Ch. des Alpes	C. alpino	Ch. sfluri
C. personata	Kletten-D.	Ch. Bardane	C. personata	Ch. mascrà
Carex	Segge	Carex, Laiche	Carice	Charetsch
C. atrata	Schwarze S.	C. noirâtre	C. abbronzata	Ch. stgir
C. curvula	Krumm-S.	C. courbé	C. curva	Ch. tort
C. firma	Polster-S.	C. ferme	C. salda	Ch. plimatsch
C. parviflora	Kleinblütige S.	C. à petites fleurs	C. nera	Ch. flur pitschna
C. sempervirens	Immergrüne S.	C. toujours vert	C. cespitosa	Ch. semperverd
Carlina simplex	Silberdistel	Carline sans tige	Cardo di San Pellegrino	Chardunet simpel
Centaurea	Flockenblume	Centaurée	Centaurea	Centaura
C. alpestris	Alpen-F.	C. des Alpes	C. alpina	C. alpestra
C. montana	Berg-F.	C. des montagnes	C. montana	C. da muntogna
C. nervosa	Federige	C. nervée	C. piumosa	C. nervada
Cerastium	Hornkraut	Céraiste	Cerastio, Peverina	Cornetta
C. latifolium	Breitblättriges H.	C. à larges feuilles	C. a foglie larghe	C. lada
C. strictum	Aufrechtes H.	C. rigide	C. eretto	C. spessa
C. trigynum	Dreigriffliges H.	C. à trois styles	C. a tre stimmi	C. da trais stigmas
C. uniflorum	Einblättriges H.	C. uniflore	C. uniforo	C. d'ina flura
Cerinthe glabra	Alpen-Wachsblume	Mélinet glabre	Cerinta Erba tortora	Tschairina glischa
Cetraria islandica	Isländisch Moos	Lichen d'Islande	Lichene d'Islanda	Erva setga (Busetga)
Chaerophyllum cicutaria	Berg-Kerbel	Chérophylle hérissé	Cerfoglio alpino	Tscherfegl d'aua
Chamorchis alpina	Zwergorchis	Chamorchis des Alpes	Orchidea nana alpina	Orchidea alpina

Latin	German	French	Italian	Rhaeto-Romanic
Chenopodium bonus-henricus	Guter Heinrich	Epinard sauvage	Chenopodio Buon Enrico, Tutta buona	Farinent d'Andri
Chrysanthemum	Margerite, Wucherblume	Chrysanthème	Margherita	Margaritta
C. adustum	Berg M.	Ch. des montagnes	M. montana	M. da muntogna
C. alpinum	Alpen-M.	Ch. des Alpes	M. alpina	M. alpina
C. halleri	Hallers M.	Ch. de Haller	M. di Haller	M. da Haller
Cicerbita alpina	Alpen-Milchlattich	Cicerbite des Alpes	Cicerbita azzurra	Latitschun alpin
Cirsium	Kratzdistel	Cirse	Cirsio	Punschun
C. acaule	Stengellose K.	C. sans tige	C. acaule	P. curt
C. eriophorum	Wollköpfige K.	C. laineux	Cardo lanaso	P. lanus
C. helenioides	Alant-K.	C. Fausse Hélénie	C. di Elena	P. variá
C. spinosissimum	Stachige K.	C. épineux	C. spinosissimo	P. d'alp
Cladonia sp.	Rentierflechte	Cladonie	Cladonia	Cladonia
Clematis	Waldrebe	Clématite	Clematide	Clematina
C. alpina	Alpenrebe	C. des Alpes	Vitalbino dei sassi	Clematina alpina
Coeloglossum viride	Hohlzunge	Coeloglossum verdâtre	Lingua cava verde	Orchidea verda
Colchicum	Zeitlose	Colchique	Colchico	Mintgiletta
C. alpinum	Alpen-Z.	C. des Alpes	C. minore	M. alpina
C. bulbocodium	Lichtblume	Bulbocode du printemps	C. di Sphagna	M. bulbina
Corallorhiza trifida	Korallenwurz	Racine de corail	Coralloriza trifida	Corallina
Coronilla vaginalis	Scheiden-Kronwicke	Coronille engainante	Cornetta guainata	Curunella vaginada
Cortusa matthioli	Heilglöckchen	Cortusa de Matthiole	Cortusa di Matthioli	Cortusa da Matthioli
Corydalis	Lerchensporn	Corydale	Colombina	Lodulera
C. lutea	Gelber L.	C. jaune	C. gialla	L. melna
C. solida	Festknolliger L.	C. solide	C. solida	L. solida
Crepis	Pippau	Crépide	Crepide, Radicchiella	Flur groma
C. aurea	Gold-Pippau	C. dorée	C. dorata	F.g. d'aur
C. conyzifolia	Dürrwurzblättriger P.	C. à feuilles de Conyze	C. maggiore	F.g. odurada
C. jacquinii	Jacquins P.	C. de Jacquin	C. di Jacquin	F.g. da Jacquin
C. pontana	Berg-P.	C. des montagnes	C. subalpina	F.g. da muntogna
C. pygmaea	Zwerg-P.	C. naine	C. pigmea	F.g. nanina
C. terglouensis	Triglav-P.	C. du Triglav	C. del monte Triglau	F.g. da portg
Crocus vernus	Frühlings-Krokus	Safran du printemps	Croco, Zafferano selvatico	Minicola da primavaira (Cavazzola)

267

Latin	German	French	Italian	Rhaeto-Romanic
Cuscuta epithymum	Thymian-Seide	Cuscute du Thym	Cuscuta del Timo	Giarsola da timian
Cyclamen europaeum	Europäische Zyklame	Cyclamen d'Europe	Ciclamino delle Alpi	Ciclama europea
Cypripedium calceolus	Frauenschuh	Cypripède, Sabot de Vénus	Pianella di Venere, Scarpetta della Madonna	Pantofla da Nossadunna
Daphne	Seidelbast	Daphné	Dafne	Dafna
D. alpina	Alpen-S.	D. des Alpes	Laureola alpina	D. alpina
D. mezereum	Gewöhnlicher S. Ziland	D. Mézéréon, Bois gentil	Fior di stecco	D. paivretta
D. striata	Gestr. S., Steinröschen	D. strié	D. delle rocce	D. strivlada
Delphinium elatum	Hoher Rittersporn	Dauphinelle elevée	Delfinio, Speron di cavaliere	Sparunetta lunga
Dianthus	Nelke	Œillet	Garofano	Negla
D. carthusianorum	Karthäuser-N.	O. des Charteux	G. selvatico	N. purpura
D. glacialis	Gletscher-N.	O. des glaciers	G. dei ghiacciai	N. da glatscher
D. silvester	Stein-N.	Girofle	G. dei boschi	N. da crap
D. superbus	Pracht-N.	O. superbe	G. da pennacchio	N. franslada
Digitalis	Fingerhut	Digitale	Digitale	Diclar
D. grandiflora	Grossblütiger F.	D. à grandes fleurs	D. a grandi fiori	D. grond
D. lutea	Gelber F.	D. jaune	D. gialla, Erba aralda	D. mellen
Doronicum grandiflorum	Grossblumige Gemswurz	Doronic à grandes fleurs	Doronico a grandi fiori	Doronica gronda
Draba	Felsenblümchen	Drave	Draba	Drava
D. aizoides	Immergrünes F.	D. Faux Aizoon	D. gialla	D. melna
D. carinthiaca	Kärntner F.	D. tomenteuse	D. di Carinzia	D. di Carnizia
Dracocephalum ruyschiana	Berg-Drachenkopf	Tête de Dragon, de Ruysch	Dracocefalo montano	Chau-drag da Ruysch
Dryas octopetala	Silberwurz	Dryade, Chénette	Camedrio alpino	Feglia chamutsch
Dryopteris	Wurmfarn	Dryoptéris	Felce	Felesch
D. dilatata	Breiter W.	D. à feuilles larges	F. certosina	F. lad
D. filix-mas	Gewöhnlicher W.	D. Fougère mâle	F. mascio	F. mastgel
Echium vulgare	Gewöhnlicher Natterkopf	Vipérine vulgaire	Echio Viperina, Erba rogna	Raspacot vulgar
Empetrum hermaphroditum	Krähenbeere	Camarine noire	Empetro nero, Erica baccifera	Muretta
Epilobium	Weidenröschen	Epilobe	Epilobio	Veschla-chaura
E. alpestre	Quirtiges W.	E. des Alpes	E. alpino	V.-ch. alpestra
E. alsinifolium	Mierenblättriges W.	E. à feuilles d'Alsine	E. a foglie di Alsina	V.-ch. da funtauna

Latin	German	French	Italian	Rhaeto-Romanic
E. angustifolium	Schmalblättriges W.	E. à feuilles étroites	E. a foglie strette	V.-ch. da guaud
E. fleischeri	Fleischers W.	E. de Fleischer	E. de Fleischer	V.-ch. da flum
Epipactis	Sumpfwurz	Epipactis	Elleborine	Orchidea
E. atropurpurea	Dunkelrote S.	E. pourpre noirâtre	E. violacea	O. brina
E. latifolia	Breitblättrige S.	E. à larges feuilles	E. comune	O. clera
E. palustris	Echte S.	E. des marais	E. palustre	O. da pali
Equisetum	Schachtelhalm	Prêle	Equiseto	Spurella
E. palustre	Sumpf-Sch.	P. des marais	E. palustre	S. da pali
E. silvaticum	Wald-Sch.	P. des forêts	E. dei boschi	S. da guaud
Erica carnea	Rote Erika	Bruyère couleur de chair	Erica, Scopa carnicina	Erica cotschna (Brutg da primavaira)
Erigeron	Berufkraut	Erigéron	Erigero	Rigera (Chanussa)
E. alpinus	Alpen-Berufkraut	E. des Alpes	E. alpino	R. alpina
E. uniflorus	Einköpfiges B.	E. à une tête	E. unifloro	R. d'ina flur
Erinus alpinus	Leberbalsam	Erine des Alpes	Erino odoroso	Erina alpina
Eriophorum	Wollgras	Linaigrette	Erioforo	Minalva
E. angustifolium	Schmalblättriges W.	L. à feuilles étroites	E. pendulo	M. stretga
E. scheuchzeri	Scheuchzers W.	L. de Scheuchzer	E. di Scheuchzer	M. da Scheuchzer
Eritrichium nanum	Himmelsherold	Eritrichium nain	Eritrichio, Miosotide nano	Araldin nanin
Erucastrum nasturtiifolium	Kressenblättrige R.	Fausse Roquette à feuilles de Cresson	Erucastro comune	Erutgetta craschun
Eryngium alpinum	Alpen-Mannstreu	Panicaut des Alpes, Chardon bleu	Calcatreppolo alpino	Chardun blau
Erysimum helveticum	Schweizer Schöterich	Vélar de Suisse	Erisimo svizzero	Stgampantina helvetica
Euphorbia cyparissias	Zypressen-Wolfsmilch	Euphorbe Faux-Cyprès	Euforbia Erba cipressina	Latg-stria cipressa
Euphrasia	Augentrost	Euphraise	Eufrasia	Avustina
E. Alpina	Alpen-A.	E. des Alpes	E. alpina	A. alpina
E. minima	Kleiner A.	E. naine	E. minima	A. nanina
E. rostkoviana	Echter A.	E. de Rostkovius, Casselunette	E. comune	A. rostkoviana
Festuca	Schwingel	Fétuque	Festuca	Fustigliun
F. halleri	Hallers. Sch.	F. de Haller	F. di Haller	F. da Haller
F. varia	Bunt-Sch.	V. bigarée	F. varia	F. variä

Latin	German	French	Italian	Rhaeto-Romanic
F. violacea	Violett-Sch.	F. violacée	F. viola	F. violet
Gagea fistulosa	Alpen-Gelbstern	Gagée fistuleuse, Etoile jaune	Gagea fistolosa	Staila melna alpina
Galeopsis	Hohlzahn	Galéopsis	Canapetta	Urticla faussa
G. angustifolia	Schmalblättriger H.	G. Ladanum	C. a foglie strette	U. f. stretga
G. speciosa	Bunter H.	G. orné	C. screziata	U. f. bella
Galium	Labkraut	Gaillet	Caglio	Rieua
G. anisophyllum	Ungleichblättriges L.	G. nain	C. nano	R. nanina
G. helveticum	Schweizer L.	G. de Suisse	C. elvetico	R. helvetica
Genista germanica	Deutscher Ginster	Genêt d'Allemagne	Ginestra spinosa, Bulimacola	Genista germanaisa
Gentiana	Enzian	Gentiane	Genziana	Giansauna (Genziana)
G. asclepiadea	Schwalbenwurz-E.	G. à feuilles d'Asclépiade	G. asclepiade	G. da pali
G. bavarica	Bayerischer E.	G. de Bavière	Genzianella tardiva	G. bavaraisa
G. brachyphylla	Kurzblättriger E.	G. à feuilles courtes	Genzianella a foglie corte	G. curta
G. campestris	Feld-E.	G. champêtre	G. campestre	G. champestra
G. ciliata	Gefranster E.	G. ciliée	G. frangiata	G. tschegliada
G. kochiana	Kochscher E., Stengelloser E.	G. de Koch	G. di Koch	G. diclar
G. lutea	Gelber E.	G. jaune	G. gialla	G. melna
G. nivalis	Schnee-E.	G. des neiges	G. delle nevi	G. da naiv
G. punctata	Punktierter E.	G. ponctuée	G. punteggiata	G. taclada
G. purpurea	Purpur-E.	G. pourprée	G. rossa	G. purpura
G. ramosa	Astiger E.	G. rameuse	G. ramosa	G. romusa
G. tenella	Zarter E.	G. délicate	G. gracile	G. tendra
G. utriculosa	Aufgeblasener E.	G. à calice renflé	G. ventricosa	G. urticla
G. verna	Frühlings-E.	G. printanière	Genzianella di primavera	G. tempriva
Geranium	Storchenschnabel	Géranium	Geranio	Gerani
G. lividum	Violetter S.	G. livide	G. stellato	G. grisch
G. rivulare	Blassblütiger S.	G. des ruisseaux	G. dei ruscelli	G. da riva
G. sanguineum	Blut-S.	G. rouge sang	G. sanguigno	G. cotschen
G. silvaticum	Wald-S.	G. des bois	G. dei boschi	G. da guaud

Latin	German	French	Italian	Rhaeto-Romanic
Geum	Nelkenwurz	Benoîte	Ambretta	Ambretta
G. montanum	Berg-N.	B. des montagnes	A. montana	A. da muntogna
G. reptans	Kriechende N.	B. rampante	A. strisciante	A. ruschnanta
Globularia	Kugelblume	Globulaire	Globularia	Globulera
G. cordifolia	Herzblättrige K.	G. à feuilles en cœur	G. a foglie cordate	G. cun feglia en cor
G. nudicaulis	Nacktstenglige K.	G. à tige nue	Margherita azzurra	G. niva
Gnaphalium	Ruhrkraut	Gnaphale	Gnafalio	Fieutrina
G. silvaticum	Wald-Ruhrkraut	G. des bois	G. selvatico	F. da guaud
G. supinum	Zwerg-R.	G. couché	G. minore	F. curta
Gymnadenia conopea	Mücken-Handwurz	Gymnadénie Moucheron	Ginnadenia delle zanzare	Ginmadenia sparunada
Gypsophila repens	Kriechendes Gipskraut	Gypsophile rampante	Gipsofila, Garofanina sdraiata	Gipsera serpentina
Hedysarum obscurum	Süssklee	Sainfoin des Alpes	Sulla dei monti, Lupinella d'Alpe	Traifegl dultsch stgir
Helianthemum	Sonnenröschen	Héliantème	Eliantemo	Gravirola
H. alpestre	Alpen-S.	H. alpestre	E. alpestre	G. alpestra
H. grandiflorum	Grossblütiges S.	H. à grandes fleurs	E. a grandi fiori	G. gronda
Helleborus niger	Christrose	Ellébore noir, Rose de Noël	Rosa di Natale	Sturnidella naira
Hepatica triloba	Leberblümchen	Hépatique à trois lobes	Erba trinità	Ravanetta
Heracleum sphondylium	Gewöhnlicher Bärenklau	Berce commune	Ercolino, Panace erculeo	Rasvenna cumina
Herminium monorchis	Herminie	Herminium à un bulbe	Orchid a un bulbo	Orchidea d'ina tschagula
Hieracium	Habichtskraut	Epervière	Jeracio, sparviere	Lantschetta
H. alpinum	Alpen-H.	E. des Alpes	J. alpino	L. alpina
H. aurantiacum	Orangerotes	E. orangée	J. croceo	L. cotschna
H. intybaceum	Weissliches H.	E. feuilles de Chicorée	J. intibaceo	L. endivia
H. pilosella	Gewöhnliches H.	E. Piloselle	Pelosetta, Pelosella	L. pailusa
H. prenanthoides	Hasenlattichartiges H.	E. Faux Prénanthe	J. a foglie di Prenanthes	L. pendusa
H. staticifolium	Grasnelkenblättriges H.	E. à feuilles de Statice	J. con foglie d'Armeria	L. niva
H. villosum	Zottiges H.	E. velue	J. villoso	L. lanusa
Hippocrepis comosa	Hufeisenklee	Hippocrépide à toupet	Sferracavallo comune	Traifegl chavagl, Tupé
Homogyne alpina	Gewöhnlicher Alpenlattich	Homogyne des Alpes	Omogine alpestre	Latitschun d'alp
Horminum pyrenaicum	Drachenmaul	Hormin des Pyrénées	Orminella pirenaica	Salvgia violetta pirenaica
Hugueninia tanacetifolia	Farnrauke	Sisymbre à feuilles de Tanaisie	Hugueninia comune	Rutgetta tanaida

Latin	German	French	Italian	Rhaeto-Romanic
Hutchinsia alpina	Alpen-Gemskresse	Cresson des Chamois	Utchinsia delle Alpi	Craschun-chamutsch alpin
Hypericum maculatum	Geflecktes Johanniskraut	Millepertuis maculé	Iperico maculato	Erva S. Gion taclada
Hypochoeris uniflora	Einköpfiges Ferkelkraut	Porcelle à une tête	Ipocheride Porcellina ispida	Purschlera d'ina flur
Juncus	Simse, Binse	Jonc	Giunco	Giunschla
J. jacquinii	Jacquins S.	J. de Jacquin	G. di Jacquin	G. da Jacquin
J. trifidus	Dreispaltige S.	J. trifide	G. trifido	G. da trais pizs
Kernera saxatilis	Kugelschötchen	Kernéra des rochers	Cochlearia delle rocce	Bagiaunetta da Kerner
Knautia silvatica	Wald-Witwenblume	Knautie des bois	Vedovella selvatica	Vaivetta da guaud
Laserpitium	Laserkraut	Laser	Laserpizio	Laserpiz
L. halleri	Hallers L.	L. de Haller	L. di Haller	L. da Haller
L. latifolium	Breitblättriges L.	L. à larges feuilles	L. a foglie larghe	L. lad
Lastrea dryopteris	Eichenfarn	Dryoptéris de Linné	Felce delle querce	Felesch da ruver
Lathyrus	Platterbse	Gesse	Cicerchia	Bagiauna
L. occidentalis	Gelbe P.	G. jaune	C. gialla	B. melna
L. pratensis	Wiesen-P.	G. des prés	C. dei prati, Erba gialletta	B. da prada
Leontodon	Löwenzahn	Liondent	Dente di leone, Leontodo	Flur-portg (Dent-liun)
L. helveticus	Schweizer L.	L. de Suisse	L. elvetico	F.-p. helvetica
L. hispidus	Steifhaariger L.	L. hispide	L. comune	F.-p. gruglia
L. montanus	Berg-L.	L. des montagnes	L. montano	F.-p. da muntogna
Leontopodium alpinum	Edelweiss	Etoile des Alpes	Leontopodio, Stella alpina	Stailalva alpina
Leucojum vernum	Märzenglöckchen	Nivéole du printemps	Campanelle comuni	Galantina tempriva
Leucorchis albida	Weissorchis	Gymnadénia blanchâtre	Orchidea candida	Orchidea alva
Ligusticum mutellina	Muttern	Ligustique Mutelline	Ligustico Erba mutellina	Muclina alpina
Lilium	Lilie	Lis	Giglio	Gilgia
L. bulbiferum	Feuer-Lilie	L. orangé	G. rosso	G. cotschna
L. martagon	Türkenbund	L. Martagon	Trubante di Turco	G. tirca
Linaria alpina	Alpen-Leinkraut	Linaire des Alpes	Linaiola d'alpe	Ginera alpina
Linnaea borealis	Moosglöckchen	Linnée boréale	Linnea boreale	Sainin da pali
Linum alpinum	Alpen-Lein	Lin des Alpes	Lino delle Alpi	Glin alpin
Lloydia serotina	Faltenlilie	Loïdie tardive	Loidia tardiva	Gilgia tardiva
Loiseleuria procumbens	Alpenazalee	Azalée des Alpes	Azalea alpina, Azalea nana	Azalea alpina
Lomatogonium carinthiacum	Saumnarbe	Lomatogonium de Carinthie	Genzianella di Carinzia	Urnatta tschairada

272

Latin	German	French	Italian	Rhaeto-Romanic
Lonicera coerulea	Blaues Geissblatt	Lonicéra bleu	Caprifoglio turchino	Chagliamorta (Bavroler) blaua
Lotus alpinus	Alpen-Hornklee	Lotier des Alpes	Loto alpina	Cornichel alpin
Lunaria rediviva	Ausdauernde Mondviole	Lunaire vivace	Lunaria comune	Lunera reviva
Luzula	Hainsimse	Luzule	Luzola	Glischella
L. lutea	Gelbe H.	L. jaune	L. gialla	G. melna
L. nivea	Schnee-H.	L. blanc de neige	L. nivale	G. da naiv
Lycopodium	Bärlapp	Lycopode	Licopodio	Patta-luf
L. annotinum	Wald-B.	L. des bois	L. gineprino	P.-l. da guaud
L. selago	Tannen-B.	L. Sélagine	L. abietino	P.-l. savigna
Matthiola vallesiaca	Walliser Levkoje	Voiler du Valais	Violaciocca alpina	Violetta vallesana
Mentha longifolia	Ross-Minze	Menthe à longues feuilles	Menta selvatica	Menta lunga
Melampyrum	Wachtelweizen	Mélampyre	Melampiro	Melampir
M. silvaticum	Wald-W.	M. des bois	M. dei boschi	M. da guaud
M. pratense	Wiesen-W.	M. des prés	M. pratense	M. da chomp
Minuartia	Miere	Minuartie	Alsina	Minuarta
M. recurva	Krummblättrige M.	M. recourbée	A. a foglie ricurve	M. storta
M. sedoides	Zwerg-M.	M. Faux Sédum	Renaiola borracina	M. pitschna
Moehringia ciliata	Bewimperte Nabelmiere	Moehringie ciliée	Meringia cigliata	Meringia tschegliada
Myosotis alpestris	Alpen-Vergissmeinnicht	Myosotis alpestre	Miosotide, Non ti scordar di me	Chalamandrin alpin
Narcissus radiiflorus	Schmalblättrige Narzisse	Narcisse à feuilles étroites	Narciso selvatico	Narcissa
Nardus stricta	Borstgras	Nard raide	Cervino, Erba cervina	Tschorf airi
Nigritella	Männertreu	Nigritelle	Nigritella	Nigretta
N. nigra	Schwarzes M.	N. noirâtre	Vaniglia d'alpe	N. stgira
N. rubra	Rotes M.	N. rouge	N. rossa	N. cotschna
Onobrychis montana	Berg-Esparsette	Sainfoin des montagnes	Fieno santo, F. di montagna	Esparsetta da muntogna
Ononis natrix	Gelbe Hauhechel	Ononis jaune	Ononide bacaja	Restabov natra
Ophrys insectifera	Fliegenorchis	Ophrys Abeille	Ofride insettifera	Mustgarella
Orchis	Orchis, Knabenkraut	Orchis	Orchidea	Orchidea
O. globosa	Kugel-O.	O. globuleux	O. globosa	O. radunda
O. latifolia	Breitblättrige O.	O. à feuilles larges	O. a foglie larghe	O. lada

Latin	German	French	Italian	Rhaeto-Romanic
O. maculata	Gefleckte O.	O. tacheté	Concordia	O. taclada
O. mascula	Männliche O.	O. mâle	O. mascolina	O. mastgel
O. sambucina	Holunder-O.	O. à odeur de Sureau	Sambucina	O. suvi
O. traunsteineri	Traunsteiners O.	O. de Traunsteiner	O. di Traunsteiner	O. da Traunstein
O. ustulata	Schwarzköpfige O.	O. brûlé	O. adusta	O. stgira
Orobanche purpurea	Violette Sommerwurz	Orobanche bleuâtre	Succiamele purpurea	Malerva purpura
Oxyria digyna	Säuerling	Oxyria	Osiria alpina	Arscholetta distigma
Oxytropis	Spitzkiel	Oxytropis	Astragalina	Astragl
O. campestris	Feld-S.	O. champêtre	A. gialla	A. champester
O. halleri	Hallers S.	O. de Haller	A. di Haller	A. da Haller
O. jacquinii	Berg-S.	O. des montagnes	A. di Jacquin	A. da muntogna
O. pilosa	Zottiger S.	O. poilu	A. peloso	A. pailus
Paeonia officinalis	Pfingstrose	Pivoine officinale	Peonia selvatica	Peonia officinala
Papaver	Mohn	Pavot	Papavero	Papaver
P. alpinum	Weisser Alpenmohn	P. des Alpes	P. alpino	P. alpin
P. aurantiacum	Gelber Alpenmohn	P. orange	P. giallo	P. mellen
Paradisia liliastrum	Paradieslilie	Paradisie	Paradisia gigliastro	Paradisia
Parnassia palustris	Studentenröschen	Parnassie	Parnassia palustre	Parnassia da pali
Pedicularis	Läusekraut	Pédiculaire	Pedicularia	Plugliuna
P. foliosa	Blattreiches L.	P. feuillée	P. gialla	P. fegliusa
P. gyroflexa	Bogenblütiges L.	P. arquée	P. giroflessa	P. storta
P. kerneri	Kerners L.	P. de Kerner	P. di Kerner	P. da Kerner
P. oederi	Buntes L.	P. d'Oeder	P. di Oeder	P. d'Oeder
P. rostrato-spicata	Hellrotes L.	P. à bec et en épi	P. carnicina	P. cun pical
P. tuberosa	Knolliges L.	P. tubéreuse	P. tuberosa	P. tuberusa
P. verticillata	Quirlblättriges L.	P. verticillée	P. verticillata	P. verticulada
Petasites	Pestwurz	Pétasite	Petasite	Patlauna
P. albus	Weisse P.	P. blanc	P. bianca	P. alva
P. paradoxus	Alpen-P.	P. paradoxal	P. nivea	P. farinusa
Petrocallis pyrenaica	Steinschmückel	Pétrocallis des Pyrénées	Petrocallide, Grazia delle rupi	Fittacrap pirenaic
Peucedanum ostruthium	Meisterwurz	Impératoire	Peucedano porporino	Rena imperiala
Phleum alpinum	Alpen-Lieschgras	Fléole des Alpes	Fleo alpino, Coda di topo alpina	Flieula alpina

274

Latin	German	French	Italian	Rhaeto-Romanic
Phyteuma	Rapunzel	Raiponce	Raponzo, Raperonzolo	Grifla
P. betonicifolium	Betonienblättrige R.	R. à feuilles de Bétoine	R. a foglie di Betonica	G. betunia
P. globulariifolium	Armblütige R.	R. à feuilles de Globulaire	R. piemontese	G. setga
P. hemisphaericum	Halbkugelige R.	R. hémisphérique	R. emisferico	G. combla
P. humile	Niedrige R.	R. naine	R. nano	G. pitschna
P. orbiculare	Rundköpfige R.	R. orbiculaire	R. rotondetto	G. radunda
P. ovatum	Hallers R.	R. ovoide	R. di Haller	G. ovala
P. scheuchzeri	Scheuchzers R.	R. de Scheuchzer	R. di Scheuchzer	G. da Scheuchzer
P. spicatum	Ährige R.	R. en épi	R. spica	G. spiada
Pinguicula	Fettblatt	Grassette	Pinguicola	Grassetta
P. Alpina	Alpen-F.	G. des Alpes	P. alpina Erba-nuta	G. alpina
P. leptoceras	Dünnsporniges F.	G. à éperon grêle	P. bianco maculata	G. cumina
P. vulgaris	Gewöhnliches F.	G. vulgaire	P. comune	G. vulgara
Plantago	Wegerich	Plantain	Piantaggine	Plantagen
P. alpina	Alpen-W., Adelsgras	P. des Alpes	P. alpina	P. alpin
P. media	Mittlerer W.	P. moyen	P. mezzo	P. mesaun
Platanthera bifolia	Zweiblättr. Breitkölbchen	Platanthère à deux feuilles	Panierino a due foglie	Platantera da dus fegls
Poa alpina	Alpen-Rispengras	Paturin des Alpes	Poa alpina	Grassitsch alpin
Polemonium coeruleum	Sperrkraut	Polémoine bleue	Polemonio ceruleo	Polemonia blaua
Polygala	Kreuzblume	Polygala	Poligala	Puliglia
P. alpestris	Berg-K.	P. alpestre	P. alpestre	P. alpestra
P. chamaebuxus	Buchsblättrige K.	P. Petit Buis	P. falso bosso	P. melna
Polygonum	Knöterich	Renouée	Poligono	Badalestg
P. alpinum	Alpen-K.	R. des Alpes	P. alpino	B. alpin
P. bistorta	Schlangen-K.	R. Bistorte, Serpentaire	Bistorta serpentina	B. da serp
P. viviparum	Brut-K.	R. vivipare	P. viviparo	B. vivipar
Polygonatum verticillatum	Quirlblättr. Salomonssiegel	Polygonate verticillé	Sigillo di Salmone verticillato	Rischalva verschlada
Polytrichum sexangulare	Widertonmoos	Polytric hexagonal	Politrico esagonale	Chavellira sexangulara
Potentilla	Fingerkraut	Potentille	Potentilla, Cinquefoglia	Potentilla
P. aurea	Gold-F.	P. dorée	Fior d'oro, P. dorata	P. d'aur
P. caulescens	Stengel-F.	P. caulescente	P. caulescente	P. lunga

Latin	German	French	Italian	Rhaeto-Romanic
P. erecta	Aufrechtes F., Tormentil	P. dressée, Tormentille	Tormentilla	P. turment
P. frigida	Frost-F.	P. des régions froides	P. gelida	P. da glatscher
P. grandiflora	Grossblütiges F.	P. à grandes fleurs	Fragolaccia trifogliata	P. gronda
P. nitida	Glänzendes F.	P. luisante	P. delle Dolomiti	P. glischenta
Prenanthes purpurea	Hasenlattich	Prénanthe pourpre	Lattuga montana	Pendusetta purpura
Primula	Schlüsselblume, Primel	Primevère	Primola	Primula
P. auricula	Aurikel, Flühblümchen	P. Auricule	Orecchia d'orso	P. auricla
P. elatior	Gewöhnliche S.	P. élevée	P. fiori giallo	P. gronda
P. farinosa	Mehl-P.	P. farineuse	P. farinosa	P. farinusa
P. glutinosa	Klebrige S.	P. glutineuse	P. vischiosa	P. glutinusa
P. halleri	Hallers S.	P. de Haller	P. di Haller	P. da Haller
P. hirsuta	Behaarte S., Rote Felsenp.	P. hérissée	P. irsuta	P. pailusa
P. integrifolia	Ganzblättrige S.	P. à feuilles entières	P. a foglie intere	P. glischa
P. veris	Frühlings-S.	P. du printemps	Fior di primavera	P. tempriva
Prunella grandiflora	Grossblütige Brunelle	Brunelle à grandes fleurs	Brunella a grandi fiori	Brinella gronda
Pulmonaria angustifolia	Schmalblättr. Lungenkraut	Pulmonaire à feuilles étroites	Polmonaria a foglie sottii	Pulmunera stretga
Pulsatilla	Kuhschelle, Anemone	Pulsatille	Anemone	Anemone
P. alpina	Alpen-K.	P. des Alpes	A. alpina	A. alpina
P. halleri	Hallers K.	P. de Haller	A. di Haller	A. da Haller
P. montana	Berg-K.	P. des montagnes	A. montana	A. da muntogna
P. sulphurea	Schwefel-A.	P. à fleurs jaunes	A. solforosa	A. sulfurusa
P. vernalis	Pelz-A., Frühlings-A.	P. du printemps	A. di primavera	A. tempriva
Pyrola	Wintergrün	Pirole	Piroletta	Pirola
P. rotundifolia	Rundblättriges W.	P. à feuilles rondes	P. a foglie rotonde	P. radunda
P. secunda	Einseitswendiges W.	P. unilatérale	P. secunda	P. pendusa
P. uniflora	Einblütiges W.	P. à une fleur	P. soldanina	P. d'ina flur
Ranunculus	Hahnenfuss	Renoncule	Ranuncolo	Ranunchel
R. aconitifolius	Eisenhutblättriger H.	R. à feuilles d'Aconit	Piè di gallo	R. tustgin
R. alpester	Alpen-H.	R. alpestre	R. alpestre	R. alpin
R. glacialis	Gletscher-H.	R. des glaciers	R. dei ghiacciai	R. da glatscher
R. languinosus	Wolliger H.	R. laineuse	R. lanuto	R. lanus
R. montanus	Berg-H.	R. des montagnes	R. delle montagne	R. da muntogna

Latin	German	French	Italian	Rhaeto-Romanic
R. parnassifolius	Herzblatt-H.	R. à feuilles de Parnassie	R. petacciolo	R. cun feglia en cor
R. pygmaeus	Zwerg-H.	R. nain	R. pigmeo	R. nanin
R. pyrenaeus	Pyrenäen-H.	R. des Pyrénées	R. dei Pirenei	R. pirenaic
R. seguieri	Seguiers H.	R. de Séguier	R. di Séguier	R. da Seguieri
R. thora	Thora-H.	R. Thora	R. tora, Erba tora	R. da tissi
Rhamnus pumila	Niederliegender Kreuzdorn	Nerprun nain	Ramno, Spin-cervino nano	Ramner pitschen
Rhaponticum scariosum	Bergscharte	Centaurée Rhapontic	Fiordaliso rapontico	Tschentaura gronda
Rhinanthus	Klappertopf	Rhinanthe	Cresta di gallo	Claffa-scarsella
R. alectorolophus	Behaarter K.	R. velue	Fistularia	C. pailusa
R. angustifolius	Schmalblättriger K.	R. à feuilles étroites	C. a foglie strette	C. cun feglia stretga
Rhizocarpon geographicum	Landkartenflechte	Rhizocarpon	Lichne geografico	Moffa da crap
Rhododendron	Alpenrose	Rosage, Rhododendron	Rododendro	Cresta-cot
R. ferrugineum	Rostblättrige A.	R. ferrugineux	R. ferrugineo, Rosa delle Alpi	C.-c. cotschna
R. hirsutum	Behaarte A., Steinrose	R. hérissé	R. peloso	C.-c. pailusa
Rosa pendulina	Alpen-Hagrose	Rosier des Alpes	Rosa alpina	Rosa alpina
Rumex	Ampfer	Oseille	Romice Rabarbero	Fegliascha
R. alpinus	Alpen-A., Blacke	O. des Alpes	R. alpino	F. alpina
R. arifolius	Aronstabblättriger A.	O. à feuilles de Gouet	R. di montagna	F. setga
R. nivalis	Schnee-A.	O. des neiges	R. delle nevi	F. da naiv
R. scutatus	Schild-A.	O. ronde	Acetosa rotonda, Erba	F. radunda
Salix	Weide	Saule	Salice	Salesch
S. helvetica	Schweizer W.	S. de Suisse	S. elvetico	S. helvetic
S. herbacea	Krautweide	S. herbacé	S. erbaceo	S. ervus
S. reticulata	Netz-W.	S. à réseau	S. reticulato	S. da rait
S. retusa	Stumpfblättrige W.	S. à feuilles émoussées	S. retuso	S. mut
Saponaria ocymoides	Kleines Seifenkraut	Saponaire rose	Saponaria falso basilico, Ocimoide rossa	Savunella cotschna
Satureja alpina	Alpen-Saturei	Sariette des Alpes	Santoreggia alpina, Melissa alpina	Saturegia alpina
Saussurea discolor	Zweifarbige Alpenscharte	Saussurée à feuilles discolores	Saussurea cordata	Barschuna varià
Saxifraga	Steinbrech	Saxifragé	Sassifraga	Fendacrap

277

Latin	German	French	Italian	Rhaeto-Romanic
S. aizoides	Bewimperte S.	S. Faux Aizoon	S. autunnale	F. Semperverd
S. aizoon	Immergrüner S.	S. Aizoon	S. sempreverde	F. puschlà
S. androsacea	Mannsschild-S.	S. Androsace	S. androsacea	F. androsa
S. aphylla	Blattloser S.	S. à tige nue	S. afilla	F. senza feglia
S. aspera	Rauher S.	S. rude	S. aspra	F. asper
S. biflora	Zweiblütiger S.	S. à deux fleurs	S. biflora	F. da duas flurs
S. bryoides	Moosartiger S.	S. mousse	S. zolfina	F. mistgel
S. caesia	Bläulicher S.	S. bleuâtre	S. verdazzurra	F. blau
S. cernua	Nickender S.	S. penchée	S. incurvata	F. pendus
S. cotyledon	Strauss-S.	S. Cotylédon	S. piramidale	F. cotiledon
S. moschata	Moschus-S.	S. musquée	S. muschiata	F. muscat
S. mutata	Veränderter S.	S. changée	S. gialla	F. midà
S. oppositifolia	Gegenblättriger S.	S. à feuilles opposées	S. rossa	F. oppost
S. rotundifolia	Rundblättriger S.	S. à feuilles rondes	S. cimbalaria, Erba della Madonna	F. radund
S. seguieri	Seguiers S.	S. de Séguier	S. sedolina	F. da Seguieri
S. stellaris	Stern-S.	S. étoilée	S. stellata	F. stailà
Scabiosa lucida	Glänzende Skabiose	Scabieuse luisante	Scabbiosa lucida	Scabbiosa glischenta
Scutellaria alpina	Alpen-Helmkraut	Scutellaire des Alpes	Scutellaria alpina	Scutella alpina
Sedum	Fetthenne, Mauerpfeffer	Sédum, Orpin	Sedo, Borracina	Grassella
S. annuum	Einjähriger M.	S. annuel	S. annuo	G. annuala
S. atratum	Dunkler M.	S. noirâtre	Pinocchina nera	G. naira
S. rosea	Rosenwurz	S. Rose	Rodiola rosea	G. rosa
S. villosum	Behaarter M.	S. velu	S. villoso	G. pailusa
Sempervivum	Hauswurz	Joubarbe	Semprevivo	Semperviv
S. alpinum	Alpen-H.	J. des Alpes	S. delle Alpi	S. alpin
S. arachnoideum	Spinnwebige H.	J. aranéeuse	S. ragnateloso	S. tessi
S. montanum	Berg-H.	J. des montagnes	S. dei monti	S. da muntogna
S. wulfenii	Gelbe H.	J. de Wulfen	S. a fiori gialli	S. da Wulfen
Senecio	Kreuzkraut	Seneçon	Senecio	Sanetsch
S. abrotanifolius	Eberreis-K.	S. à feuilles d'Auron	S. a foglie di Abrotano	S. d'asseus
S. alpinus	Alpen-K.	S. des Alpes	S. delle Alpi	S. alpin
S. capitatus	Kopfiges K.	S. en tête	S. capitato	S. cun chau

Latin	German	French	Italian	Rhaeto-Romanic
S. carniolicus	Krainer K.	S. de la Carniole	S. carniolico	S. carniolic
S. doronicum	Gemswurz-K.	S. Doronic	S. mezzano	S. doronic
S. fuchsii	Fuchs-K.	S. de Fuchs	S. di Fuchs	S. da Fuchs
S. incanus	Graues K.	S. blanchâtre	S. bianco-cotonoso	S. grisch
S. rupester	Felsen-K.	S. des rochers	S. montanino	S. da crap
S. uniflorus	Einköpfiges K.	S. à un capitule	S. unifloro	S. d'ina flur
Sesleria disticha	Zweizeiliges Kopfgras	Seslerie distique	Sesleria distica	Sesleria
Sibbaldia procumbens	Sibbaldie	Sibbaldia couchée	Sibbaldia prostrata	Sibbaldia giaschigl
Silene	Leimkraut	Silène	Silene	Silena
S. dioeca	Rote Waldnelke	S. dioïque	Licne diurna, Fiamma	S. cotschna
S. exscapa	Stielloses L.	S. sans tige	S. a cuscinetto	S. senza manti
S. flos-jovis	Jupiternelke	S. Fleur de Jupiter, œillet de Dieu	Crotonella fior di Giove	S. da Jupiter
S. liponeura	Rote Alpennelke	S. des Alpes, Viscaire	Crotonella alpina	S. glischenta
S. nutans	Nickendes L.	S. penché	S. ciondola	S. pendusa
S. quadridentata	Strahlensame	S. à quatre dents	S. delle fonti	S. da quatter dents
S. rupestris	Felsen-L.	S. des rochers	S. delle rupi	S. da crap
S. vulgaris	Gewöhnliches L.	S. enflé	Strigoli, Bubbolino	S. cumina
Soldanella	Soldanelle	Soldanelle	Soldanella	Soldanella
S. alpina	Alpen-S.	S. des Alpes	S. alpina	S. alpina
S. pusilla	Kleine S.	Petite S.	S. piccola	S. pitschna
Solidago alpestris	Alpen-Goldrute	Solidage alpestre	Verga d'oro	Saldagen alpester
Sorbus aucuparia	Vogelbeerbaum	Sorbier des oiseleurs	Sorbo degli uccellatori	Culaischen
Stachys alpina	Alpen-Ziest	Epiaire des Alpes	Stregona alpina	Chalesch-spina alpin
Stipa pennata	Federgras	Plumet, Stipe pennée	Stipa delle fate	Stipa plimada
Swertia perennis	Moorenzian	Swertie vivace	Swertia perenne	Tarauta
Synotoma comosum	Schopfrapunzel	Raiponce chevelue	Raponzolo chiomoso	Grifla puschlada
Taraxacum alpinum	Alpen-Pfaffenröhrchen	Pissenlit des Alpes	Tarassaco alpino	Latitschun alpin
Teucrium montanum	Berg-Gamander	Germandrée des montagnes	Teucrio montano	Giamander da muntogna
Thalictrum	Wiesenraute	Pigamon	Pigamo	Ruta
T. aquilegiifolium	Akeleiblättrige W.	P. à feuilles d'Ancolie	P. colombino	R. alpina
T. minus	Kleine W.	Petit Pigamon	P. minore	R. pitschna
Thesium alpinum	Alpenflachs	Thésium des Alpes	Tesio alpino	Glin fauss alpin

279

Latin	German	French	Italian	Rhaeto-Romanic
Thlaspi	Täschelkraut	Tabouret	Tlaspide, Erba storna	Tastgetta
T. corymbosum	Doldentraubiges T.	T. à feuilles rondes	T. corymbosum	T. umbellada
T. montanum	Berg-T.	T. des montagnes	T. montanina	T. da muntogna
T. rotundifolium	Rundblättriges T.	T. à feuilles rondes	T. dei ghiacci, Iberella	T. radunda
Thymus polytrichus	Alpen-Thymian	Thym des Alpes	Timo alpino	Timian alpin
Tofieldia calyculata	Kelch-Liliensimse	Tofieldia à calicule	Tofieldia a calicetto	Schervina cumina
Tozzia alpina	Tozzie	Tozzie des Alpes	Tozzia alpina	Tozzin alpin
Trichophorum alpinum	Alpen-Haarbinse	Trichophorum des Alpes	Tricoforo alpino	Minalva alpina
Trientalis europaea	Siebenstern	Trientalis d'Europe	Trientalis	Trientala europea
Trifolium	Klee	Trèfle	Trifoglio	Traifegl
T. alpestre	Hügel-K.	T. alpestre	T. alpestre	T. alpester
T. alpinum	Alpen-K.	T. des Alpes	T. alpino	T. alpin
T. badium	Braun-K.	T. brun	T. giallo bruno	T. brin
T. montanum	Berg-K.	T. des montagnes	T. montano	T. da muntogna
T. nivale	Schnee-K.	T. des neiges	T. delle nevi	T. da naiv
T. rubens	Purpur-K.	T. pourpre	T. rosseggiante	T. cotschnent
T. thalli	Thals K.	T. de Thalius	T. cespitoso	T. da Thalius
Trollius europaeus	Trollblume	Boule d'or	Botton d'oro, Paparia	Targnols
Tussilago farfara	Huflattich	Tussilage, Pas-d'Ane	Tossilaggine, Farfugio	Tschilendra (Pei-pulein)
Vaccinium	Heidelbeere	Airelle	Mirtillo	Granidla
V. gaultherioides	Alpen-Moorbeere	A. des marais	M. falso	Gighidra da pali
V. myrtillus	Heidelbeere	Myrtille	M. nero	Izun nair
V. vitis-idaea	Preiselbeere	A. rouge	M. rosso	Gighidra
Valeriana	Baldrian	Valériane	Valeriana	Valeriana
V. celtica	Keltischer B., Speik	V. celtique	V. celtica	V. celtica
V. montana	Berg-B.	V. des montagnes	V. montana	V. da muntogna
V. supina	Zwerg-B.	V. naine	V. strisciante, Stellina	V. nanina
V. tripteris	Dreiblatt-B.	V. triséquée	V. trifogliata	V. triala
Veratrum album	Weisser Germer	Vératre blanc	Veratro bianco, Elabro bianco	Baloma alva
Verbascum crassifolium	Dickblättrige Königskerze	Molène à feuilles épaisses	Tassobarbasso di monti	Mulaina grossa
Veronica	Ehrenpreis	Véronique	Veronica	Veronica
V. alpina	Alpen-E.	V. des Alpes	V. alpina, Erba gualda alpina	V. alpina

280

Latin	German	French	Italian	Rhaeto-Romanic
V. aphylla	Blattloser E.	V. à tige nue	V. senza foglie	V. senza feglia
V. bellidioides	Rosetten-E.	V. Fausse Pâquerette	V. falsa Margherita	V. bella
V. fruticans	Felsen-E.	V. buissonnante	V. delle rocce	V. chagliada
V. fruticulosa	Halbstrauchiger E.	V. sous-ligneuse	V. fior di Rosa	V. bassa
V. tenella	Zarter E.	V. délicate	V. tenella	V. delicata
Vicia	Wicke	Vesce	Veccia	Vitscha
V. cracca	Vogel-W.	V. Cracca	V. montanina	V. d'utschè
V. silvatica	Wald-W.	V. des bois	V. delle selve	V. da guaud
Vincetoxicum officinale	Schwalbenwurz	Dompte-venin official	Vincetossico comune	Ventschatissi officinal
Viola	Veilchen, Stiefmütterchen	Violette	Viola	Viola
V. biflora	Zweiblütiges V.	V. à deux fleurs	V. gialla	V. da duas flurs
V. calcarata	Langsporniges S.	V. éperonnée	V. speronata, V. di monti	V. d'alp
V. lutea	Gelbes S.	V. jaune	V. gialla	V. melna
V. rupestris	Sand-V.	V. des rochers	V. rupestre	V. da crap
V. tricolor	Feld-S.	V. tricolore, Pensée des champs	V. tricolore	V. da trais colurs

281

Subject Index

(for botanical terms, see the glossary, Chapter 6.2., p. 88)

283

286

287

290

291

293

298

299

Origin of the material used in Figures and Plates

This book includes reproductions from original colour slides, and drawings.

The sources of the slides are as follows:

Margarita Egger, Zumikon: **98,4**

Mark Greuter, Adliswil: **4,**2; **15,**2; **60,**4; **81,**2; **97,**2.

Fritz Hutzli, Vechigen: **70,**1.

Elias Landolt, Zürich: **1,**1; **1,**2; **2,**1; **4,**1; **4,**4; **5,**3; **6,**4; **7,**1; **7,**3; **8,**4; **9,**2; **10,**3; **11,**2; **12,**2; **12,**4; **17,**1; **18,**2; **18,**3; **19,**2; **19,**3; **19,**4; **20,**2; **20,**4; **21,**3; **21,**4; **22,**1; **22,**4; **25,**2; **26,**3; **28,**1; **28,**2; **29,**4; **32,**3; **34,**2; **36,**3; **37,**1; **38,**1; **38,**3; **38,**4; **39,**1; **40,**1; **40,**2; **40,**3; **40,**4; **45,**4; **46,**4; **47,**2; **48,**2; **48,**3; **48,**4; **49,**1; **49,**2; **49,**4; **50,**4; **51,**4; **52,**1; **52,**4; **53,**1; **53,**3; **55,**1; **55,**4; **58,**2; **58,**3; **60,**4; **61,**1; **63,**1; **64,**3; **65,**3; **66,**2; **66,**3; **67,**2; **70,**2; **71,**2; **72,**2; **75,**3; **76,**2; **77,**2; **79,**1; **79,**4; **81,**4; **83,**1; **83,**3; **84,**4; **86,**3; **88,**1; **88,**2; **88,**3; **90,**1; **90,**3; **93,**4; **94,**4; **95,**3; **96,**4; **98,**2; **99,**4; **100,**2; **102,**3; **102,**4; **103,**4; **104,**1; **104,**2; **104,**3; **105,**4; **107,**3; **108,**4; **109,**1; **110,**3; **110,**4; **111,**1; **111,**2; **111,**3; **111,**4; **112,**3; **113,**2; **114,**3; **115,**2; **115,**4; **116,**1; **117,**2; **117,**3; **118,**3; **119,**1; **119,**2; **119,**3; **120,**1; **120,**2; **120,**4.

Walter Matheis, Bronschhofen: **9,**3; **16,**1; **16,**4; **21,**2; **26,**1; **36,**2; **37,**4; **38,**2; **41,**1; **42,**3; **46,**2; **47,**4; **48,**1; **53,**2; **62,**2; **73,**2; **80,**4; **95,**4; **107,**2; **108,**3.

Hans Sigg, Winterthur: **1,**3; **1,**4; **2,**2; **2,**3; **2,**4; **3,**1; **3,**2; **3,**3; **3,**4; **4,**3; **5,**1; **5,**2; **5,**4; **6,**1; **6,**2; **6,**3; **7,**2; **7,**4; **8,**1; **8,**2; **8,**3; **9,**1; **9,**4; **10,**1; **10,**2; **10,**4; **11,**1; **11,**3; **11,**4; **12,**1; **12,**3; **13,**1; **13,**2; **13,**3; **13,**4; **14,**1; **14,**2; **14,**3; **14,**4; **15,**1; **15,**3; **15,**4; **16,**2; **16,**3; **17,**2; **17,**3; **17,**4; **18,**1; **18,**4; **19,**1; **20,**1; **20,**3; **21,**1; **22,**2; **22,**3; **23,**1; **23,**2; **23,**3; **23,**4; **24,**1; **24,**2; **24,**3; **24,**4; **25,**1; **25,**3; **25,**4; **26,**2; **26,**4; **27,**1; **27,**2; **27,**3; **27,**4; **28,**3; **28,**4; **29,**1; **29,**2; **29,**3; **30,**1; **30,**2; **30,**3; **30,**4; **31,**1; **31,**2; **31,**3; **31,**4; **32,**1; **32,**2; **32,**4; **33,**1; **33,**2; **33,**3; **34,**1; **34,**3; **34,**4; **35,**1; **35,**2; **35,**3; **35,**4; **36,**1; **36,**4; **37,**2; **37,**3; **39,**2; **39,**3; **39,**4; **41,**2; **41,**3; **41,**4; **42,**1; **42,**2; **42,**4; **43,**1; **43,**2; **43,**3; **43,**4; **44,**1; **44,**2; **44,**3; **44,**4; **45,**1; **45,**2; **45,**3; **46,**1; **46,**3; **47,**1; **47,**3; **49,**3; **50,**1; **50,**2; **50,**3; **51,**1; **51,**2; **51,**3; **52,**2; **52,**3; **53,**4; **54,**1; **54,**2; **54,**3; **54,**4; **55,**2; **55,**3; **56,**1; **56,**2; **56,**3; **56,**4; **57,**1; **57,**2; **57,**3; **57,**4; **58,**1; **58,**4; **59,**1; **59,**2; **59,**3; **59,**4; **60,**1; **60,**2; **60,**3; **61,**2; **61,**3; **61,**4; **62,**1; **62,**3; **62,**4; **63,**2; **63,**3; **63,**4; **64,**1; **64,**2; **64,**4; **65,**1; **65,**2; **65,**4; **66,**1; **66,**4; **67,**1; **67,**3; **67,**4; **68,**1; **68,**2; **68,**3; **68,**4; **69,**1; **69,**2; **69,**3; **69,**4; **70,**3; **70,**4; **71,**1; **71,**3; **71,**4; **72,**1; **72,**3; **72,**4; **73,**1; **73,**3; **73,**4; **74,**1; **74,**2; **74,**3; **74,**4; **75,**1; **75,**2; **75,**4; **76,**1; **76,**3; **76,**4; **77,**1; **77,**3; **77,**4; **78,**1; **78,**2; **78,**3; **78,**4; **79,**2; **79,**3; **80,**1; **80,**2; **80,**3; **81,**1; **81,**3; **82,**1; **82,**2; **82,**3; **82,**4; **83,**2; **83,**4; **84,**1; **84,**2; **84,**3; **85,**1; **85,**2; **85,**3; **85,**4; **86,**1; **86,**2; **86,**4; **87,**1; **87,**2; **87,**3; **87,**4; **88,**4; **89,**1; **89,**2; **89,**3; **89,**4; **90,**2; **90,**4; **91,**1; **91,**2; **91,**3; **91,**4; **92,**1; **92,**2; **92,**3; **92,**4; **93,**1; **93,**2; **93,**3; **94,**2; **94,**3; **95,**1; **95,**2; **96,**1; **96,**2; **96,**3; **97,**1; **97,**3; **97,**4; **98,**1; **98,**3; **99,**1; **99,**2; **99,**3; **100,**1; **100,**3; **100,**4; **101,**1; **102,**2; **101,**3; **101,**4; **102,**1; **102,**2; **103,**1; **103,**2; **103,**3; **104,**4; **105,**1; **105,**2; **105,**3; **106,**1; **106,**2; **106,**3; **106,**4; **107,**1; **107,**4; **108,**1; **108,**2; **109,**2; **109,**3; **109,**4; **110,**1; **110,**2; **112,**1; **112,**2; **112,**4; **113,**1; **113,**3; **113,**4; **114,**1; **114,**2; **114,**4; **115,**1; **115,**3; **116,**2; **116,**3; **116,**4; **117,**1; **117,**4; **118,**1; **118,**2; **118,**4; **119,**4; **120,**3.

Erwin Steinmann, Chur: **33,**4.

René Widmer, Zürich: **94,**1.

Figs 2, 3, 4, 29, 32, 34, 40, 42, 43, 46, 49, 50 and 51 are scaled-down reproductions from: Hess. H. E., Landolt E. and Hirzel R. 1976–1980. Flora der Schweiz. Birkhäuser Publ. Basle.

Colour Plates